Dynamics

This book is in

THE ADDISON-WESLEY SERIES IN THE
ENGINEERING SCIENCES

Mechanics and Thermodynamics

Howard W. Emmons

Consulting Editor

Dynamics

VOLUME I

PARTICLES, RIGID BODIES, AND SYSTEMS

by

ROBERT L. HALFMAN

Department of Aeronautics and Astronautics
Massachusetts Institute of Technology

ADDISON-WESLEY PUBLISHING COMPANY, INC.

READING, MASSACHUSETTS · PALO ALTO · LONDON

The views of space and time which I wish to lay before you have sprung from the soil of experimental physics, and therein lies their strength.

H. Minkowski

PREFACE

This is the first of a pair of volumes which forms a single coordinated treatment of the dynamics of particles, groups of particles, rigid bodies, and systems. The bulk of the material has evolved slowly over the years in a classroom atmosphere and reflects the needs of the student as well as those of the instructor.

Although undergraduate dynamics has often been presented as a self-contained subject fully developed in the distant past, an attempt has been made here to show its interrelationship with many neighboring disciplines and to indicate how it is continuously evolving as a working tool. Principles of elasticity, electromagnetism, fluid mechanics, and automatic control have been employed occasionally in illustrative examples, and the bases of the various approximations and idealizations have been examined, insofar as it seemed feasible. Thus in Chapter 4, the principles of particle dynamics are applied to bodies of variable mass (such as accelerating and rotating rockets with high-speed internal flow) and are also developed in the forms useful in fluid mechanics. In a similar vein, in Chapter 6, the concept of principal axes of inertia is related to the torques which act on a satellite in a nonuniform gravitational field.

This point of view, in which the student is shown many directions to choose from as he proceeds in his later studies, is particularly evident in the second volume, entitled *Dynamics: Systems, Variational Methods, and Relativity.* The treatment of both linear and nonlinear systems (Chapters 7, 8, and 9) is not a drill in detailed techniques, but rather a stimulating broad look at the fundamental ideas. Similarly, the variational calculus (Chapter 10) is developed separately from the classical variational principles of dynamics and applied largely to the newer area of performance optimization (Chapter 11). In turn, the ideas underlying special and general relativity (Chapter 12), as they affect dynamics, are not subordinated to a formal rigorous analytical development, but are examined in simple illustrative situations. The detailed formalism in these areas can come later for the student.

Of course, the entire presentation is strongly colored by my own interests and background. I am not primarily interested in classical dynamics as a preliminary to studying modern particle physics. I would rather try to help the modern engineer develop competence in transforming real problems in dynamics into appropriate mathematical forms which he can then manipulate to produce useful conclusions. Thus in many instances in the text, more realistic problems have been substituted for the traditional carefully selected ones in which all the sticky points have been assumed

out of existence. The boredom of a purely logical development has sometimes been interrupted by a stimulating glimpse of more difficult problems
yet to come.

The strong emphasis on moving reference frames and on inertial, accelerating, and rotating observers reflects my interest in vehicles and their
behavior, whether on the ground, in the air, or in orbit. My students have
very strongly reinforced my own inclination to make the study of relative
motion a less impersonal process by visualizing a set of observers who are
introduced in Chapter 2. To those of you who are skeptical of this somewhat novel (and therefore undignified) approach, I can only say—try it
and see.

The presentation in two volumes rather than one was dictated by con-
sideration of flexibility for the instructor and cost for the student. Thus
the first volume can provide, on a selective basis, a good one-semester
course of study in about the junior year, based on a solid year of physics
and one and one-half or two years of mathematics. This is the way it has
been used in the Department of Aeronautics and Astronautics at M.I.T.
However, there is plenty of material in the first volume for several se-
mesters, and even for a review course for incoming graduate students whose
dynamics needs strengthening. The second volume offers a wealth of
material appropriate to the senior elective or graduate level which can be
selected, and occasionally amplified, according to the instructor's needs.
Especially recommended is a full-year course using selections from both
volumes to take advantage of the fact that they were written as a single
coordinated unit. Numerous illustrative examples form an integral part
of the text in both volumes, and a substantial offering of problems is ap-
pended to each chapter.

Mathematical tools are used as required, without apology, according to
the general professional practice at this time, and may require a bit of
updating of instructor background in a few areas. The simple matrix
algebra introduced for coordinate transformations is gradually employed
in other situations. Eigenvalue problems and the corresponding diagonalization of matrices arise in the addition of angular displacements of a rigid
body, the finding of principal axes of inertia, and the handling of vibration
problems with multiple degrees of freedom. The inertia tensor is treated as
such, and both vector and scalar forms are developed for many of the
associated principles. In general, I have purposely avoided singling out a
favorite special form (such as vector analysis) and sticking to it through
thick and thin. As a corollary, the subject matter has not been selected to
illustrate mathematical techniques, but to give a balanced presentation of
a broad area of dynamics.

Nevertheless, the student is assumed to have only a standard background in calculus, such as represented by Thomas' *Calculus and Analytic*

Geometry. Some background in differential equations is also needed for the chapters on system and variational dynamics. Somewhat unusual topics, such as elementary matrices, are developed as needed in the text. The new mathematics is carefully introduced in familiar physical situations and, in turn, new physical situations are handled only with relatively familiar mathematical techniques. In this way, Fourier series and the Laplace transform are introduced quite naturally in the later chapters on system dynamics, and some properties of adjoint equations which are useful in the variational chapters are introduced to study simple nonself-adjoint linear systems. For much the same reason, Lagrange's equations are introduced in limited form in connection with both particle and rigid-body dynamics and then given a thorough mathematical treatment in Chapters 10 and 11.

I would like to acknowledge the very substantial assistance of my colleagues and students at the Massachusetts Institute of Technology during the formative stages of this material and, in particular, note my debt to my own teacher, Manfred Rauscher, now in Zurich. The encouragement offered by Howard Emmons of Harvard during the writing of the manuscript and the expert assistance by the staff of the publisher are deeply appreciated, as are the efforts of the many people who have helped with the various preliminary sets of class notes and with the manuscript. In particular, the bulk of the typing and proofing was most ably carried out by Barbara Faure and Barbara Marks. The later stages of development of the manuscript were supported, in part, by funds made available under the substantial grant to M.I.T. by the Ford Foundation for the development of undergraduate engineering education. This support at key times made possible a substantially accelerated and improved effort.

January, 1962   R. L. H.
Meredith, N.H.

CONTENTS

CHAPTER 1

PRINCIPLES AND PROBLEMS OF DYNAMICS

1-1 Introduction. Dynamics has often been cited as a discipline in which many difficult and involved problems have been solved by elaborate analytical techniques and concepts based upon a very few fundamental ideas. You have already developed an acquaintance with these fundamentals by studying carefully chosen illustrative problems in your course in physics. You have used quantitatively the ideas of force, mass, and motion; moment of a force, center of mass, angular velocity are not new terms. You have also gained considerable experience in other fields since first encountering the ideas of dynamics and now have a considerably strengthened arsenal of mathematical tools which you can use. Your study of the properties and uses of materials has provided some insight into the nature of various forces, stresses, interactions, and the many facets of the idea of static equilibrium. You have worked with many kinds of physical quantities in many situations.

Now is an excellent time for a renewed exploration of the field of dynamics to gain experience in critically applying the fundamentals to more difficult situations. We will no longer stick to problems which fit our fundamental ideas most neatly and simply but will inquire about what problems are of professional interest. We will attempt to relate much of the elegant and idealized classical analytical dynamics of particles and rigid bodies to the realities of our current problems.

In many interesting situations, the concepts of Newton's laws and the conservation of mass must be supplemented by the fundamental ideas of areas neighboring that of dynamics. We must include the appropriate material force-deformation properties if we are interested in dynamic stresses and strains, whereas the laws of thermodynamics are particularly important to most fluid dynamics problems. In some cases we must deal with forces and fields of electromagnetic origin and perhaps energy released or absorbed by chemical or nuclear reaction. While the main emphasis of our work will certainly be on dynamics, interrelationships such as these will be pointed out rather than hidden.

A person interested in the problems associated with the motion of vehicles soon finds himself deeply embroiled in dynamics. He may be studying the over all flight paths or trajectories of submarines, aircraft, or spacecraft, or perhaps their response to control inputs. He may be concerned with the dynamic stability of a flexible aircraft at supersonic speeds, the vibrations of a helicopter or a slender missile balanced on its tail of fire.

1

His attention may be drawn to the complex flow patterns around a vehicle or through its power plant. He may be looking at the whirling gyros and spinning turbines within a vehicle, or he may be trying to stabilize a telescope mounted on an oscillating satellite.

1-2 **An historical view.** There are many ways to gain perspective and experience in dynamics. A rewarding experience is to browse leisurely through the shelf in a library which contains Mach, Appell, Lamb, Milne, Whitaker, Newton, Poincaré, Routh, Einstein, Rayleigh, and many others. Glance at the prefaces, the chapter headings, and the dates of publication. Read more closely whatever strikes your eye. Once you have located such a shelf, you will find yourself returning again and again.

Another helpful way is to look critically at how the fundamental ideas in dynamics have developed over the years.* Three separate stages can be traced—geometry, kinematics, and dynamics. *Geometry* has origins in the concepts of areas and proportions used by the Egyptians and later formalized and extended by the Greeks. This Euclidean geometry is quite familiar and useful to us. In Euclidean space, we have no trouble with the translations and rotations of triangles or rigid bodies and the underlying concept of congruence because it is homogeneous and isotropic. Its properties are unrelated to the distribution of matter or to the motion of the matter and are uniform throughout.

Other systems of geometry consistent with the ideas of rigid bodies and congruence were developed in the early part of the last century. Hyperbolic geometry, in which space is infinitely extended in all directions, came first and then Riemann's finite curved but unbounded geometries. A simple two-dimensional example of the latter is the geometry of the surface of a sphere where great circles are analogous to Euclid's straight lines, but nevertheless, all intersect each other. Of course Euclidean geometry was not only available but also eminently suitable to the development of early dynamics, and its practical monopoly was maintained until challenged by the needs of Einstein's gravitational theory developed early in this century.

Kinematics, the study of the motion of a body, relies on a concept of time and its passage. The Newtonian idea of a completely independent and absolute time has had a very useful and fruitful working relationship with the flat and homogeneous Euclidean geometry, but it could not satisfy the simultaneous demands of dynamical and electromagnetic theory. Newton's absolute time permits the use of radar like time signals to synchronize clocks of stationary observers, but unfortunately, it requires an infinite

---

* Many excellent historical treatments have been written. The point of view presented here follows the stimulating chapter by H. P. Robertson in Ref. 1. (References are listed at the end of the book.)

transmission speed when the observers are in different states of motion. The speed of electromagnetic propagation may be so nearly infinite that in many situations the use of Newtonian time results in no practical error. However, at the beginning of this century, the concept of the fundamental independence of time and space had to be abandoned, except as an approximation, in favor of a space-time continuum.

In Newton's day, homogeneity of absolute Euclidean space forced the conclusion that there was no preferred position or orientation; that is, there was no preferred origin or preferred coordinate system. Also, since the concept of motion was related to change in position with passage of independent time, observers at different positions could talk, without ambiguity, about simultaneous events and separations between points in space.

The third stage to be traced is that of *dynamics* itself. Since dynamics relates the motion of a physical body to its interactions with its surroundings, the question is soon asked, what is the natural state of motion of a body? If all the sources of interaction are removed, will the body tend toward a preferred point, will it come to rest, or will it do something less obvious? Of course this procedure is unrealizable physically; but if our isolation of one interaction after another leads us to a sound postulate or law for the motion of an isolated body, we have taken a tremendous step.

The idea of a preferred point is so foreign to Euclidean geometry that it was naturally discarded. The second idea of the body coming to rest was tried at some length, fruitlessly, by Aristotle in ancient times. Since neither velocity nor position could be considered absolute, it was logical to examine acceleration as a candidate. Galileo's work at the end of the Middle Ages led to the result that there are preferred reference systems in which the deviation of a body from uniform motion (or rest) is always attributable to external influences. These preferred reference systems, called "inertial" or "Galilean," are, at worst, in uniform translation (without angular velocity) with respect to each other. Thus if we can identify in any situation a reference system which is Galilean (within the desired accuracy), we can speak of absolute acceleration (and absolute angular velocity). These ideas are embodied in Newton's first law of motion.

Newton's third law, which states that the actions of two bodies upon each other are always equal and directly opposite, leads quantitatively, through the study of accelerations in an interaction, to the ideas of inertia and mass. The idea that the mass of a body is an inherent constant follows easily. Both of these ideas of Newton's time had to be modified later because electromagnetic forces between moving particles do not follow the third law (see Example 4–4 and Goldstein, Ref. 2, p. 4), and the constant mass idea does not survive the reassessments following the kinematic upheavals of the newer space-time relativity.

Newton's second law is a simple statement of the way in which a body deviates from uniform motion under external influences. It embodies the useful concept of force as related to mass and acceleration. We must be wary of forces because they have a way of disappearing just when we think we understand them. Thus, centrifugal and Coriolis forces, often seen by non-Galilean observers, can be eliminated by transferring to a Galilean reference system. These forces, often called kinematic forces, have the peculiar property of imparting to a particle an acceleration dependent only on its position and velocity, not on its mass; that is, the force is directly proportional to the particle's mass. Gravitational force, although apparently very similar, requires for its elimination a far more radical change in both the geometrical and kinematical framework as demonstrated by Einstein in his gravitational theory which he called *general relativity*. Although the transformation to a Galilean reference system will be very useful in many dynamics problems, we will not find it advantageous to go to the trouble of eliminating gravitational force, because it means abandoning the very convenient Euclidean geometry.

Following Newton, then, with his homogeneous Euclidean space and his independent time, we have *the classical principle of relativity*. As stated by Robertson (Ref. 1) it asserts the "complete relativity of position and velocity, in the sense that it is impossible by any mechanical experiment to determine an absolute position or an absolute velocity. There exists a set of privileged reference frames, the Galilean, ... [and] any acceleration, including rotation, relative to such a frame is absolute, in the sense that it has a common measure for all Galilean observers."

Although the idea of absolute velocity seemed undefinable by mechanical means, a strong effort was made in the nineteenth century to attain this end by optical or other electromagnetic means. Keynoted by the famous Michelson-Morley experiment, the attempts to find a stationary reference frame, the luminiferous ether, also failed. Of course the results did not fit the classical principle of relativity either, and many attempts were made to explain the discrepancies. The idea of bodily contraction in the direction of motion introduced by Fitzgerald and expanded by Lorentz finally led Einstein to modify drastically the concept of time.

Instead of an absolute, true, independent time, a time interrelated with basically Euclidean spatial coordinates in a *flat four-dimensional space-time continuum* seemed far more satisfactory. This concept had little effect on the Newtonian dynamics in the usual applications where all velocities were much smaller than that of light. Yet this change made it possible to postulate "a set of intrinsically indistinguishable inertial reference frames, between which the Lorentzian transformations obtain, which define the natural state of motion for the description of both electromagnetic and mechanical phenomena." (Robertson, Ref. 1, p. 36)

Unfortunately this *theory of relativity*, called "special relativity" by Einstein, does nothing to clarify the ideas of gravitational force or permit it to be eliminated, as with centrifugal and Coriolis forces, by a kinematical transformation.   In another tremendous forward step, Einstein in his *gravitational theory* discarded the flat Euclidean geometry and found that gravitational forces disappear in a *curved space-time continuum* in which properties of the inertial mass determine the curvatures.   As one consequence, this development finally accounts for the historically troublesome anomaly in the motion of the perihelion of Mercury.   Another interesting consequence of this gravitational theory, which postulates space-time curvatures dependent on the distribution of matter, is that we have lost the earlier relativity of position and velocity.   One observer in principle can distinguish himself from another by measurement and comparison of space-time curvatures in their neighborhoods.*

In almost all of our problems in dynamics, we will find it sufficiently accurate and far more convenient to retain the concepts of Euclidean geometry, an independent time, and the classical relativity of position and velocity.   We are thus required to deal with gravitation in the Newtonian fashion and base our description of motion on Galilean or inertial reference frames.   Fortunately these concepts are relatively familiar to us and must be abandoned only when we attempt to handle dynamics problems involving very high velocities.   Some examples are the obtaining of thrust by the high-speed expulsion of particles such as ions and the ever-intriguing twin paradox of space travel, in which the stay-at-home twin may age faster than his more venturesome brother (see Examples 12–5 and 12–9).†

1–3 The scope of our task. The study of dynamics can take many forms, depending on the background and interests of the student and the teacher. In this book we will emphasize and illustrate aspects of dynamics which are of importance to flight vehicles and the many related fields.   We will not emphasize those elegant portions of classical dynamics associated with Hamilton and Jacobi which serve as a valuable preparation for quantum mechanics and atomic physics on a submicroscopic scale.   We are more interested in the macroscopic view where solids and fluids can be considered to be continuous distributions of matter over regions of space appreciable to our human senses.

---

* For this reason the term "general relativity" seems more suitable for the flat Lorentzian space-time to which Einstein unfortunately applied the name "special relativity." Einstein's "general relativity" is gradually becoming known somewhat more accurately as his "gravitational theory."

† References to chapters beyond 7 are to Volume 2.

In this book, we will not attempt any substantial investigation of fluid mechanics, which, with its intimate relationship to thermodynamics, warrants a thorough separate effort. Nevertheless, we will draw on its principles when the needs of our problems require. Similarly, we will draw on the ideas and principles of the statics of deformable solids in many instances. However, our central aim will be to gain experience and understanding of problems in the *dynamics of solids*. Now these solids may be quite flexible or quite rigid, and they may be submerged in fluids or connected to other solids. We may be interested in their motions, deformations, or stresses. Of one thing we can be sure: they will not be standing still.

Particularly for the more rigid solids, two very useful and therefore important approximations can often be made. If we are interested in the overall motion of a body, especially when the body is small compared with the scope of its motion, or when it does not rotate, we can often approximate its motion by watching the motion of a single representative particle instead. This is much more convenient mathematically and is a serviceable stratagem in a surprisingly large number of situations. In other problems we will have to admit to the finite size of the body in studying its overall motion but will be able to ignore the small deformations associated with its flexibility. Thus, in large-scale maneuvers, an aircraft may be susceptible to analysis as a particle, whereas in its rotational response to pilot control movements, it may be considered a rigid body. However, when we analyze its response to gusty air, neither idealization will be adequate for two reasons: (1) the elastic deformations of the flexible wings appreciably alter the unsteady loads applied by the rough air flow and (2) the elastic deformations of the wings alter the magnitude of the stresses in the structure.

A glance at the table of contents indicates that following a study of kinematics, we will look at the dynamics of particles, various groupings of particles, rigid bodies, and dynamic systems. We will also explore relativistic dynamics and some of the elegant variational principles. Throughout, we will try to emphasize the translation of complex physical problems into the simplest possible mathematical formulations consistent with the nature and required accuracy of the answers we are seeking.

Mathematically speaking, our problems can take on a variety of forms. Basically they involve interrelations among distributions in space of force, mass, and motion which are functions of time. Because of Newton's second law, force and position are two integrations or differentiations apart, and we may want to go either way. Forces known as functions of time or position lead to differential equations to be integrated as in the case of a simple pendulum. Alternatively, specified motions may be used to predict loads or stresses through a differentiation process. Of course we may start in the middle and go either way if we can state our problem in terms of work and kinetic energy or impulse and momentum.

The mathematical forms which we may encounter range from simple integration or differentiation processes through ordinary differential equations, partial differential equations (for the continuous flexible bodies), to sets of simultaneous ordinary or partial differential equations (when the motions in the various coordinates are interrelated). We will find use for vectors, a few tensors, determinants, matrices, and some operational methods. The relatively unfamiliar mathematical tools will be employed first in familiar physical situations, and vice versa.

1-4 Theory and experiment. In the field of dynamics and in many other fields, the adequate solution of a particular problem, whether of a scientific or an engineering nature, can usually be obtained in several ways. Sometimes it is possible to make direct measurements of the relevant physical quantities during an actual occurrence of the process or situation under study. More often we must resort to the study of *a model of the actual problem* for reasons of feasibility, cost, or convenience. This model, whether a mathematical or physical one, is normally carefully designed to emphasize those aspects of the problem which significantly influence the answers we seek while minimizing or ignoring those factors we believe irrelevant. Thus its formulation is based on our experience and understanding of the fundamental principles involved.

As an illustration, suppose we want to find the vibration frequencies of an aircraft wing. If the wing is available and we have the proper excitation and measurement equipment, the most logical and straightforward approach is usually to shake the wing and measure its response. If the wing has not yet been fabricated, we can build a simplified model of it, leaving out many irrelevant details but carefully representing the proper distributions of mass and structural stiffness. This model may well be a conveniently scaled interconnection of masses and springs which is vibrated in the laboratory, or it could be a set of differential equations whose characteristic values are extracted by analog or digital computation.

Different problems may require drastically different types of approach. Thus, in an initial exploratory investigation into a new field or phenomenon, the primary aim may be to establish which physical quantities have a significant influence and which can be safely ignored. Complex, abstract, analytical techniques have little relevance here. The application of a well-developed intuitive sense in the form of a few barely quantitative experiments is far more likely to prove fruitful. On the other hand, a comprehensive survey of the vibration characteristics of an entire jet transport may entail considerable manipulation of high-order matrices on a high-speed computer or, alternatively, the carefully synchronized application of many shakers and the simultaneous recording of many response-measuring instruments. Still different approaches must be made to the ultraprecise measurements or analyses frequently attempted by a physicist or astronomer. In short, a few minutes of careful and critical sizing up of the nature of a problem in relation to the techniques and principles available for its solution may save weeks of fruitless effort.

The process of going from an actual complex physical problem to a model suitable for analysis or laboratory use often involves more than just the elimination of irrelevant details. The model may have to be further simplified to reduce it to manageable size and form. These more drastic approximations often represent a calculated balance between the effort required for the solution and the probable adequacy of the answers. It is quite usual to compare the results obtained from various different approximations and from both analytical and experimental approaches in trying to find the sometimes elusive answers to difficult problems.

CHAPTER 2

KINEMATICS

To prepare for a systematic and comprehensive attack on the many and varied problems in dynamics in which we are interested, it is well to become familiar first with whatever means are available for describing the motion of the objects under study. We find ourselves concerned with freely moving bodies which are usually hard to keep track of. They are not restricted to motion in one plane and, in fact, they must often be observed from other freely moving bodies. Thus, before beginning an intensive study of the interaction of forces and motion, we will spend considerable time studying *kinematics*, the technique of describing motion. [In the terms of Section 1–2, we will restrict ourselves (until Chapter 12) to a flat Euclidean space and an independent and absolute time.]

In most of our problems, we are certainly interested in watching the motion of bodies of finite size. Nevertheless, we can often accomplish our purpose by watching the motion of just one representative particle in the body in situations where the orientation of the body is either not relevant or does not change. When the size of the body is small compared with the distance it travels, we may even be able to represent it with sufficient accuracy as a single particle even though, in other problems, the same body may appear to have almost infinite extent. Thus, in formulating laws of planetary motion, Kepler's viewpoint of the earth as a particle is quite different from the appearance of the earth to an outfielder chasing a bouncing baseball.

In the many situations where we must keep track of more than one particle in a body, we will find it useful to relate the motions of the other points in the body to that of a single representative point. In the case of rigid bodies, we often watch translation of and rotation around the center of mass. For these reasons, we will devote considerable effort to studying the various ways of describing quantitatively the motion of a particle. We will not standardize on a single notation or approach because we should have an understanding of the relative advantages of the various techniques encountered in practice.

2–1 Kinematics of a particle. The simplest motion of a particle (the mathematicians speak of motion of a point) is *rectilinear translation* or motion along a straight line (Fig. 2–1). Using O as a reference point, we can define the position or displacement of the particle P as s. As we know, the change in displacement with time can be very usefully defined as

$$v = \lim_{\Delta t \to 0} \frac{\Delta s}{\Delta t} = \frac{ds}{dt},$$ (2-1)

where v is called the instantaneous velocity. (Here Δ represents a small but finite increment in a variable.) In general, v also changes with time, which leads to the definition of acceleration as

$$a = \lim_{\Delta t \to 0} \frac{\Delta v}{\Delta t} = \frac{dv}{dt} = \frac{d^2 s}{dt^2}.$$ (2-2)

We could continue such a series of definitions indefinitely if we wanted to but would find very little use for them. In fact, acceleration would be of as little practical importance as its derivative (sometimes called jerk) if Newton had been able to relate force directly to velocity instead of acceleration.

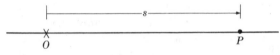

Fig. 2-1. Rectilinear translation of a particle.

Translation of a particle along a *path all in one plane* differs from rectilinear translation in that the velocity and acceleration can change direction as well as change magnitude (Fig. 2-2). Notice that the velocity of the particle P is tangent to the path because it must point in the direction in which P is going at this instant. Note also that it might be useful to remember that velocity and acceleration fall into that special class of quantities which can be represented by vectors; that is, they have magnitude, line of action, and sense, and can be combined and resolved according to the parallelogram rule. This is important because it will permit us to use vector algebra and a little vector calculus, if it seems to be worthwhile.

There may be ambiguity in applying the vector concept to the displacement of P unless we are careful to distinguish between the distance s traveled along the path and the position of P with respect to the origin O. As shown in Fig. 2-2 the position of P can be represented by the vector **R** from O to P which has both magnitude and direction. The distance s has only a magnitude and not a direction and thus is a scalar rather than a vector quantity.

We will often find it necessary to observe the rate of change of a vector quantity, and no such process is closer to our experience than watching rate of change of position and calling it velocity. From a pictorial point of view, it is easy in planar motion to watch the changes in the position

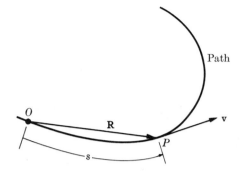

FIG. 2–2.   The motion of a particle in one plane.

vector **R** as P moves along the path.   If we sketch the positions of **R** at
equal successive intervals Δt of time, we can estimate the velocity of P
as shown in Fig. 2–3(a).

The direction of the velocity is tangent to the path, and its magnitude
is indicated by the distance from one position vector head to the next
divided by Δt.   We note that the change in a position vector **R**, from one
instant to another, is made up of a swinging as well as a stretching.

Let's now apply what we have learned about rate of change of position
vector to watch the rate of change of velocity.   As we have noted, it is
easy to see the change in a vector if it is plotted at each instant from the
same reference point.   This was natural for the displacement vector but
must be contrived for the velocity vector.   As shown in Fig. 2–3(b), we
can plot the successive velocities of P from a common point which we

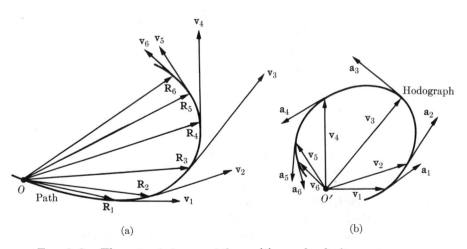

FIG. 2–3.   The rate of change of the position and velocity vectors.

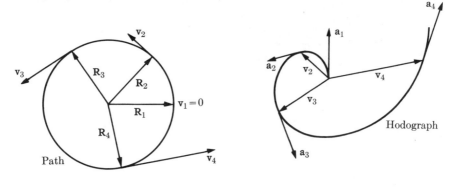

(a)   (b)

FIG. 2–4.   Accelerated circular motion of a particle.

FIG. 2–5.   A path in three dimensions.

FIG. 2–6.   Reference directions in the plane of a curve.

may call O'. It is then quite apparent that the velocity is changing direction while it stretches and then begins to shrink.

If we visualize the path of the particle as being generated by the head of the position vector $\mathbf{R}$ as it follows P, we should also be able to visualize a curve generated simultaneously in Fig. 2–3(b) by the head of the velocity vector $\mathbf{v}$. This curve is usually called the *hodograph*. Note that the rate of movement of the velocity vector head along the hodograph can be interpreted as acceleration. Observe also that at each instant the acceleration vector is tangent to the hodograph. We will use these ideas later to watch the rate of change of many vector quantities.

EXAMPLE 2-1. Let's watch the motion of a point on the rim of a phonograph record while it is speeding up from rest. In Fig. 2-4(a) the center of the record has been chosen as a convenient origin and the displacement vector is shown at a number of equal time intervals. Observe that the path is a circle, but the velocity is increasing in size as well as changing direction. Thus the hodograph generated by the tip of the velocity vector (Fig. 2-4b) is not a circle nor is the acceleration vector perpendicular to the corresponding velocity vector. Part of the acceleration represents stretching of the velocity vector and part represents its swinging. By comparison, the velocity vector represents, in Fig. 2-4(a), only the swinging of the fixed-length displacement vector. ▲*

The extension of these ideas to *particle motion in three-dimensional space* is not difficult in principle but is aided by a further mobilization of the tools of kinematics. As illustrated in Fig. 2-3, when the path of a particle is entirely within a single plane, all of the velocity and acceleration vectors needed to help describe the particle's motion are also in the same plane. The directions associated with the tangent to the path and the perpendicular to the path are quite easily visualized. If we look at Fig. 2-5, which represents a path in space, we find that although the tangent may still be easily visualized, the choice of a useful perpendicular direction is more complicated. At any point on the path there are an infinite number of directions perpendicular to the tangent. Since we are interested in watching the rate of change of the velocity vector, which we know can change by stretching and swinging, we might well choose as our preferred perpendicular to the path the direction in which **v** is swinging at a given instant. This direction, called the *normal direction*, together with the tangent, defines the plane of the curve at the given point (*A* in Fig. 2-6). The perpendicular to this plane, although of little practical use, is called the *binormal direction*.

To see how these directions are quite naturally employed in the description of the motion of particle *P* in space, let's make an excursion into the use of *vector symbolism*, including some ideas of vector differentiation. If you have seen this development before, exercise your mind by trying to remember and anticipate the steps rather than follow them dully with only a flicker of recognition.

---

* Throughout the book, the black triangle signifies the end of an example.

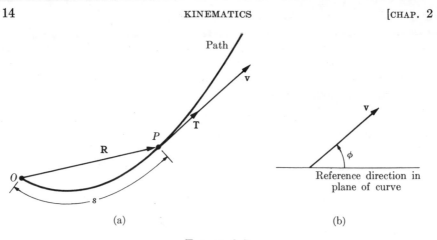

Figure 2-7

Let us watch particle P move along a path in space as illustrated in Fig. 2-7. We can measure the distance traveled by P along the path by the scalar s. The position of P relative to a conveniently located observer at O may be called the vector $\mathbf{R}$. The velocity of P is its rate of change of position, which can be written symbolically as

$$\mathbf{v} = \frac{d\mathbf{R}}{dt}. \tag{2-3}$$

The meaning of the derivative with respect to time of the vector $\mathbf{R}$ can be illustrated by introducing ds, the change in s during the time interval dt.

$$\mathbf{v} = \frac{d\mathbf{R}}{dt} = \frac{d\mathbf{R}}{ds} \cdot \frac{ds}{dt}.$$

We recognize the scalar ds/dt as the speed of P along the path. To understand the significance of $d\mathbf{R}/ds$, let's return to its definition:

$$\frac{d\mathbf{R}}{ds} = \lim_{\Delta s \to 0} \frac{\Delta \mathbf{R}}{\Delta s},$$

where $\Delta\mathbf{R}$ is the change in $\mathbf{R}$ during an interval Δt, and Δs is the corresponding change in s. The ratio can be thought of as the chord of an arc divided by the length of the arc. As $\Delta s \to 0$, this ratio approaches unity and has the direction of $\Delta \mathbf{R}$, which in the limit is the tangent direction. Thus, $d\mathbf{R}/ds$ can be thought of as a unit vector always tangent to the path.

$$\frac{d\mathbf{R}}{ds} = \mathbf{T}. \tag{2-4}$$

Thus,
$$\mathbf{v} = \mathbf{T}\frac{ds}{dt},$$
(2–5)

which, in words, says the velocity $\mathbf{v}$ has a magnitude ds/dt directed along the tangent to the path. Note that the direction of $\mathbf{T}$ and $\mathbf{v}$ are always changing. This direction can be represented (Fig. 2–7b) by ϕ and the change in direction of $\mathbf{T}$ by

$$\frac{d\mathbf{T}}{d\phi} = \mathbf{N},$$
(2–6)

where $\mathbf{N}$ is a unit vector in the normal direction [inward along the perpendicular in the plane of the curve (Fig. 2–6)]. Equation (2–6) arises from the idea that since $\mathbf{T}$ is a unit vector, it cannot stretch but can only swing. If it swings an amount $d\phi$, its change is its length times $d\phi$ directed along the normal. Since its length is unity, the ratio of $d\mathbf{T}$ and $d\phi$ is also unity.

Now, look at the acceleration of P which is the rate of change of $\mathbf{v}$.

$$\mathbf{a} = \frac{d\mathbf{v}}{dt} = \frac{d}{dt}\left(\mathbf{T}\frac{ds}{dt}\right)$$
$$= \frac{d\mathbf{T}}{dt}\frac{ds}{dt} + \mathbf{T}\frac{d^2s}{dt^2}.$$
(2–7)

We can write

$$\frac{d\mathbf{T}}{dt} = \frac{d\mathbf{T}}{d\phi}\frac{d\phi}{ds}\frac{ds}{dt} = \mathbf{N}K\frac{ds}{dt}.$$
(2–8)

Here K represents $d\phi/ds$, the curvature of the path, and is the reciprocal of the radius of curvature ρ. Thus the acceleration

$$\mathbf{a} = \frac{d\mathbf{v}}{dt} = \mathbf{T}\frac{d^2s}{dt^2} + \mathbf{N}K\left(\frac{ds}{dt}\right)^2$$
(2–9)

is formally represented as a stretching in the tangent direction and a swinging in the normal direction.

2–2 Coordinate systems and transformations. Although the preceding development follows elegantly from the ideas of rate of change and vector quantities, its usefulness in many practical problems is surpassed by the use of reference directions which do not change with time. Thus our observer at O in Fig. 2–7 may prefer to set up the fixed *cartesian reference directions X, Y, and Z* as shown in Fig. 2–8. He can, if he wishes, define unit vectors $\mathbf{i}$, $\mathbf{j}$, and $\mathbf{k}$ along these fixed directions with the result that

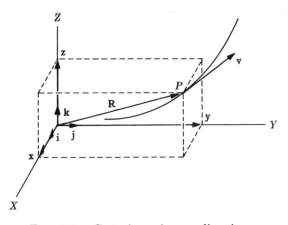

FIG. 2–8. Cartesian reference directions.

this set of unit vectors has zero rate of change. This leads us to the idea

$$\mathbf{R} = \mathbf{x} + \mathbf{y} + \mathbf{z} = \mathbf{i}x + \mathbf{j}y + \mathbf{k}z, \qquad (2\text{–}10)$$

where x, y, and z are the magnitudes of the vector components $\mathbf{x}$, $\mathbf{y}$, and $\mathbf{z}$ of $\mathbf{R}$. The velocity becomes

$$\mathbf{v} = \frac{d\mathbf{R}}{dt} = \mathbf{i}\frac{dx}{dt} + \mathbf{j}\frac{dy}{dt} + \mathbf{k}\frac{dz}{dt}$$

$$= \mathbf{i}v_x + \mathbf{j}v_y + \mathbf{k}v_z$$

$$= \mathbf{v}_x + \mathbf{v}_y + \mathbf{v}_z, \qquad (2\text{–}11)$$

and the acceleration

$$\mathbf{a} = \mathbf{i}\frac{d^2x}{dt^2} + \mathbf{j}\frac{d^2y}{dt^2} + \mathbf{k}\frac{d^2z}{dt^2}$$

$$= \mathbf{i}a_x + \mathbf{j}a_y + \mathbf{k}a_z$$

$$= \mathbf{a}_x + \mathbf{a}_y + \mathbf{a}_z. \qquad (2\text{–}12)$$

As a matter of actual practice, we often do not take the trouble to write the unit vectors, and many people use the notation

$$R = x \mathbin{+\mkern-8mu+} y \mathbin{+\mkern-8mu+} z,$$

$$v = v_x \mathbin{+\mkern-8mu+} v_y \mathbin{+\mkern-8mu+} v_z, \qquad (2\text{–}13)$$

$$a = a_x \mathbin{+\mkern-8mu+} a_y \mathbin{+\mkern-8mu+} a_z,$$

where the sign $\mathbin{+\mkern-8mu+}$ is used, somewhat recklessly, to indicate that we are dealing with the sum of vectors rather than scalars.

A different approach to keeping track of the particle P uses no formal vector notation at all and deals only in relations among components. Thus, we say that the components of particle position are x, y, and z. The components of particle velocity can be written

$$v_x = \frac{dx}{dt}, \qquad v_y = \frac{dy}{dt}, \qquad v_z = \frac{dz}{dt}, \qquad (2\text{–}14)$$

and, similarly,

$$a_x = \frac{dv_x}{dt} = \frac{d^2x}{dt^2}, \qquad a_y = \frac{dv_y}{dt} = \frac{d^2y}{dt^2}, \qquad a_z = \frac{dv_z}{dt} = \frac{d^2z}{dt^2}. \qquad (2\text{–}15)$$

You may wonder why we do not use one of these systems and forget the others. The answer is largely a matter of practicability. The elegant vector notation is particularly useful in the derivation of complex results because many ideas are self-contained in this shorthand kind of notation. When it comes to solving a numerical problem, however, the details of the computation must not be submerged, and you will find yourself writing equations in the form of Eqs. (2–13), (2–14), and (2–15). We will shift, whenever it is convenient, from notation to notation. At times this will exasperate you, but it will result eventually in a working understanding of each form.

Before we leave the kinematics of a particle, we should also look at the systems of cylindrical and spherical coordinates because they will be of

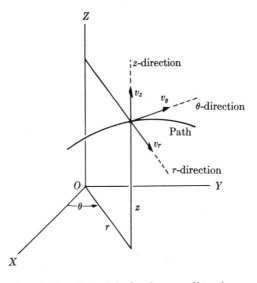

FIG. 2–9. Cylindrical reference directions.

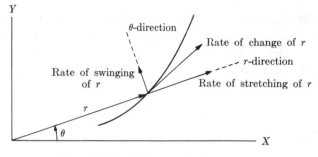

FIG. 2–10. The rate of change of r.

considerable aid to us in solving problems which involve some degree of line or point symmetry. To put it differently, in the cartesian system of Fig. 2–8, we used three perpendicular lengths to make up the position vector **R**. At times it is convenient to use two lengths and one angular coordinate and at other times one length and two angular coordinates.

Let's look first at the *cylindrical coordinates* illustrated in Fig. 2–9. The situation can be simplified considerably if we notice that the z-coordinate is unchanged from Fig. 2–8, and we can still say that z can stretch but not swing. Thus,

$$v_z = \frac{dz}{dt}, \qquad a_z = \frac{dv_z}{dt} = \frac{d^2z}{dt^2}. \qquad (2\text{--}16)$$

Since r and θ replace x and y, they can best be viewed by looking down along the z-axis (Fig. 2–10). Note that the stretching and swinging of r replace the changes in both x and y. In the limiting time interval dt the change in magnitude of r is dr in the r-direction. The change in position, $r\, d\theta$, is a result of the swinging of r by the amount $d\theta$. We can then write the velocity component in the r-direction as

$$v_r = \frac{dr}{dt}, \qquad (2\text{--}17)$$

and we can write the component in the θ-direction as

$$v_\theta = r\frac{d\theta}{dt}. \qquad (2\text{--}18)$$

The total velocity can be written as the vector sum of these three perpendicular components,

$$v = v_z \mathrel{+\!\!\!+} v_r \mathrel{+\!\!\!+} v_\theta. \qquad (2\text{--}19)$$

Looking now at the components of acceleration in the $r\theta$-plane, we observe in Fig. 2–11 that v_r and v_θ are simultaneously swinging and

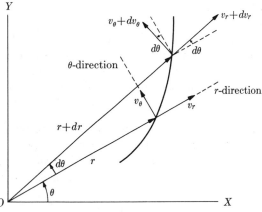

FIG. 2–11. The rates of change of v_r and v_θ.

stretching as P moves along the path. Remembering that the sizes of dv_r, dv_θ, and $d\theta$ are exaggerated for pictorial clarity and actually represent the changes in the limit as dt approaches zero, we note that the change in v_r consists of two parts. First is the change in the r-direction which, in the limit, is dv_r because $d\theta$ is so small. Second is the change of v_r in the θ-direction which results from its swinging an amount $d\theta$. The magnitude of the change is $v_r\, d\theta$. Similarly v_θ has a change in the θ-direction of dv_θ and in the negative r-direction of $v_\theta\, d\theta$. Dividing these changes by the time interval in which they took place and collecting the contributions in the r- and θ-directions, we have

$$a_r = \frac{dv_r}{dt} - v_\theta \frac{d\theta}{dt},$$

$$a_\theta = \frac{dv_\theta}{dt} + v_r \frac{d\theta}{dt}. \tag{2–20}$$

These can be written in an alternative form by introducing Eqs. (2–17) and (2–18) which give

$$a_r = \frac{d^2r}{dt^2} - r\left(\frac{d\theta}{dt}\right)^2,$$

$$a_\theta = r\frac{d^2\theta}{dt^2} + 2\frac{dr}{dt}\frac{d\theta}{dt}. \tag{2–21}$$

Note that half of the last term in the second equation came from dv_θ/dt because in v_θ (Eq. 2–18) both r and $d\theta/dt$ change magnitude with time. The total acceleration of P is then

$$a = a_z \nrightarrow a_r \nrightarrow a_\theta. \tag{2–22}$$

It is important to realize that the velocity **v** made up of components v_r, v_θ, v_z and the acceleration **a** with components a_r, a_θ, a_z refer to the motion of P seen by an observer to whom the axes XYZ of Fig. 2–9 appear stationary. By contrast, an observer who rides along on r as it swings at the rate $d\theta/dt$ sees a much simpler motion for P. To him P is always in the stationary rZ-plane and its entire motion can be easily related to the stretching of r and z.

EXAMPLE 2–2. Suppose a certain lighthouse keeper finds it convenient to come down from the light by sliding at constant speed down the spiral railing of the stairway. His path is then a spiral of constant radius and pitch. His position **R** measured from the top of the spiral axis has the components

$$r = a, \quad \text{(the radius)}$$
$$\theta = bt,$$
$$z = -ct,$$

where the constants b and c are related to the pitch of the spiral. The velocity components are

$$v_r = \frac{dr}{dt} = 0,$$

$$v_\theta = r\frac{d\theta}{dt} = ab,$$

$$v_z = \frac{dz}{dt} = -c.$$

The acceleration components become

$$a_r = \frac{d^2r}{dt^2} - r\left(\frac{d\theta}{dt}\right)^2 = -ab^2,$$

$$a_\theta = r\frac{d^2\theta}{dt^2} + 2\frac{dr}{dt}\frac{d\theta}{dt} = 0,$$

$$a_z = \frac{d^2z}{dt^2} = 0,$$

which represents simply a horizontally inward acceleration. Can you write all of the components for the case where somebody greases the railing so that the poor man's speed increases linearly with time? ▲

It is often necessary to transform expressions written in terms of one set of coordinates into the corresponding expressions in another set. If we see how this works in the case of the two relatively familiar sets, carte-

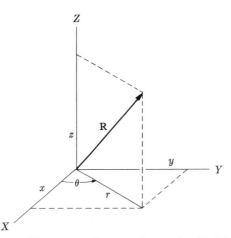

FIG. 2–12. The position vector in cartesian and cylindrical coordinates.

sian and cylindrical, we may later be able to use the *coordinate transformation techniques* in more difficult situations.

Looking at Fig. 2–12, we can write the relationships between the sets of components of the position vector **R**.

$$x = r \cos \theta, \qquad y = r \sin \theta, \qquad z = z. \tag{2–23}$$

Or, in the other way,

$$r = \sqrt{x^2 + y^2}, \qquad \theta = \tan^{-1}\frac{y}{x}, \qquad z = z. \tag{2–24}$$

However, **R** is the simplest quantity we might want to transform. Let's look next at the general vector quantity **A** which has components A_x, A_y, A_z or A_r, A_θ, A_z as shown in Fig. 2–13(a). Since A_z is the same in both systems, a look at the XY- or $r\theta$-plane in Fig. 2–13(b) helps indicate the other transformation relations,

$$
\begin{aligned}
A_x &= A_r \cos \theta - A_\theta \sin \theta, \\
A_y &= A_r \sin \theta + A_\theta \cos \theta, \\
A_z &= A_z.
\end{aligned}
\tag{2–25}
$$

If the vector we are interested in happens to be the velocity **v**, we can immediately write

$$
\begin{aligned}
v_x &= v_r \cos \theta - v_\theta \sin \theta, \\
v_y &= v_r \sin \theta + v_\theta \cos \theta, \\
v_z &= v_z.
\end{aligned}
\tag{2–26}
$$

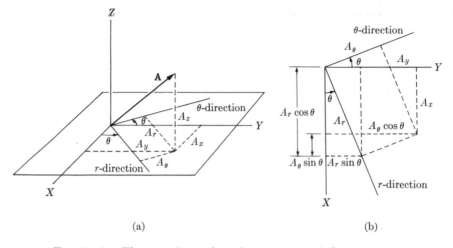

FIG. 2–13. The transformation of components of the vector **A**.

We can also reproduce the position component relations [Eq. (2–23)] from the general relations [Eq. (2–25)] by setting

$$A_x = x, \qquad A_r = r,$$
$$A_y = y, \qquad A_\theta = 0,$$
$$A_z = z, \qquad A_z = z.$$

Note that the transformation equations for **A** [Eq. (2–25)] typically have the form of a set of algebraic simultaneous equations. Rewriting them to illustrate this, we have

$$A_x = (\cos\theta)A_r + (-\sin\theta)A_\theta + (0)A_z,$$
$$A_y = (\sin\theta)A_r + (\cos\theta)A_\theta + (0)A_z, \qquad (2\text{--}25)$$
$$A_z = (0)A_r + (0)A_\theta + (1)A_z.$$

Using Cramer's rule and the concept of determinants, we can solve for the inverse expressions of A_r, A_θ, A_z in terms of the cartesian components. For example,

$$A_r = \frac{\begin{vmatrix} A_x & -\sin\theta & 0 \\ A_y & \cos\theta & 0 \\ A_z & 0 & 1 \end{vmatrix}}{\begin{vmatrix} \cos\theta & -\sin\theta & 0 \\ \sin\theta & \cos\theta & 0 \\ 0 & 0 & 1 \end{vmatrix}} = \frac{(\cos\theta)A_x + (\sin\theta)A_y + (0)A_z}{1}.$$

The complete set is

$$A_r = (\cos\theta)A_x + (\sin\theta)A_y + (0)A_z,$$
$$A_\theta = (-\sin\theta)A_x + (\cos\theta)A_y + (0)A_z, \qquad (2\text{--}27)$$
$$A_z = (0)A_x + (0)A_y + (1)A_z.$$

Mathematically speaking, the cylindrical components can be obtained by multiplying the cartesian components by a quantity which is certainly not a simple factor but rather more like an array of factors. *Matrix notation* is ideal for this situation involving a set of simultaneous equations. In this useful form Eq. (2–27) becomes

$$\begin{Bmatrix} A_r \\ A_\theta \\ A_z \end{Bmatrix} = \begin{bmatrix} \cos\theta & \sin\theta & 0 \\ -\sin\theta & \cos\theta & 0 \\ 0 & 0 & 1 \end{bmatrix} \begin{Bmatrix} A_x \\ A_y \\ A_z \end{Bmatrix}. \qquad (2\text{--}28)$$

The rule for the multiplication of the two matrices on the right is just that which will produce the right-hand side of Eq. (2–27). (Some of the properties of matrices are illustrated in Appendix A.)* As an example on a smaller scale

$$\begin{bmatrix} a & b \\ c & d \end{bmatrix} \begin{Bmatrix} x \\ y \end{Bmatrix} = \begin{Bmatrix} e \\ f \end{Bmatrix}$$

is equivalent to

$$ax + by = e,$$
$$cx + dy = f.$$

After you gain some familiarity with matrices, you will be writing Eq. (2–28) in the simpler form

$$\{A_{\text{cyl}}\} = [\theta_{\text{rot}}]\{A_{\text{cart}}\}. \qquad (2\text{--}29)$$

Note that the transformation from cartesian to cylindrical coordinates really is just a rotation of coordinate axes by the angle θ. Hence it is reasonable that $[\theta_{\text{rot}}]$ is merely a function of θ. Note also that all the properties of the transformation are contained in this matrix.

It would appear simple enough to solve Eq. (2–29) for $\{A_{\text{cart}}\}$ by dividing by $[\theta_{\text{rot}}]$, but remember that we are dealing with arrays of quantities,

---

* Matrices will be used in increasingly difficult situations as we go along, so learn the basic notation here and use Appendix A as needed. Other sets of simultaneous algebraic equations appear in Chapter 5 and in Chapter 9.

not simple factors. Instead, let's define a matrix $\lfloor\theta_{\text{rot}}\rfloor^{-1}$, called the inverse of $[\theta_{\text{rot}}]$, such that

$$[\theta_{\text{rot}}]^{-1}[\theta_{\text{rot}}] = [1], \tag{2-30}$$

where

$$[1] = \begin{bmatrix} 1 & 0 & 0 \\ 0 & 1 & 0 \\ 0 & 0 & 1 \end{bmatrix} \tag{2-31}$$

and is called the unit matrix. If we premultiply both sides of Eq. (2-29) by the inverse transformation matrix as follows:

$$\begin{aligned} [\theta_{\text{rot}}]^{-1}\{A_{\text{cyl}}\} &= [\theta_{\text{rot}}]^{-1}[\theta_{\text{rot}}]\{A_{\text{cart}}\} \\ &= [1]\{A_{\text{cart}}\} \\ &= \{A_{\text{cart}}\}, \end{aligned} \tag{2-32}$$

we have the equivalent of our original Eq. (2-25). Comparison will show that

$$[\theta_{\text{rot}}]^{-1} = \begin{bmatrix} \cos\theta & -\sin\theta & 0 \\ \sin\theta & \cos\theta & 0 \\ 0 & 0 & 1 \end{bmatrix}. \tag{2-33}$$

Thus for a simple rotation of coordinates, the inverse transformation matrix $[\theta_{\text{rot}}]^{-1}$ is simply the original matrix $[\theta_{\text{rot}}]$ with corresponding terms transposed across the main diagonal.

As a last set of coordinates let's look at *spherical coordinates*, the one involving one length and two angles, which happens to arise quite naturally in problems such as radar tracking, gun laying, and orbit calculations. As shown in Fig. 2–14, the θ-direction is unchanged from cylindrical coordinates, and the r- and z-directions are replaced by the R- and ϕ-directions.* In order to find the expressions for the components of velocity of P as it moves along the path, we can again watch the stretching and swinging of the displacement vector **R**. The stretching is all in the R-direction so

$$v_R = \frac{dR}{dt}. \tag{2-34}$$

---

* It is often more convenient to define ϕ from the Z-axis down to R in problems in which Z is the axis of symmetry. Then ϕ is a positive rotation about the θ-direction and, when $\theta = \phi = 0$, the ϕ-, θ-, and R-directions coincide with X, Y, and Z. In Fig. 2–14, the R-, θ-, and ϕ-directions correspond, respectively, to X, Y, and Z for $\theta = \phi = 0$. See the problems at the end of the chapter.

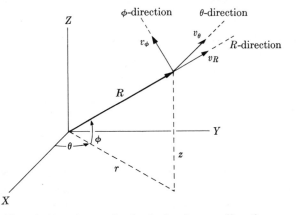

Fig. 2–14. A set of spherical reference directions.

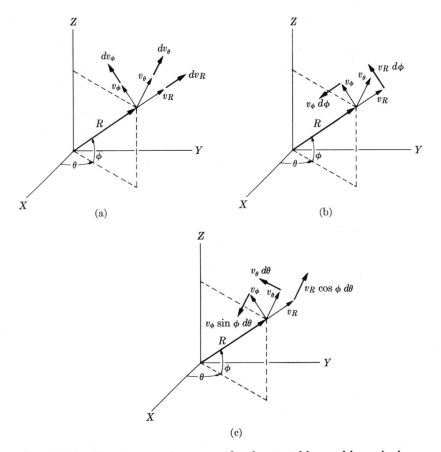

Fig. 2–15. The changes of v_R, v_θ, and v_ϕ by stretching and by swinging.

The swinging results partly from a change in θ and partly from a change in ϕ. The change $d\phi$ swings R a distance $R\,d\phi$ in the ϕ-direction so

$$v_\phi = R\frac{d\phi}{dt}. \tag{2–35}$$

The change $d\theta$ swings R a distance $R\cos\phi\,d\theta$ in the θ-direction, and thus

$$v_\theta = R\cos\phi\frac{d\theta}{dt}. \tag{2–36}$$

To obtain quickly the components of acceleration in spherical coordinates, we can watch the stretching and swinging of v_R, v_θ, and v_ϕ. Thus in Fig. 2–15(a) we can see the stretching of each velocity component. In Fig. 2–15(b), we see the swinging due to a change $d\phi$ in ϕ. Note that v_θ remains parallel to the XY-plane and does not change direction as ϕ changes. The variations in velocity components caused by a change $d\theta$ in θ are shown in Fig. 2–15(c). Note that the tail of v_ϕ swings further than the head in the θ-direction so that the net change in v_ϕ is in the negative θ-direction. Also the swinging of v_θ is parallel to the XY-plane and not directly in either the R- or ϕ-directions. Thus when we collect contributions in these directions, the term $v_\theta\,d\theta$ will have to be broken into $v_\theta\cos\phi\,d\theta$ in the negative R-direction and $v_\theta\sin\phi\,d\theta$ in the positive ϕ-direction.

If we visualize these changes taking place during the time dt, we can write

$$a_R = \frac{dv_R}{dt} - v_\phi\frac{d\phi}{dt} - v_\theta\cos\phi\frac{d\theta}{dt},$$

$$a_\theta = \frac{dv_\theta}{dt} + v_R\cos\phi\frac{d\theta}{dt} - v_\phi\sin\phi\frac{d\theta}{dt}, \tag{2–37}$$

$$a_\phi = \frac{dv_\phi}{dt} + v_\theta\sin\phi\frac{d\theta}{dt} + v_R\frac{d\phi}{dt}$$

for the components of acceleration. Substituting the expressions in Eqs. (2–34) through (2–36) for the velocity components, we get an alternative form

$$a_R = \frac{d^2R}{dt^2} - R\left(\frac{d\phi}{dt}\right)^2 - R\cos^2\phi\left(\frac{d\theta}{dt}\right)^2,$$

$$a_\theta = R\cos\phi\frac{d^2\theta}{dt^2} + 2\left(\frac{dR}{dt}\cos\phi - R\sin\phi\frac{d\phi}{dt}\right)\frac{d\theta}{dt}, \tag{2–38}$$

$$a_\phi = R\frac{d^2\phi}{dt^2} + R\cos\phi\sin\phi\left(\frac{d\theta}{dt}\right)^2 + 2\frac{dR}{dt}\frac{d\phi}{dt}.$$

If we note that the transformation from cylindrical to spherical coordinates is merely a rotation of the coordinate axes through an angle ϕ

about the θ-direction, we can use the techniques already developed in the previous section. Remembering that transforming to $R\phi$- from rz-coordinates is analogous to going to $r\theta$- from xy-coordinates, we can write [following Eq. (2-28)]

$$\begin{Bmatrix} A_R \\ A_\theta \\ A_\phi \end{Bmatrix} = \begin{bmatrix} \cos \phi & 0 & \sin \phi \\ 0 & 1 & 0 \\ -\sin \phi & 0 & \cos \phi \end{bmatrix} \begin{Bmatrix} A_r \\ A_\theta \\ A_z \end{Bmatrix}. \qquad (2\text{--}39)$$

We can check this for the case where **A** is the displacement vector **R** which has only one component in spherical coordinates and two in cylindrical coordinates. Equation (2–39) becomes

$$\begin{Bmatrix} R \\ 0 \\ 0 \end{Bmatrix} = \begin{bmatrix} \cos \phi & 0 & \sin \phi \\ 0 & 1 & 0 \\ -\sin \phi & 0 & \cos \phi \end{bmatrix} \begin{Bmatrix} r \\ 0 \\ z \end{Bmatrix},$$

which gives the three equations

$$R = r \cos \phi + z \sin \phi,$$
$$0 = 0,$$
$$0 = -r \sin \phi + z \cos \phi.$$

Or, alternatively, from the last equation,

$$\phi = \tan^{-1} \frac{z}{r}.$$

Note that if we want to make a transformation from cartesian to spherical coordinates we can substitute Eq. (2–29) into Eq. (2–39) as

$$\{A_{\text{sph}}\} = [\phi_{\text{rot}}]\{A_{\text{cyl}}\} = [\phi_{\text{rot}}][\theta_{\text{rot}}]\{A_{\text{cart}}\}. \qquad (2\text{--}40)$$

Since the matrix $[\phi_{\text{rot}}]$ is analogous to $[\theta_{\text{rot}}]$, the determinant of its array should be unity, and its inverse can be formed by transposing terms across the main diagonal.

$$[\phi_{\text{rot}}]^{-1} = \begin{bmatrix} \cos \phi & 0 & -\sin \phi \\ 0 & 1 & 0 \\ \sin \phi & 0 & \cos \phi \end{bmatrix}. \qquad (2\text{--}41)$$

EXAMPLE 2–3. Suppose a jet transport T is flying past the ground radar station O, as shown in Fig. 2–16, with its position and velocity given

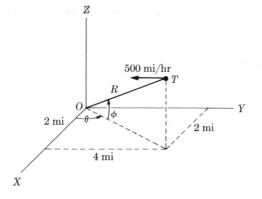

FIGURE 2–16

in terms of the cartesian coordinate system. To find its coordinates and velocity components as seen in the spherical coordinate system natural to the radar, which measures range R, azimuth θ, and elevation ϕ, let's use Eq. (2–40). To find the position in spherical coordinates, set

$$\{A_{\text{sph}}\} = \begin{Bmatrix} R \\ 0 \\ 0 \end{Bmatrix} \quad \text{and} \quad \{A_{\text{cart}}\} = \begin{Bmatrix} 2 \\ 4 \\ 2 \end{Bmatrix}$$

with

$$[\phi_{\text{rot}}][\theta_{\text{rot}}] = \begin{bmatrix} \cos\phi\cos\theta & \cos\phi\sin\theta & \sin\phi \\ -\sin\theta & \cos\theta & 0 \\ -\sin\phi\cos\theta & -\sin\phi\sin\theta & \cos\phi \end{bmatrix}.$$

This gives

$$R = 4.9 \text{ miles}, \qquad \theta = 63.4°, \qquad \phi = 24.1°.$$

To find the velocity components, set

$$\{A_{\text{cart}}\} = \begin{Bmatrix} v_x \\ v_y \\ v_z \end{Bmatrix} = \begin{Bmatrix} 0 \\ -500 \\ 0 \end{Bmatrix}$$

and obtain

$$\{A_{\text{sph}}\} = \begin{Bmatrix} v_R \\ v_\theta \\ v_\phi \end{Bmatrix} = \begin{Bmatrix} -408 \\ -224 \\ 183 \end{Bmatrix}.$$

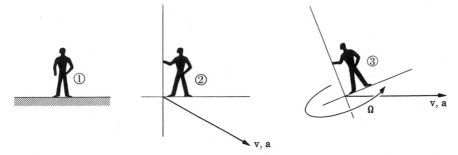

Fig. 2–17.   Three kinds of observers: ① who will not accelerate or rotate, ② who will accelerate but not rotate, and ③ who will accelerate and rotate.

2–3 Motion relative to translating observers. In many situations of practical interest, we find ourselves forced to describe the motion of bodies while we are simultaneously moving with respect to some more basic reference. The driver of an automobile who pulls into the left lane to pass a slowly moving car must be able to judge such relative motion quite well. Otherwise, he may not be able to return to his lane before he reaches a curve or meets an oncoming car. On the other hand, it is often to our advantage to adopt *purposely* the viewpoint of a moving observer in order to see a much simpler and more tractable picture of some complicated phase of a motion. Thus the description of the combustion process and subsequent flow through the nozzle of a rocket engine can usually be made most advantageously by an observer riding on the rocket rather than one on the ground despite the fact that we may also be interested in the trajectory of the rocket vehicle itself. Similarly, the deformations and oscillations of an aircraft wing in a violent maneuver are often most easily described by an observer moving with the aircraft's center of mass.

Although the above ideas can be implemented by the definition of moving axes or reference systems, most people find it very helpful to use a less impersonal approach which allows them to separate the concept of an observer from the axis system he chooses to employ. To use this latter idea, we can define *three kinds of observers* for whom we will find much useful work in the course of the book. Because Newton differentiates sharply between accelerated observers and unaccelerated or Galilean observers,* we will certainly need the services of an unaccelerated observer whom we shall designate ① (see Fig. 2–17). Such an observer, who is linearly unaccelerated and nonrotating, can be moving at constant velocity but, in many situations, may be essentially stationary. Then he may be called a "fixed" observer.

---

* See Chapters 1 and 3.

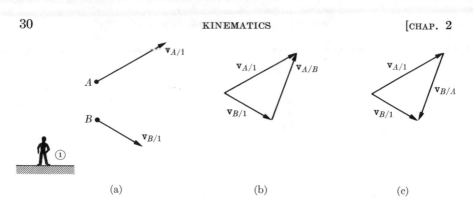

FIG. 2–18. Relative velocities of translating observers.

We shall designate as ② an observer who is entirely willing to accelerate linearly and tell us what he sees, but who will not rotate. We will call the more daring fellow who is also willing to rotate ③. Any one of these observers can use any of the techniques of describing motion which we have developed in the preceding sections of this chapter. However, we must learn how to transfer from the observations of one observer to those of another.

Concentrating for the moment on observers ① and ②, let's look at Fig. 2–18(a) in which points A and B are moving in an arbitrary fashion, as seen by our fixed (that is, unaccelerated) observer ①. If we require our nonrotating friend ② to adopt the motion of B so that he has B's velocity and acceleration at each instant, we can call $\mathbf{v}_{A/B}$ the velocity of A seen by ② from B and write (see Fig. 2–18b)

$$\mathbf{v}_{A/1} = \mathbf{v}_{B/1} + \mathbf{v}_{A/B}. \qquad (2\text{–}42)$$

In words, the velocity of observer ② moving with B plus the velocity he sees for A is just the velocity of A seen by ①. Similarly, for accelerations, we can differentiate Eq. (2–42) to get

$$\mathbf{a}_{A/1} = \mathbf{a}_{B/1} + \mathbf{a}_{A/B}. \qquad (2\text{–}43)$$

Note that if observer ② moves with A instead of B, we can write (see Fig. 2–18c)

$$\mathbf{v}_{B/1} = \mathbf{v}_{A/1} + \mathbf{v}_{B/A}, \qquad \mathbf{a}_{B/1} = \mathbf{a}_{A/1} + \mathbf{a}_{B/A}.$$

Comparison with the previous equations gives the results

$$\mathbf{v}_{A/B} = -\mathbf{v}_{B/A}, \qquad \mathbf{a}_{A/B} = -\mathbf{a}_{B/A},$$

which are almost intuitive to most of us because of our extensive experience with linear relative motion.

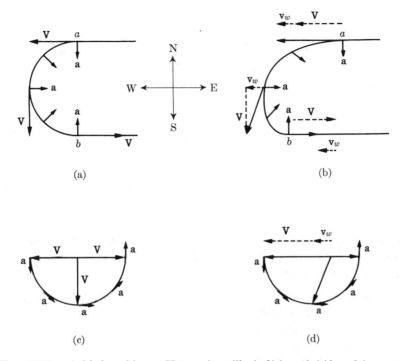

FIG. 2–19. A bird making a U-turn in still air [(a) and (c)] and in an east wind [(b) and (d)].

EXAMPLE 2–4. Suppose we are watching a bird which is flying straight west when it decides to make a smooth 180° turn and head back east. If we idealize the motion slightly, we can say that the bird's speed V is constant and the turn is semicircular, as shown in Fig. 2–19(a). The bird's acceleration will be zero except during the turn from a to b, when it will be radially inward and of constant magnitude. Of course the picture we have described is as it would be seen from the ground in still air. If there is a horizontal wind $\mathbf{v}_w$ blowing from the east, we can postulate that the motion would look like Fig. 2–19(a) only to an observer drifting with the wind, since the bird maneuvers and flies primarily with respect to the air rather than the ground. Such a drifting observer can be visualized as being supported by a balloon.

The bird's velocity as seen from the ground is now the instantaneous $\mathbf{V}$ plus $\mathbf{v}_w$, which corresponds to the path shown in Fig. 2–19(b). Observe that since the wind velocity is assumed constant, both observers see the same time-history of acceleration. Thus they see the same shape for the hodograph of the bird's motion but disagree on the relative position of the origin from which the velocity vectors are plotted. Note that the drifting

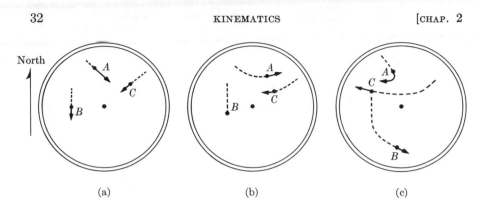

(a)   (b)   (c)

FIG. 2–20. Targets on the radarscope of a ship which (a) has constant speed, (b) is slowing down, and (c) is turning to the right.

observer (Fig. 2–19c) sees only the swinging of the velocity vector **V**, whereas the ground observer (Fig. 2–19d) sees both the stretching and the swinging in varying proportions. ▲

EXAMPLE 2–5. To be on the bridge of an ocean liner moving north through the fog at speed V is a situation where we would naturally adopt the identity of a moving observer. If we look at the display on the radarscope, we can see the positions of other ships relative to us at the center, and if we plot their paths with time indications along them, we can estimate their velocities relative to us. As shown in Fig. 2–20(a), we can identify A as a ship which will pass to starboard, B as a stationary buoy or lightship, and C as a ship on a collision course with us. Actually, C is moving over the ocean in a northwesterly direction, but note how dramatic a collision course appears to an observer on one of the ships.

So far we have assumed that our velocity is constant. Suppose our captain decides to reverse the engines and decelerate to avoid a collision. From our point of view, the objects A, B, and C will suddenly acquire a northward acceleration **a** and may trace out subsequent paths as shown in Fig. 2–20(b) even though their captains have given no orders. Suppose that instead of reversing engines we put the rudder hard over and achieve a considerable rate of turn to the right. Can you see that the motions of A, B, and C will be as shown in Fig. 2–20(c)? We are now rotating, accelerating observers, and our point of view can become drastically distorted (as we will see in Section 2–4). ▲

Cartesian and other coordinate systems can sometimes fit very nicely into this situation of linear relative motion. As shown in Fig. 2–21, we can observe the motion of point P from a fixed system $X_F Y_F Z_F$ and from a parallel but translating system $X_T Y_T Z_T$. We are presuming no connection between the motions of P and the translating system. At any instant

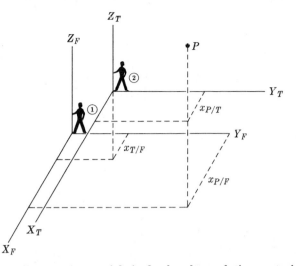

FIG. 2–21. Coordinates of a particle in fixed and translating cartesian systems.

P will have coordinates in both axis systems. The x-coordinates are related, as

$$x_{P/F} = x_{P/T} + x_{T/F}, \qquad (2\text{–}44)$$

with similar relations for y and z. If we look at the rate of change of these coordinates by differentiating Eq. (2–44), we get

$$\frac{dx_{P/F}}{dt} = \frac{dx_{P/T}}{dt} + \frac{dx_{T/F}}{dt},$$

which is nothing more than

$$v_{x_{P/F}} = v_{x_{P/T}} + v_{x_{T/F}}. \qquad (2\text{–}45)$$

Also, it follows that

$$a_{x_{P/F}} = a_{x_{P/T}} + a_{x_{T/F}}. \qquad (2\text{–}46)$$

Although the use of subscripts begins to get complicated, note that we do not need to specify vector addition in Eqs. (2–44, 2–45, 2–46) because all the X-components are in the same direction and can be added algebraically. The same is true for the Y- and Z-components. Thus we have three algebraic equations in X, Y, and Z such as Eq. (2–45) in place of each vector equation such as Eq. (2–42).

EXAMPLE 2–6. Let's look at a helicopter landing on a moving ship in a crosswind, as shown in Fig. 2–22(a). If we postulate that the ship has a forward speed of 20 knots, that a 20-knot wind is blowing perpendicular

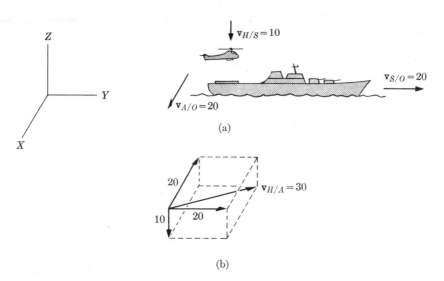

FIG. 2–22. A helicopter descending in a crosswind onto a moving ship.

to the ship's course, and that the helicopter appears to a man on the ship
to be descending vertically at 10 knots, we might ask for the velocity of
the helicopter through the air. We can use parallel sets of cartesian coordinates moving with the ship, the wind, the helicopter, and the ocean
oriented as shown.

The component of velocity in the X-direction of the helicopter with
respect to the air can be written as

$$v_{xH/A} = v_{xH/S} + v_{xS/O} + v_{xO/A} = 0 + 0 - 20 = -20 \text{ knots.}$$

Visualizing the velocity of the ocean with respect to the air is not so difficult if we imagine that we are hanging below a balloon which is drifting
with the air. Thus the air appears to be stationary to us (no wind in our
faces), but the ocean is moving in the negative X-direction.

In the Y-direction, we can write

$$v_{yH/A} = v_{yH/S} + v_{yS/O} + v_{yO/A} = 0 + 20 + 0 = 20 \text{ knots,}$$

and in the Z-direction,

$$v_{zH/A} = v_{zH/S} + v_{zS/O} + v_{zO/A} = -10 + 0 + 0 = -10 \text{ knots.}$$

The resultant velocity of the helicopter through the air in which it is flying is shown in the vector diagram of Fig. 2–22(b). The pilot must set

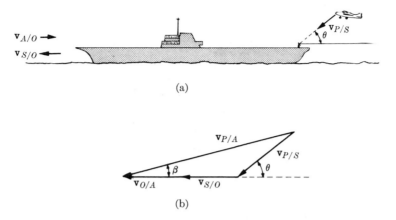

(a)

(b)

FIG. 2–23. The approach to an aircraft carrier steaming into the wind.

the controls for a slanting 30-knot flight in order to descend "vertically" toward the ship at 10 knots. ▲

EXAMPLE 2–7. Situations in which translating observers find it convenient to use coordinates other than cartesian are quite common. A Navy pilot making a landing approach on a carrier is more interested in his glide path angle and slant distance (polar coordinates) than in his horizontal and vertical coordinates. If the carrier is employing a gyro-stabilized mirror landing system (Fig. 2–23a), the mirror is very much like our nonrotating observer ②. The gyro system prevents the pitch and roll of the carrier from rotating the mirror. However, the linear motions of the carrier are transmitted to the mirror, and for it to present the needed glide path angle information to the approaching pilot, they must be taken into account. In fact, it is the motion of the carrier relative to the air mass that counts because the mirror should be set to require the proper motion of the aircraft with respect to the air (Fig. 2–23b).

It is a question of some importance in the design of the landing system whether the side and particularly the vertical motions of the carrier at the mirror location will be large enough to distort appreciably the indications of the mirror to the pilot. If necessary, the instantaneous translations of the mirror could be measured, and, after suitable computation, correction signals could be put continuously into the gyro system to rotate the mirror slightly to compensate for its changing linear motion.

Another situation in which noncartesian coordinates are naturally used is in radar searching by picket aircraft. The radar measures the motion of a target directly in spherical coordinates and their rates of change. However, if the radar information is to be transmitted back to the carrier and used there, it must be modified to account for the linear motion of the

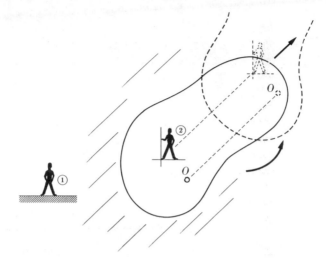

FIG. 2–24.   A nonrotating observer ② moving with point O of a rigid body in planar motion sees only rotation about O.

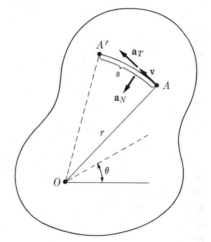

FIG. 2–25.   Motion of a particle A in a rigid body rotating about a fixed axis through O.

picket plane.   Whether this corrective information is put in spherical coordinate form or whether the original radar data are transformed into cartesian form before the data are combined is a matter of manipulative convenience. ▲

One of the most rewarding uses of the linearly moving observer ② is in the study of rigid-body motion.   If we visualize a rigid body moving in a general fashion as shown in Fig. 2–24, we can ask observer ② to assume

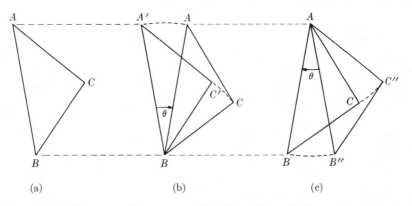

FIG. 2–26. Planar motion as a combination of translation and rotation.

exactly the linear motion of a point in the body such as O. Observer ②
will then say that, to him, point O is completely stationary and the rigid
body is simply rotating about the fixed point O. Observer ①, who can
see the translation of O, can readily separate the general rigid-body motion
into *translation plus rotation* by combining his observations with those of
②. We will study the kinematics of rigid-body rotations in some depth
in Chapter 5, where we will examine the implications of the fact that,
although angular velocity and acceleration are vector quantities, angular
displacement is not quite a vector. Let's restrict ourselves here to studying the relative motion of various points in the same rigid body.

   If we further restrict ourselves at first to *planar motion of the rigid body*
in which the motion of any point of the body remains in the same plane,
our observer ②, when moving with a given point O, will see just simple
rotation about a fixed axis through O (Fig. 2–25). The motion of some
other point A in the body can be described in terms of the angular position θ of the body, its rate of change, and the radial distance r. With the
idea that in a rigid body the separation of any two points remains constant,
the motion of A to A' can be related to the angular displacement θ as
(Fig. 2–25)

$$s = r\theta. \tag{2–47}$$

The linear velocity of A at any instant is tangent to its path and just the
swinging of r so that

$$v = r\frac{d\theta}{dt}. \tag{2–48}$$

The acceleration of A is partly the stretching of v in the tangential direction

$$a_T = r\frac{d^2\theta}{dt^2} \tag{2–49a}$$

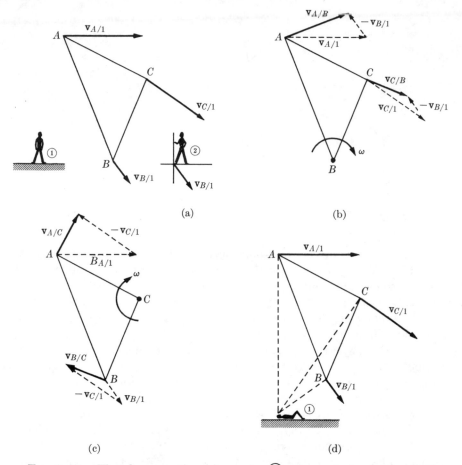

FIG. 2–27. The planar motion (a) seen by ① appears to be simple rotation to observers translating with points on the body in (b) and (c) and to a stationary observer at the instantaneous center (d).

and partly the swinging of v at the rate $d\theta/dt$ in the normal direction

$$a_N = \left(r \frac{d\theta}{dt} \right) \frac{d\theta}{dt}. \qquad (2\text{--}49b)$$

The ordinary symbols for the angular velocity and angular acceleration vectors are $\boldsymbol{\omega}$ and $\boldsymbol{\alpha}$ which in this special fixed-axis rotation are simply

$$\omega = \frac{d\theta}{dt}, \qquad \alpha = \frac{d\omega}{dt} = \frac{d^2\theta}{dt^2}. \qquad (2\text{--}50)$$

In order to visualize how *planar motion* can be considered a sum of translation plus rotation, look at the flat, triangular, rigid body in Fig.

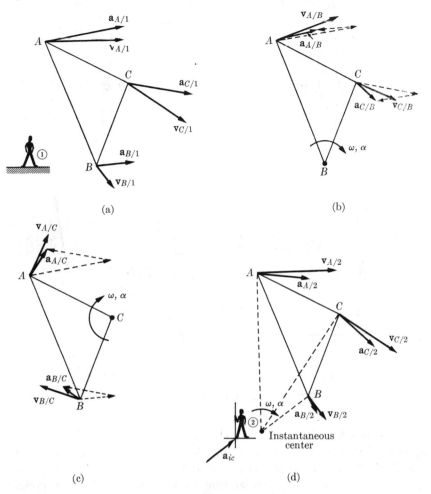

FIG. 2–28. The planar motion of Fig. 2–27 including acceleration.

2–26(a). If it moves to the position ABC in Fig. 2–26(b), we can think of the displacement as a translation A–A', B–B, C–C' and a clockwise rotation A'–A, C'–C of a magnitude θ about B. Alternatively, it could have been considered a translation as shown in Fig. 2–26(c) of A–A, B–B'', C–C'' and a clockwise rotation about A. Note that the magnitude and sense of the rotation θ is the same in both instances, but the translation to A is longer than that to B.

If we presume that our triangular rigid body ABC has at its corners the velocities seen by ① as in Fig. 2–27(a), let's call in observer ② and ask him to move with corner B. To him, B will appear stationary and A and C will have the velocities shown in solid lines in Fig. 2–27(b). Note that $\mathbf{v}_{A/B}$ and $\mathbf{v}_{C/B}$ are perpendicular to and proportional to the length

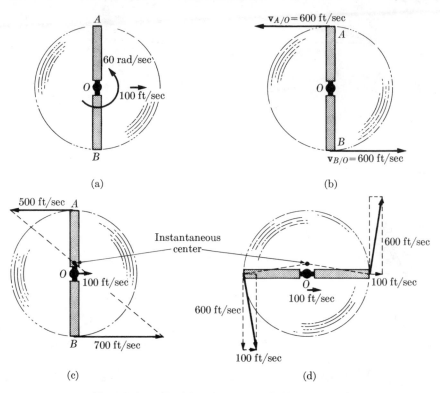

FIG. 2–29. Looking down on a helicopter rotor.

of the lines AB and CB, respectively. If we had asked ② to assume the motion of C instead of B, he would have seen the motion depicted in Fig. 2–27(c). Realize from the vector diagrams that $\mathbf{v}_{B/C}$ is just $-\mathbf{v}_{C/B}$, so ② must see the same angular velocity ω regardless of which point he follows. His linear velocity, however, does depend on which point he follows.

Note, also, that if our observer ① happens at the given instant to be at the intersection of the perpendiculars from the velocity vectors (Fig. 2–27d), he will see pure rotation at the rate ω. His position is often called *the instantaneous center* and corresponds to that point in the rigid body (or an imagined extension of it) which instantaneously has zero velocity.

Normally, of course, the corners of our triangle will have accelerations as well as velocities. Do the accelerations shown in Fig. 2–28(a) look reasonable? Let's ask ② to move again with B and sketch what he sees in Fig. 2–28(b). Here the tangential and normal components seem entirely compatible with fixed-axis rotation about B at an ω which is increasing with time. The picture for ② moving with point C (Fig. 2–28c)

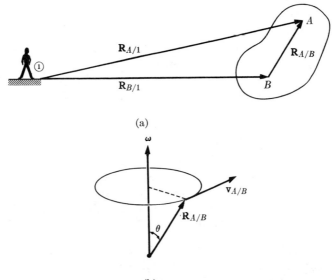

(a)

(b)

FIG. 2–30. The motion of A as seen by observer ② moving with point B in the same rigid body.

is similarly reasonable. However, an observer ① at the instantaneous center will not see fixed-axis rotation. This is only seen by an observer ② (in Fig. 2–28d) who has the acceleration of the point of the body at the instantaneous center.

EXAMPLE 2–8. Suppose a helicopter is traveling forward at 100 ft/sec while the two-bladed 20-ft-diameter rotor turns at 60 rad/sec (Fig. 2–29a). The velocities of the blade tips (consider the blades AOB our rigid body) as seen by the pilot are shown in Fig. 2–29(b). The tip velocities and instantaneous center as seen by a stationary observer are shown in Fig. 2–29(c), and again a quarter of a revolution later in Fig. 2–29(d). Note that in (d) the instantaneous center is in the same geometric location on the rotor disk as in (c) but is no longer a point on the blade. Therefore the point moving with the blade which is the instantaneous center in (c) has no velocity in (c) but certainly has an acceleration. Can you find it? ▲

These same ideas of relative motion of various points in a rigid body will be derived in *formal vector notation* in order to illustrate the ease with which general relationships can be established by using vector symbolism.

For the rigid body in Fig. 2–30(a), we can write the position of A as seen by observer ① as

$$\mathbf{R}_{A/1} = \mathbf{R}_{B/1} + \mathbf{R}_{A/B}. \tag{2–51}$$

Formally, we can find an expression for the velocity of A by differentiating Eq. (2–51). Thus,

$$\frac{d\mathbf{R}_{A/1}}{dt} = \frac{d\mathbf{R}_{B/1}}{dt} + \frac{d\mathbf{R}_{A/B}}{dt}, \qquad (2\text{–}52\text{a})$$

or

$$\mathbf{v}_{A/1} = \mathbf{v}_{B/1} + \mathbf{v}_{A/B}. \qquad (2\text{–}52\text{b})$$

Since A and B are on the same rigid body, $\mathbf{R}_{A/B}$ cannot stretch but can only swing. If we say that observer ② is moving with B, he will see an angular velocity $\boldsymbol{\omega}$ for the body about an axis through B. If we represent $\boldsymbol{\omega}$ by a vector along the axis, the swinging of $\mathbf{R}_{A/B}$ which is the velocity of A as seen by observer ② moving with B, can be written as*

$$\mathbf{v}_{A/B} = \boldsymbol{\omega} \times \mathbf{R}_{A/B}.$$

Thus, we can write

$$\mathbf{v}_{A/1} = \mathbf{v}_{B/1} + \boldsymbol{\omega} \times \mathbf{R}_{A/B}. \qquad (2\text{–}52\text{c})$$

To find a similar relation for accelerations, we can differentiate Eq. (2–52c) to obtain

$$\mathbf{a}_{A/1} = \mathbf{a}_{B/1} + \frac{d\boldsymbol{\omega}}{dt} \times \mathbf{R}_{A/B} + \boldsymbol{\omega} \times \frac{d\mathbf{R}_{A/B}}{dt}. \qquad (2\text{–}53\text{a})$$

Here again the last term can only involve a change by swinging, so we have

$$\mathbf{a}_{A/1} = \mathbf{a}_{B/1} + \frac{d\boldsymbol{\omega}}{dt} \times \mathbf{R}_{A/B} + \boldsymbol{\omega} \times (\boldsymbol{\omega} \times \mathbf{R}_{A/B}). \qquad (2\text{–}53\text{b})$$

These relationships are entirely compatible with our earlier ideas in this section on planar motion. Equation (2–52c) says that to get the velocity of A, we must add to the velocity of B a term $\omega R_{A/B}$ perpendicular to the radius from B to A. Equation (2–53b) says that to get the acceleration of A, we must add to the acceleration of B an $R\alpha$-term perpendicular to $\mathbf{R}_{A/B}$ and an $\omega^2 R$-term along $R_{A/B}$.

2–4 Motion relative to rotating observers. Until now, we have made no use of our observer ③ who is willing to rotate [except in passing in Fig. 2–20(c) for the radar display on the turning ship]. Before we study the general case of making observations in a rotating reference space, we should look at the two special cases of rotating systems of axes, which we have already studied; namely, cylindrical and spherical coordinates. If

---

* Remember that the vector cross product represents a vector perpendicular to the two constituent vectors as shown in Fig. 2–30(b) with the magnitude $\omega R_{A/B} \sin \theta$. See your mathematics text for review of vector algebra.

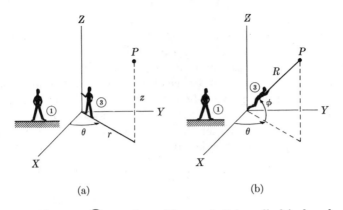

FIG. 2–31. Observer ③ rotating with r and R in cylindrical and spherical coordinates, respectively.

you look back at our derivations, you will see that when we were writing expressions for velocity and acceleration components of point P, we were adopting the viewpoint of observer ① in Fig. 2–31. Thus when we write

$$v_r = \frac{dr}{dt}, \qquad (2\text{–}17)$$

$$v_\theta = r\frac{d\theta}{dt}, \qquad (2\text{–}18)$$

$$v_z = \frac{dz}{dt}, \qquad (2\text{–}16)$$

the vector sum of these components represents the velocity of P as seen by ① standing at the fixed origin (Fig. 2–31a).

Let us call in our observer ③, who is willing to rotate, and ask him to stand at the origin so that he does not translate. At the same time, however, we will ask him to stand on r and ride around with it at the rate $d\theta/dt$. Observer ③ finds that in order to watch P as it moves, he does not have to turn his head to left or right. He sees changes in only the r- and z-distances and does not see the coordinate θ, its changes, or even any need for such a coordinate. Thus he sees v_r and v_z, but not v_θ. Similarly, in the expressions for acceleration components seen by ① in the cylindrical reference directions, our observer ③ sees only the bracketed terms.

$$a_r = \left[\frac{d^2r}{dt^2}\right] - r\left(\frac{d\theta}{dt}\right)^2, \qquad a_\theta = r\frac{d^2\theta}{dt^2} + 2\frac{dr}{dt}\frac{d\theta}{dt}, \qquad (2\text{–}21)$$

$$a_z = \left[\frac{d^2z}{dt^2}\right]. \qquad (2\text{–}16)$$

The other terms must be added to his observations in order to obtain components of absolute acceleration. They represent the distortion introduced by the rotation of observer ③ in this situation.

Looking now at spherical coordinates (Fig. 2–31b), our nonrotating observer ① sees the velocity and acceleration components in Eqs. (2–34) through (2–37), as we previously derived them. An observer ③ who rides on the axis R, however, finds he is always looking directly at P, and its motion appears to be either directly toward him or away from him. Thus he sees only the two bracketed terms in Eqs. (2–34) and (2–38)

$$v_R = \left[\frac{dR}{dt}\right], \tag{2-34}$$

$$v_\phi = R\frac{d\phi}{dt}, \tag{2-35}$$

$$v_\theta = R\cos\phi\,\frac{d\theta}{dt}, \tag{2-36}$$

$$a_R = \left[\frac{d^2R}{dt^2}\right] - R\left(\frac{d\phi}{dt}\right)^2 - R\cos^2\phi\left(\frac{d\theta}{dt}\right)^2,$$

$$a_\theta = R\cos\phi\,\frac{d^2\theta}{dt^2} + 2\left(\frac{dR}{dt}\cos\phi - R\frac{d\phi}{dt}\sin\phi\right)\frac{d\theta}{dt}, \tag{2-38}$$

$$a_\phi = R\frac{d^2\phi}{dt^2} + 2\frac{dR}{dt}\frac{d\phi}{dt} + R\sin\phi\cos\phi\left(\frac{d\theta}{dt}\right)^2.$$

The other terms can be thought to be necessary to remove the distortion from his observations so that he may obtain components of absolute velocity and acceleration.

Leaving these specialized cases of rotating observers, let's look, in a more general situation, at the difference between the observations of a nonrotating and a rotating observer. We will assume that both observers have the same translational motion and that the only difference between ② and ③ is that ③ is rotating at the angular velocity $\boldsymbol{\Omega}$. Let's visualize them as moving with point O in Fig. 2–32(a) as they watch the motion of point P. We will draw the vector $\boldsymbol{\Omega}$ through O with a little platform for ③ to stand on. (If you would prefer to think of point O as being stationary, this can easily be done by thinking of yourself as having the same motion as O; then O appears fixed.)

Both observers ② and ③ agree to use the vector $\mathbf{R}$ to describe the position of P at the instant t. To help visualize the changes in the time interval dt, we will sketch the circle centered on $\boldsymbol{\Omega}$, which contains P at time t (Fig. 2–32b), and which ② would call the path of P if ③ said P was stationary. The position of P at time $t + dt$ for a more general motion

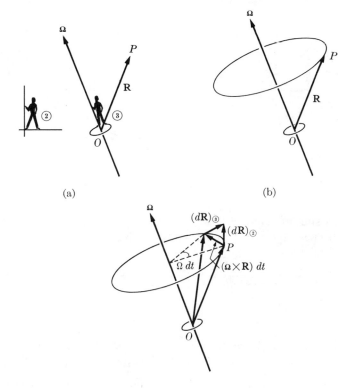

(a)   (b)

(c)

Fig. 2–32. Position and changes in position seen by observers ② and ③ who have the same translational motion.

of P is sketched in Fig. 2–32(c). Observer ② says P moved up to the left $(d\mathbf{R})_②$. He arrived at this conclusion by comparing the new position of P with the old position. Rotating observer ③ differs, however, because his idea of the original position of P is not the same as for ②. The reference space in which ③ mentally marked out $\mathbf{R}$ is a space rotating at the rate $\boldsymbol{\Omega}$. Thus ③ has rotated through an angle $\boldsymbol{\Omega}\,dt$, and what he called the original position vector $\mathbf{R}$ has rotated the same amount. He then says that P has moved up to the right $(d\mathbf{R})_③$. The relationship between these observations is, from Fig. 2–32(c),

$$(d\mathbf{R})_② = (d\mathbf{R})_③ + (\boldsymbol{\Omega} \times \mathbf{R})\,dt.$$

If we divide by the time interval (happily they don't disagree on this), we get

$$\left(\frac{d\mathbf{R}}{dt}\right)_② = \left(\frac{d\mathbf{R}}{dt}\right)_③ + \boldsymbol{\Omega} \times \mathbf{R}. \qquad (2\text{–}54a)$$

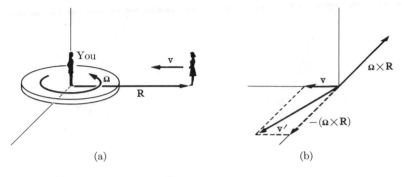

FIGURE 2-33

In order to simplify notation, we will use a prime to denote observer ③ and the absence of a prime to denote ②. Thus

$$\frac{d\mathbf{R}}{dt} = \frac{d'\mathbf{R}}{dt} + \mathbf{\Omega} \times \mathbf{R}, \tag{2-54b}$$

or

$$\mathbf{v} = \mathbf{v}' + \mathbf{\Omega} \times \mathbf{R}. \tag{2-54c}$$

Apparently observers ② and ③ while watching the same point P agree at any instant on its position ($\mathbf{R} = \mathbf{R}'$) but disagree on its velocity.

EXAMPLE 2-9. Suppose you are standing on a turntable rotating at the rate $\mathbf{\Omega}$ when a girl enters the room and walks straight toward you at the velocity $\mathbf{v}$ (Fig. 2-33a). What do you see for her velocity? Solving Eq. (2-54c) for your observation, we have

$$\mathbf{v}' = \mathbf{v} - \mathbf{\Omega} \times \mathbf{R},$$

which gives the vector picture in Fig. 2-33(b). Thus, to keep her in view, you must swivel your head to the right. To you, she is following a spiral course, whereas the nonrotating observer ② says she is walking straight toward you. ▲

So far our observers ② and ③ have been comparing observations of the rate of change of a position vector. They are quite willing to observe rate of change of any vector quantity such as $\mathbf{A}$ in Fig. 2-34. In general $\mathbf{A}$ will not originate at either observer if it is not a position vector like $\mathbf{R}$, but both observers can watch $\mathbf{A}$ stretch and swing. They will differ on the swinging of $\mathbf{A}$ by $\mathbf{\Omega}$, so, by analogy with Fig. 2-32 and Eq. (2-54b),

$$\frac{d\mathbf{A}}{dt} = \frac{d'\mathbf{A}}{dt} + \mathbf{\Omega} \times \mathbf{A}. \tag{2-55}$$

In words, two observers, one of whom rotates at the rate $\mathbf{\Omega}$, differ on the rate of change they see for the vector quantity $\mathbf{A}$ by the amount $\mathbf{\Omega} \times \mathbf{A}$. This general result is often called the *Theorem of Coriolis.*

Using this theorem we should be able to extend Eq. (2–54c) for velocities to accelerations. We must be careful when we talk of differentiating an equation, however, because there is a difference between the derivatives or rates of change seen by observers ② and ③. (Remember that for Eq. (2–54c) both observers have exactly the same linear motion in order to agree on the particle's position vector $\mathbf{R}$. Usually this restriction is unnecessary for the application of the Coriolis theorem.) If we take the derivative or rate of change of Eq. (2–54c) as seen by ②, we have

$$\frac{d\mathbf{v}}{dt} = \frac{d\mathbf{v}'}{dt} + \frac{d\mathbf{\Omega}}{dt} \times \mathbf{R} + \mathbf{\Omega} \times \frac{d\mathbf{R}}{dt}.$$

To interpret the first term on the right-hand side, we can think of $\mathbf{v}$ as $\mathbf{A}$ in Eq. (2–55). We can then write

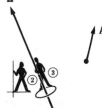

FIG. 2–34. Observers ② and ③ watch the general vector $\mathbf{A}$.

$$\frac{d\mathbf{v}'}{dt} = \frac{d'\mathbf{v}'}{dt} + \mathbf{\Omega} \times \mathbf{v}' = \mathbf{a}' + \mathbf{\Omega} \times \mathbf{v}',$$

where $\mathbf{a}'$ is the acceleration of P seen by ③; that is, the rate of change ③ sees of $\mathbf{v}'$. Combining these two equations with Eq. (2–54), we obtain the result

$$\mathbf{a} = \mathbf{a}' + \frac{d\mathbf{\Omega}}{dt} \times \mathbf{R} + 2\mathbf{\Omega} \times \mathbf{v}' + \mathbf{\Omega} \times (\mathbf{\Omega} \times \mathbf{R}), \qquad (2\text{–}56)$$

which relates the accelerations of P seen by observers ② and ③. You will have the opportunity in problems at the end of the chapter to show that the velocity and acceleration expressions in cylindrical and spherical coordinates can be considered special cases of Eqs. (2–54) and (2–56). Note that if the origin O of both observers ② and ③ is linearly accelerated at the rate $\mathbf{a}_0$, then the absolute acceleration of P is given by

$$\mathbf{a} = \mathbf{a}_0 + \left[\mathbf{a}' + \frac{d\mathbf{\Omega}}{dt} \times \mathbf{R} + 2\mathbf{\Omega} \times \mathbf{v}' + \mathbf{\Omega} \times (\mathbf{\Omega} \times \mathbf{R}) \right]. \quad (2\text{–}57)$$

EXAMPLE 2–10. For an application of the acceleration expression [Eq. (2–56)] look again at the problem of Fig. 2–33. Let's specify that the girl's velocity $\mathbf{v}$ is constant and see if you on your rotating platform observe any acceleration for her. Solving Eq. (2–56) for $\mathbf{a}'$ and noting that

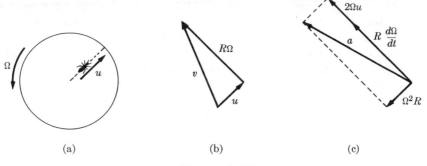

$$(a)\qquad\qquad\qquad (b)\qquad\qquad\qquad (c)$$

FIGURE 2–35

a is equal to zero, we have

$$\mathbf{a}' = -\frac{d\mathbf{\Omega}}{dt} \times \mathbf{R} - 2\mathbf{\Omega} \times \mathbf{v}' - \mathbf{\Omega} \times (\mathbf{\Omega} \times \mathbf{R}).$$

The first term is similar to the $R\alpha$-term we have seen before. The last term corresponds to the familiar $\Omega^2 R$-term. The middle term is not so familiar and is often called the *Coriolis acceleration*. Thus the girl does not appear unaccelerated to you as you watch her traverse a spiral path. Try plotting the individual acceleration terms and see if they seem reasonable to you in terms of the spiral path you saw in Example 2–9. ▲

EXAMPLE 2–11. Returning to our accelerating phonograph record of Example 2–1, we now notice an ant walking from the center toward the rim (Fig. 2–35a). He says his velocity is constant in both magnitude and direction (he proceeds perpendicular to the grooves), and therefore he is unaccelerated. What do we, as stationary observers, see?

To find his velocity we use Eq. (2–54c) to obtain

$$v = u +\!\!\!+ R\Omega$$

as shown in Fig. 2–35(b). Equation (2–56) gives his acceleration as

$$a = a' +\!\!\!+ R\frac{d\Omega}{dt} +\!\!\!+ 2\Omega u +\!\!\!+ \Omega^2 R,$$

shown in Fig. 2–35(c). (Remember a' is zero in this case.) Suppose another ant is standing on the south rim of the record. Does the first ant appear to him to be accelerating? ▲

EXAMPLE 2–12. Watching satellites from the surface of the earth is a situation in which we find ourselves to be rotating observers, whether we

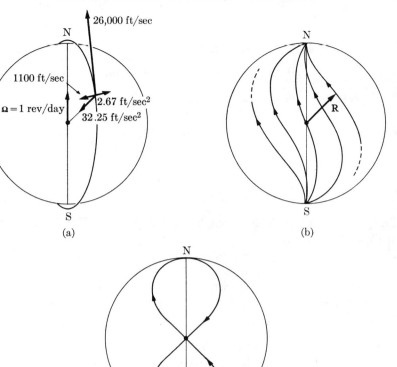

(a)   (b)

(c)

FIGURE 2–36

like it or not. Suppose we are watching a near satellite on a circular pole-to-pole orbit as it crosses 45° north latitude. To a nonrotating observer at the earth's center, the satellite moves at a constant speed of 26,000 ft/sec in a circular path and has an acceleration toward the earth's center of 32 ft/sec². We are standing on the earth's surface at 45° and rotating with it. What do we observe for the satellite's velocity and acceleration?

As a first step, note that any two observers on the earth who appear stationary to each other will completely agree on the velocity and acceleration of a particle which they both observe. They will disagree only on its position by the distance separating them. Thus we can use directly the observations of observer ③ stationed at the earth's center O, who is rotating with the earth at one revolution per day (see Fig. 2–36a). The satellite's velocity as seen by ③ is thus, for R of about 4000 mi,

$$\mathbf{v}' = \mathbf{v} - \mathbf{\Omega} \times \mathbf{R}$$
$$= 26{,}000 \text{ north} \nrightarrow 1100 \text{ west (in ft/sec)}.$$

The acceleration seen by ③ (and thus by us) is

$$\mathbf{a}' = \mathbf{a} - \frac{d\mathbf{\Omega}}{dt} \times \mathbf{R} - 2\mathbf{\Omega} \times \mathbf{v}' - \mathbf{\Omega} \times (\mathbf{\Omega} \times \mathbf{R})$$

$$= \mathbf{a} - \frac{d\mathbf{\Omega}}{dt} \times \mathbf{R} - 2\mathbf{\Omega} \times \mathbf{v} + \mathbf{\Omega} \times (\mathbf{\Omega} \times \mathbf{R})$$

$$= 32.25 \text{ radially in} \nrightarrow 0 \nrightarrow 2.67 \text{ east} \nrightarrow 0.08 \text{ in normal to } \mathbf{\Omega} \text{ (in ft/sec}^2).$$

The projection down onto the earth's surface of the satellite's path is shown in Fig. 2–36(b).

A satellite at a height to make just one revolution per day will remain over one point on the earth's equator if launched in an equatorial orbit. Its velocity and acceleration will be zero as seen from the earth. If it is launched in a polar orbit, can you see that the projection on the earth of its path is given by Fig. 2–36(c)? ▲

Before leaving the subject of relative motion, we should be aware of one important idea. We have looked at the motion of a particle P from the point of view of stationary and translating observers ① and ②, respectively, and have derived the relations

$$\mathbf{v}_{P/1} = \mathbf{v}_{P/2} + \mathbf{v}_{2/1} \quad \text{and} \quad \mathbf{a}_{P/1} = \mathbf{a}_{P/2} + \mathbf{a}_{2/1}. \quad (2\text{--}58)$$

Suppose we think for the moment that ② is really stationary and ① is accelerating. Remembering that $v_{2/1}$ and $a_{2/1}$ are the negatives of $v_{1/2}$ and $a_{1/2}$, we can solve Eq. (2–58) for what we now believe to be the motion seen by a stationary observer. We will get

$$\mathbf{v}_{P/2} = \mathbf{v}_{P/1} + \mathbf{v}_{1/2} \quad \text{and} \quad \mathbf{a}_{P/2} = \mathbf{a}_{P/1} + \mathbf{a}_{1/2}. \quad (2\text{--}59)$$

Note that Eqs. (2–59) have exactly the same form as Eqs. (2–58). Apparently *the form of the equations gives no indication as to which observer is stationary.* In fact, either set holds even if both observers are accelerating.

To show a similar result, look at the relations that we derived between the observations of observers ② and ③ who have the same linear motion although ③ rotates as well.

$$\mathbf{v} = \mathbf{v}' + \mathbf{\Omega} \times \mathbf{R}, \quad (2\text{--}54)$$

$$\mathbf{a} = \mathbf{a}' + \frac{d\mathbf{\Omega}}{dt} \times \mathbf{R} + 2\mathbf{\Omega} \times \mathbf{v}' + \mathbf{\Omega} \times (\mathbf{\Omega} \times \mathbf{R}). \quad (2\text{--}56)$$

Let's, for the moment, assume that ③ is really nonrotating and ②
rotates at $-\mathbf{\Omega}$ (which we will call $\mathbf{\Omega}'$). Solving for $\mathbf{v}'$ and $\mathbf{a}'$, we get

$$\mathbf{v}' = \mathbf{v} + \mathbf{\Omega}' \times \mathbf{R},$$

$$\mathbf{a}' = \mathbf{a} + \frac{d\mathbf{\Omega}'}{dt} \times \mathbf{R} + 2\mathbf{\Omega}' \times \mathbf{v} + \mathbf{\Omega}' \times (\mathbf{\Omega}' \times \mathbf{R}). \tag{2-60}$$

This set is completely analogous to Eqs. (2–54) and (2–56). We can then
deduce that these equations may be used even when both ② and ③ are
rotating, provided $\mathbf{\Omega}$ represents the difference between the angular velocities of ③ and ②.

PROBLEMS

2–1. The lighthouse keeper in Example 2–2 finds it convenient to come down
from the light by sliding down the spiral railing of the stairway. His path is
thus a spiral of constant diameter and pitch.

(a) If he slides at a constant speed, what does his hodograph look like, and
what is the magnitude and direction of his acceleration?

(b) If, one day, he loses control and he finds his speed increasing at a constant
rate, what shape does his hodograph take?

2–2. A particle moves in an elliptical path with constant speed. At what
points is the magnitude of acceleration (a) a maximum, (b) a minimum? Explain
your reasoning in some detail and sketch the shape of the hodograph.

2–3. Water drips from a faucet at the uniform rate of n drops per second. Find
the distance x between two adjacent drops as a function of the time t since the
second drop leaves the faucet. Neglect air resistance by assuming only a constant
vertical acceleration g.

2–4. Explain the differences in the meanings and implications of the symbols

$$\frac{ds}{dt}, \quad \frac{d\mathbf{R}}{dt}, \quad \dot{\mathbf{R}}, \quad \ddot{\mathbf{R}}, \quad \frac{dv}{dt},$$

remembering that the dot is a popular shorthand notation for d/dt.

2–5. Suppose a satellite is observed to follow an elliptical path around a celestial
body with the body's center at one focus. It is also observed that the component
of the satellite's velocity perpendicular to the position vector $\mathbf{R}$ from the focus is
inversely proportional to the magnitude of $\mathbf{R}$. (a) Sketch a large ellipse and plot
the satellite's velocity vector at a number of points. (b) Sketch the hodograph
for the satellite's motion. (c) Demonstrate graphically that the satellite's acceleration is always directed along $\mathbf{R}$.

2–6. Suppose a particle follows a path such that the component of its velocity
perpendicular to its position vector $\mathbf{R}$ is inversely proportional to the magnitude
of $\mathbf{R}$. Show analytically that the particle's acceleration is always directed along $\mathbf{R}$.

2–7. An expert pilot of a light airplane cruising at $V = 200 \text{ mi/hr}$ suddenly
pulls up into a loop which is a perfect circle in the vertical plane. If he notices

that his speed is only 100 mi/hr as he goes over the top and if we assume that his speed v varies with height h gained as $v^2 = V^2 - 2gh$ ($g = 32.2$ ft/sec^2), (a) find the radius of the loop, (b) sketch the shape of the hodograph, and (c) find the airplane's acceleration **a** when it has come halfway down again.

2–8. A child is riding a "horse" which moves up and down sinusoidally ($h = h_0 \sin at$) relative to a merry-go-round which rotates about the vertical at the constant rate Ω. If the child is at the distance c from the axis of rotation, (a) sketch the hodograph of the child's motion, and (b) find an expression for his acceleration in terms of Ω, c, h_0, a, and t.

2–9. Sketch the hodograph of a point on the rim of a wheel rolling at constant speed. What happens to the hodograph if the wheel is accelerating?

2–10. A sailor is in the "crow's nest" 100 ft up the mast on an old sailing vessel, which is rolling on the waves. If we assume that the angular motion of the mast from the vertical is in one plane and is given by $\theta = \sin t/2$, (a) sketch the path and hodograph of the sailor's linear motion indicating his velocity and acceleration at several instants, and (b) find, analytically, expressions for his acceleration when θ is zero and when it is a maximum.

2–11. Set up in cartesian coordinates expressions for the position, velocity, and acceleration of a particle P on the rim of a wheel of radius c rolling at the constant angular velocity ω along a horizontal straight line. Show that the particle's acceleration is always directed toward the center of the wheel.

2–12. A "guinea pig" pilot in a whirling-arm centrifuge is positioned 30 ft from the axis of rotation. In starting the test the arm is speeded up from 0 to 30 rev/min in 5 sec at a steady rate. What is the total acceleration of the pilot at the instant the arm is going 25 rev/min? Does this exceed the constant acceleration encountered when testing at 30 rev/min?

2–13. If the barrel of a gun is swinging about its base at the constant angular velocity Ω when the shell is fired, the shell follows a curved path as it traverses the barrel. Find the component of the shell's acceleration normal to the barrel's axis just before the shell emerges at its muzzle velocity of 6000 ft/sec.

2–14. (a) Show that the determinant of the elements of the transformation matrix from cartesian to cylindrical coordinates is equal to unity. (b) Show the same result for the transformation matrix from cartesian to spherical coordinates.

2–15. Start with

$$\begin{Bmatrix} a_x \\ a_y \\ a_z \end{Bmatrix} = \frac{d^2}{dt^2} \begin{Bmatrix} x \\ y \\ z \end{Bmatrix}$$

and show that

$$\begin{Bmatrix} a_r \\ a_\theta \\ a_z \end{Bmatrix} = [\theta_{\text{rot}}] \frac{d^2}{dt^2} \left([\theta_{\text{rot}}]' \begin{Bmatrix} r \\ 0 \\ z \end{Bmatrix} \right),$$

and then expand the result to get the usual expressions for acceleration in cylindrical coordinates.

2–16. In cylindrical coordinates, we can define the unit vectors $\mathbf{u}_r$, $\mathbf{u}_\theta$, $\mathbf{u}_z$ in the three perpendicular coordinate directions.

(a) Since unit vectors cannot change magnitude but only direction, evaluate

$$\frac{d\mathbf{u}_r}{d\theta}, \quad \frac{d\mathbf{u}_\theta}{d\theta}, \quad \frac{d\mathbf{u}_z}{d\theta}.$$

(b) Start with $\mathbf{R} = r\mathbf{u}_r + z\mathbf{u}_z$ and differentiate to find expressions for $\mathbf{v}$ and $\mathbf{a}$. Check your results against Eqs. (2–16) through (2–21).

2–17. In the spherical coordinates of Fig. 2–14, we can define the unit vectors $\mathbf{u}_R$, $\mathbf{u}_\theta$, $\mathbf{u}_\phi$ in the three perpendicular coordinate directions.

(a) Evaluate the derivatives of these unit vectors with respect to θ and to ϕ.

(b) Using these results, start with $\mathbf{R} = R\mathbf{u}_R$ and formally differentiate to obtain expressions for velocity and acceleration. Check your results against Eq. (2–38).

2–18. A large narrow-beam radar tracking antenna is trying to locate a satellite by rotating in the scanning mode (in spherical coordinates)

$$\theta = 0.0001\, t,$$
$$\phi = 1 + 0.0025 \sin 2t.$$

What is the acceleration of the feed horn if it is located 40 ft from the center of rotation?

2–19. The expressions for the components of velocity and acceleration in the spherical coordinates in which ϕ is measured down from the Z-axis rather than up from the XY-plane are

$$v_\phi = R\dot\phi, \qquad a_\phi = R\ddot\phi + 2\dot R\dot\phi - R\dot\theta^2 \sin\phi \cos\phi,$$
$$v_\theta = R\dot\theta \sin\phi, \qquad a_\theta = R\ddot\theta \sin\phi + 2\dot R\dot\theta \sin\phi + 2R\dot\theta\dot\phi \cos\phi,$$
$$v_R = \dot R, \qquad a_R = \ddot R - R\dot\phi^2 - R\dot\theta^2 \sin^2\phi.$$

Derive these expressions (a) by watching the stretching and swinging first of $\mathbf{R}$ and then of the components of velocity, and (b) by a matrix coordinate transformation from cylindrical coordinates.

2–20. The position of a satellite (Fig. 2–37) in space may be described in terms of the constants Ω and i locating its orbit plane and the polar coordinates R and u in the orbit plane as illustrated. Find the cartesian coordinates of the satellite in terms of Ω, i, u, R.

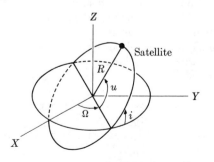

FIGURE 2–37

2–21. On a canted-deck aircraft carrier, one catapult is directed 15° to the left of the ship's fore-and-aft axis. How much of a "crosswind" does the pilot experience at takeoff if the catapult gives him a speed of 80 mi/hr relative to the carrier? Assume the carrier is heading at 25 mi/hr directly into a wind of 15 mi/hr.

2–22. Referring to the bird making a U-turn in the air in Example 2–4 and Fig. 2–19, sketch the bird's path over the ground and its hodograph if it makes the same turn in (a) a tailwind for which $v_w = V$, and (b) a crosswind for which $v_w = \frac{1}{2}V$.

2–23. Suppose you are flying a glider at a steady airspeed of 40 mi/hr. Because it has no engine, the glider is sinking downward through the air at 3 mi/hr.

(a) You are headed north on the windward side of a long east-west mountain range where the 20 mi/hr wind from the north is inclined upward at 10°. What are your vertical and horizontal speeds relative to the ground?

(b) Suppose, instead, you are maintaining under the same wind conditions a path over the ground that is directly east. What is your heading?

2–24. In Example 2–5 and Fig. 2–20, we watched, on a ship's radarscope, the approach of another ship C on a collision course 45° off the starboard bow. Assume that our speed is 30 knots and that the speed of ship C relative to us is 20 knots at a range of 3 nautical miles when our captain reverses engines and causes us to decelerate at about $\frac{1}{10}$ knot/sec. Find the path of C's blip on the radarscope and calculate the minimum separation of the two ships.

2–25. A "flying saucer" (of radius c) recently was seen moving at constant speed V in a horizontal circular path of radius A. It was, of course, also spinning about a vertical axis through its own center at the constant angular velocity ω.

(a) Locate the saucer's instantaneous center by graphical construction and then use it to indicate the velocity **v** relative to the ground of an arbitrary point P on the saucer's rim.

(b) Find the acceleration of P as seen by a nonrotating observer moving with the center of the saucer.

(c) What is the acceleration of P as seen from the ground?

2–26. An inexperienced driver starting his car from rest on icy pavement spins his $2\frac{1}{2}$ ft diameter rear wheels at 4 rev/sec while achieving a constant 3 ft/sec/sec acceleration. Five seconds after starting, find the velocity and acceleration relative to the ground of the point on the wheel in contact with the ground.

2–27. A half-cylinder (Fig. 2–38) is rocking back and forth sinusoidally without slipping, as shown, such that $\theta = \sin 2t$.

(a) As it goes through the neutral position of $\theta = 0$, what is the acceleration of the point in contact with the stationary surface?

(b) When the half-cylinder is at the maximum angle of $\theta = 1$ radian, what is the acceleration of the point then in contact?

2–28. Can you find the instantaneous centers for the rigid bodies shown in (a), (b), and (c) of Fig. 2–39? In which case does the body have the largest angular velocity? Does (c) lead you to a restriction on velocities for points in the same rigid body? If so, what is it?

2–29. If you are rotating on your merry-go-round at 10 rev/min as the girl in Examples 2–9 and 2–11 approaches at a speed of 3 ft/sec from a 50-ft distance,

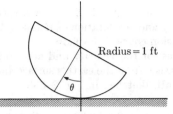

FIGURE 2–38

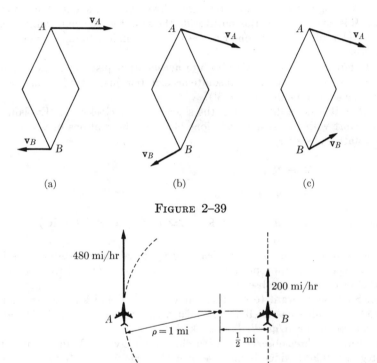

FIGURE 2–39

FIGURE 2–40

find her path as it appears to you and sketch the shape of the corresponding hodograph.

2–30. Let's return to the ant, in Example 2–11, walking radially on the phonograph record at what he calls constant speed. Do other ants clinging to the record see him walking at constant speed? Can we generalize this conclusion and make the statement that any group of observers who appear to each other to be stationary will agree on the velocity and acceleration of a particle they are all watching?

2–31. The pilot of airplane A (Fig. 2–40) is traveling at 480 mi/hr in a steady turn of radius $\rho = 1$ mi and thus is both rotating and accelerating when he sees another plane B 1.5 mi to his right. If B has an airspeed of 200 mi/hr as shown, (a) what are the velocity and acceleration of B as seen by the pilot of A? (b) Are the airplanes on a collision course? Explain.

2–32. Find expressions for the velocity and acceleration of a 24-hr satellite in a circular polar orbit as seen from the earth's surface and see if they are consistent with the trace of the path sketched in Fig. 2–36(c).

2–33. What would a ground observer see for the apparent motion of a 24-hr satellite whose circular orbit is in a plane only very slightly inclined to the equatorial plane?

2–34. A flying saucer rotating counterclockwise about its axis of symmetry at the rate Ω is hovering over Boston. Inside the saucer a crewman walks at a constant speed V directly from one rim observation window to another 60° around the saucer.

(a) Compare the crewman's absolute acceleration just before he leaves the first window ($v' = 0$) with his absolute acceleration just after he starts walking toward the second window ($v' = V$).

(b) Does it make a difference if the saucer rotates clockwise? Explain.

2–35. Start with the general relations between observations of a nonrotating and a rotating observer,

$$\mathbf{R} = \mathbf{R}',$$

$$\mathbf{v} = \mathbf{v}' + \mathbf{\Omega} \times \mathbf{R}',$$

$$\mathbf{a} = \mathbf{a}' + \frac{d\mathbf{\Omega}}{dt} \times \mathbf{R}' + 2\mathbf{\Omega} \times \mathbf{v}' + \mathbf{\Omega} \times (\mathbf{\Omega} \times \mathbf{R}'),$$

and specialize to the usual cylindrical and spherical coordinate systems by, in each case, specifying appropriately the angular velocity $\mathbf{\Omega}$ and the observations $\mathbf{v}'$ and $\mathbf{a}'$ of the rotating observer.

2–36. Suppose we want to use the unit vectors $\mathbf{i}$, $\mathbf{j}$, and $\mathbf{k}$ for a cartesian axis system XYZ which has itself the angular velocity components Ω_x, Ω_y, and Ω_z. Find expressions for $d\mathbf{i}/dt$, $d\mathbf{j}/dt$, and $d\mathbf{k}/dt$.

2–37. Suppose three observers are watching a force vector $\mathbf{F}$ and want to figure its integral ($\int_{t_1}^{t_2} \mathbf{F} dt$) which is impulse over the time interval t_1 to t_2. Observer ① claims $\mathbf{F}$ is constant in magnitude and direction and calculates an impulse of $\mathbf{F}(t_2 - t_1)$.

(a) Observer ② while accelerating linearly but not rotating also calculates the impulse of the force vector $\mathbf{F}$. Does he agree with ①?

(b) Observer ③ rotates at constant angular velocity such that he makes a complete revolution in the time interval $t_2 - t_1$. What resultant impulse does he see for the force vector $\mathbf{F}$?

2–38. Suppose two observers rotating at different constant rates watch a particle, which the first observer says is stationary. What does the particle's motion appear to be to the second observer (a) if both observers are rotating about the same axis, (b) if the observers are rotating about stationary but parallel axes?

CHAPTER 3

DYNAMICS OF PARTICLES

3–1 Inertial reference systems. As we discussed in Chapter 1, the successful application of Newton's brand of dynamics with its Euclidean space, independent time, and complete relativity of position and velocity, depends entirely on the use of adequate inertial reference systems. These inertial or Galilean systems must permit, in a given situation, an accurate enough reference from which to measure linear acceleration and angular velocity, and thus permit application of Newton's second law.

We say accurate enough because a perfectly unaccelerated system is an idealization in the sense that it is unattainable in the laboratory. On a given body, we can reduce and minimize one disturbing influence after another in trying to obtain our ideal "natural state of motion," but we cannot eliminate them completely. Gravity, which must be considered a disturbing influence in Newtonian mechanics, is particularly difficult to minimize. We can visualize the successive steps of moving our laboratory away from the earth, out of our solar system, and then out of the Milky Way galaxy, but we cannot actually do it.* We can only infer that we would get successively better concepts of unaccelerated motion. So far this inference has seemed to work well. Whenever our usual nearby reference has not been unaccelerated enough, we have been able to get answers which check observations by going to a more distant but less accelerated reference system. You will find in many older texts the statement that all motion should be referred to the fixed stars. As more and more has been learned about the motions of stars and galaxies, we find the phrase appearing in relatively recent texts as "the fixed stars." How much longer this procedure will work is difficult to say because we are devising and using instruments every year which measure accelerations more and more accurately.

Note that our reference system or Galilean observer must be nonrotating as well as unaccelerated. In our process above, of minimizing one disturbing influence after another on a body to permit it to assume unaccelerated rectilinear motion, we should realize that such a motion appears unaccelerated only to an unaccelerated observer who is also nonrotating. It can thus be used as a criterion for zero angular velocity as well as zero linear acceleration for a reference system or observer. We should also remember

---

* On a cosmological scale, gravity is not at all well understood. See Chapter 12 and also Sciama, Ref. 4, Part II of *The Unity of the Universe.*

that all these efforts at defining an inertial observer or reference frame are based on Euclidean space and an absolute independent time. Even in ordinary situations where extreme precision is required, it may occasionally be necessary to adopt the space-time concepts of Chapter 12.

Let's look at some of the numbers involved. An observer standing on the surface of the earth has both an angular velocity and a linear acceleration as a result of the rotation of the earth about its polar axis. His angular velocity is that of the earth, one revolution per day. Alternatively, this is 6.9×10^{-4} rev/min, or 7.3×10^{-5} rad/sec. The linear acceleration is entirely centripetal and approximately $0.11 \cos \phi$ ft/sec/sec where ϕ is his latitude. His acceleration due to the motion of the earth's center around the sun is again centripetal toward the sun and about 0.019 ft/sec/sec. It would seem that for a very large number of practical problems we can, without significant error, use a reference system right on the surface of the earth or perhaps at its center and call it inertial or Galilean. We must just be sure in a given situation that we choose an inertial reference system and its observer ① unaccelerated enough for the purposes for which they are used.

EXAMPLE 3–1. In some cases it is very easy to get a good answer to a problem on the basis of quite incorrect assumptions. We have all done it at one time or another. An example is the study of satellite motion around the earth. We use a nonrotating earth-centered observer ① whose sun-induced acceleration is only 0.019 ft/sec^2, which is quite small compared with the earth-induced accelerations of low-altitude satellites. However, we soon find ourselves calculating, on the same basis, orbits of far satellites, including the moon. A quick calculation shows that the moon's acceleration in orbit around the earth is only 0.0088 ft/sec^2, or less than half that of our earth-centered observer. Yet our answer is not very incorrect. Let's write the equations using a sun-centered observer ① and see what is happening. With the symbols shown in Fig. 3–1, we can write the vector equations

$$\mathbf{R}_{M/E} = \mathbf{R}_{M/S} - \mathbf{R}_{E/S} \quad \text{and} \quad \mathbf{a}_{M/E} = \mathbf{a}_{M/S} - \mathbf{a}_{E/S},$$

where $\mathbf{a}_{M/E}$ is the acceleration of the moon seen by our earth-centered nonrotating observer ②. Using Newton's law of gravitation and remem-

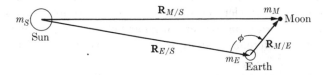

FIGURE 3–1

bering that the moon is attracted by both the sun and the earth, we find the total external force $\mathbf{F}$ acting on the moon is

$$\mathbf{F} = \mathbf{F}_{M/S} + \mathbf{F}_{M/E} = -\gamma m_M \left(\frac{m_S}{R_{M/S}^2} \frac{\mathbf{R}_{M/S}}{R_{M/S}} + \frac{m_E}{R_{M/E}^2} \frac{\mathbf{R}_{M/E}}{R_{M/E}} \right),$$

where γ is the universal gravitational constant. By substituting for $R_{M/S}$ and remembering that $R_{M/E} \ll R_{E/S}$, we see that the first term on the right becomes

$$-\gamma m_M m_S \frac{\mathbf{R}_{M/S}}{R_{M/S}^3} = -\frac{\gamma m_M m_S (\mathbf{R}_{E/S} + \mathbf{R}_{M/E})}{(R_{E/S}^2 + R_{M/E}^2 - 2R_{E/S}R_{M/E}\cos\phi)^{3/2}}$$

$$= -\frac{\gamma m_M m_S (\mathbf{R}_{E/S} + \mathbf{R}_{M/E})}{R_{E/S}^3 \left(1 - 2\dfrac{R_{M/E}}{R_{E/S}}\cos\phi + \dfrac{R_{M/E}^2}{R_{E/S}^2} \right)^{3/2}}$$

$$= \frac{-\gamma m_M m_S}{R_{E/S}^3} (\mathbf{R}_{E/S} + \mathbf{R}_{M/E})$$

$$\times \left(1 + 3\frac{R_{M/E}}{R_{E/S}}\cos\phi + \cdots \right).$$

Employing Newton's second law to relate the total gravitational force on the moon $\mathbf{F}$ to its absolute acceleration $\mathbf{a}_{M/S}$, we get

$$\mathbf{a}_{M/S} = \mathbf{a}_{E/S} + \mathbf{a}_{M/E} = \frac{-\gamma m_S \mathbf{R}_{E/S}}{R_{E/S}^3} - \frac{\gamma m_E \mathbf{R}_{M/E}}{R_{M/E}^3} - \frac{\gamma m_S}{R_{E/S}^2}$$

$$\times \frac{R_{M/E}}{R_{E/S}} \left(\frac{\mathbf{R}_{M/E}}{R_{M/E}} + 3\frac{\mathbf{R}_{E/S}}{R_{E/S}}\cos\phi \right) + \cdots,$$

after cancelling m_M from both sides. If we look for a moment at Newton's second law, written for the earth acted upon by sun and moon, as

$$\mathbf{a}_{E/S} = -\frac{\gamma m_S \mathbf{R}_{E/S}}{R_{E/S}^3} + \frac{\gamma m_M \mathbf{R}_{M/E}}{R_{M/E}^3},$$

we can substitute this in the previous equation and obtain

$$\mathbf{a}_{M/E} = -0.0088 \frac{\mathbf{R}_{M/E}}{R_{M/E}} - (0.0088) \left(\frac{1}{83} \right) \frac{\mathbf{R}_{M/E}}{R_{M/E}}$$

$$- (0.019)(0.0026) \left[\frac{\mathbf{R}_{M/E}}{R_{M/E}} + 3\frac{\mathbf{R}_{E/S}}{R_{E/S}}\cos\phi \right] + \cdots,$$

where the first term on the right represents Newton's second law for the moon in the earth's field with accelerations measured relative to the earth's center. The remaining terms are a measure of the error committed in this, our original process, and are only of the order of one percent. The first of the error terms which contains the ratio 1/83 of moon to earth mass will disappear, as we will see in a later section (3–5), if our observer ② is moved to the center of mass of the earth-moon system. The remaining error terms can be attributed to the nonuniformity rather than absolute strength of the sun's gravitational field. If the earth and moon had instead been in a uniform parallel gravitational field, it would have had no effect on their relative motion since it would have imparted the same absolute accelerations to each. Note that this result is related to the property of gravitational fields of producing, on a particle, forces proportional to the particle's mass so that its absolute acceleration is independent of its mass. ▲

3–2 Newton's second law. Often the most difficult part of a problem in dynamics is the process of assessing a physical situation so that we may idealize it sufficiently for it to be represented by a tractable mathematical problem. Too much enthusiasm can result in oversimplification and a misleading answer; too little can keep our high-speed computers whirring night and day.

If we plan to use directly Newton's second law, which says that for a particle of mass m the external forces on the particle are related vectorially to its absolute acceleration,

$$\sum \mathbf{F} = m\mathbf{a}_{\text{abs}}, \tag{3–1}$$

then we should deal only with problems in which the relevant body of matter can be adequately represented as a particle. To be sure that we have the body completely identified (most experienced people strongly recommend that we actually draw a *free-body diagram*), we should make a sketch of the relevant body entirely separate from any surrounding material. Such a free-body diagram simplifies (and thus makes less subject to error) the process of identifying all the forces acting on the body. This is particularly true of the contact forces applied at the surface of the body. Make sure that the so-called distant-acting forces like gravity are also identified. By comparing the characteristics of the body's motion with those of the applied forces, we can choose the type of reference system and notation which appears to offer the most convenience. This is particularly true for the kinematics of the problem and is the main reason we looked at so many techniques in Chapter 2.

In the *natural coordinates* of Section 2–1, which are particularly convenient for finding forces which produce a given motion, Newton's second law can be written as

$$\Sigma\mathbf{F} = m\mathbf{a}_{\text{abs}} = m\left[\mathbf{T}\frac{d^2s}{dt^2} + \mathbf{N}K\left(\frac{ds}{dt}\right)^2\right] \tag{3-2a}$$

or in scalar form

$$\Sigma F_T = m\frac{dv}{dt}, \qquad \Sigma F_N = mKv^2 = \frac{mv^2}{\rho}. \tag{3-2b}$$

Written in the *cartesian coordinates* of Section 2–2, the second law becomes, in the usual scalar form (absolute acceleration of course),

$$\Sigma F_x = ma_x = m\frac{d^2x}{dt^2},$$

$$\Sigma F_y = ma_y = m\frac{d^2y}{dt^2}, \tag{3-3}$$

$$\Sigma F_z = ma_z = m\frac{d^2z}{dt^2}.$$

In *cylindrical coordinates*, it is written as

$$\Sigma F_r = ma_r = m\left[\frac{d^2r}{dt^2} - r\left(\frac{d\theta}{dt}\right)^2\right],$$

$$\Sigma F_\theta = ma_\theta = m\left(r\frac{d^2\theta}{dt^2} + 2\frac{dr}{dt}\frac{d\theta}{dt}\right), \tag{3-4}$$

$$\Sigma F_z = ma_z = m\frac{d^2z}{dt}.$$

In *spherical coordinates*, we write

$$\Sigma F_R = ma_R = m\left[\frac{d^2R}{dt^2} - R\left(\frac{d\phi}{dt}\right)^2 - R\cos^2\phi\left(\frac{d\theta}{dt}\right)^2\right],$$

$$\Sigma F_\theta = ma_\theta = m\left[R\cos\phi\frac{d^2\theta}{dt^2} + 2\left(\frac{dR}{dt}\cos\phi - R\sin\phi\frac{d\phi}{dt}\right)\frac{d\theta}{dt}\right], \tag{3-5}$$

$$\Sigma F_\phi = ma_\phi = m\left[R\frac{d^2\phi}{dt^2} + R\cos\phi\sin\phi\left(\frac{d\theta}{dt}\right)^2 + 2\frac{dR}{dt}\frac{d\phi}{dt}\right].$$

For a *particle A in a rigid body* in terms of the absolute motion of *B* in the same body (Section 2–3),

$$\Sigma\mathbf{F} = m\mathbf{a}_{A/1} = m\left[\mathbf{a}_{B/1} + \frac{d\boldsymbol{\omega}}{dt}\times\mathbf{R}_{A/B} + \boldsymbol{\omega}\times(\boldsymbol{\omega}\times\mathbf{R}_{A/B})\right]. \tag{3-6}$$

For a *particle A seen by a linearly accelerating observer* ② whose absolute acceleration is $\mathbf{a}_{2/1}$ [Eq. (2–43)],

$$\sum \mathbf{F} = m\mathbf{a}_{A/2} + m\mathbf{a}_{2/1}. \tag{3–7a}$$

Finally, *for a particle viewed by a rotating observer* ③ [Eq. (2–56)] whose linear acceleration is zero,

$$\sum \mathbf{F} = m\left[\mathbf{a}' + \frac{d\boldsymbol{\Omega}}{dt} \times \mathbf{R} + 2\boldsymbol{\Omega} \times \mathbf{v}' + \boldsymbol{\Omega} \times (\boldsymbol{\Omega} \times \mathbf{R})\right]. \tag{3–7b}$$

If ③ has the absolute linear acceleration $\mathbf{a}_{3/1}$, Eq. (3–7b) must have the additional term $m\mathbf{a}_{3/1}$.

In the examples which follow, each of these forms will be used. In some cases we will try to find loads and stresses from given motions; in others we will look for the reverse. In all cases we will examine the important assumptions underlying the treatment.

In those situations where we are trying to predict stresses or deformations, it is particularly useful to make the dynamic problem appear in the more familiar static form. Thus, instead of writing

$$\sum \mathbf{F} = m\mathbf{a}_{\text{abs}}, \tag{3–1}$$

we can think of $-m\mathbf{a}_{\text{abs}}$ as representing an *inertia force* and write an equation of so-called dynamic equilibrium:

$$\sum \mathbf{F} + (-m\mathbf{a}_{\text{abs}}) = 0. \tag{3–8}$$

This is called *D'Alembert's principle*. The two points of view are indicated in Fig. 3–2, where the conventional use of a dotted arrow indicates the inertia force. Note that an inertia force is never seen by an inertial observer ①. In an alternative view, D'Alembert's principle says that an observer ② moving with a particle sees no motion for the particle and must instead, in applying Newton's law, visualize the inertia force equal to the negative of the particle's acceleration times its mass. Similarly, a

(a)   (b)

FIG. 3–2.   (a) The Newtonian, and (b) the D'Alembert points of view.

rotating observer ③ may find it convenient to speak of centrifugal and Coriolis forces.

EXAMPLE 3–2. Let's look at some simple vehicle maneuvers so that we can investigate the forces associated with them. A basic maneuver is the constant-speed, steady, horizontal turn. (Note that we quite naturally use the services of an observer on the surface of the earth. Is he unaccelerated enough for this problem?) Looking down on the vehicle in Fig. 3–3, let's neglect, for the moment, the orientation and size of the vehicle and characterize it by a particle of mass m moving along a circular path at speed V. Thinking in terms of the tangential and normal directions and using Eq. (3–2b), we can immediately predict the net forces which must be acting on the mass m.

$$\Sigma F_T = m\frac{dv}{dt} = m\frac{dV}{dt} = 0,$$

$$\Sigma F_N = m\frac{v^2}{\rho} = \frac{mV^2}{\rho}.$$

No net tangential force is required, but we do need a centripetal force inversely proportional to the radius of curvature.

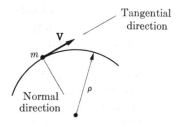

FIGURE 3–3

If our vehicle is an automobile on an unbanked curve, we can draw a free-body diagram like that in Fig. 3–4(a). The only distant-acting force of consequence is the gravitational attraction of the earth; we are omitting the centrifugal force due to the earth's rotation as well as the effect of sun and moon. Contact forces are just those on the tires if we neglect the integrated pressure of the surrounding air. Note that in the vertical (binormal) direction, we can only conclude from our analysis of a particle that the four vertical tire forces add up to be equal and opposite to W. If we want to find the relative sizes of V_1, V_2, V_3, and V_4, we must use a more sophisticated model of the automobile and form of Newton's second law.

The resultant of the horizontal components of the tire forces must be normal to the path in a constant-speed turn and large enough to equal

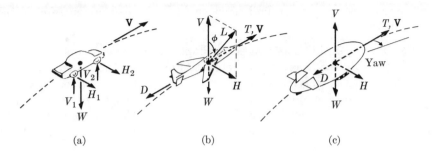

(a)   (b)   (c)

FIG. 3–4.   Vehicles in steady turns to the right.

mV^2/ρ. The maximum possible size of these frictional forces depends on the coefficient of friction μ between tires and ground.* Thus the maximum speed or minimum radius would be given by

$$\frac{V^2}{\rho} = \mu g.$$

If the vehicle is an airplane the picture looks somewhat different. Instead of neglecting the effect of surface pressure of the surrounding air, we find that it contributes the largest net force. This is largely due to the remarkable ability of wings to induce efficiently large air forces almost perpendicular to the direction of motion. To take advantage of this property to turn as well as support the airplane, we bank the airplane and simultaneously increase the wing force by increasing the angle of attack. During the steady turn then, the free-body diagram (Fig. 3–4b) shows the air pressure integral in two components, the lift and the drag. The effect of the engines is indicated as thrust T. Thus, for a bank angle ϕ,

$$H = L \sin \phi = W \tan \phi$$

or

$$\frac{V^2}{\rho} = g \tan \phi.$$

Also,

$$T - D = 0.$$

The minimum radius turn calls for a maximum lift at low speed and is

---

* The coefficient of friction μ between two surfaces is usually defined as the ratio of the maximum tangential friction force F to the normal force N; that is $\mu = F/N$. Quite interestingly the maximum friction force is not particularly dependent on the area of contact, as one might suppose, but is very nearly linearly related to the normal force.

limited by the stalling characteristics of the wing. At higher speeds the strength of the structure may be the limiting factor.

If our vehicle is an airship, surface ship, or submarine (Fig. 3–4c), we can see no efficient mechanism for producing side force, such as a wing. Instead, the side force must be generated inefficiently by the pressures induced on the entire hull when kept at an angle of yaw to its direction of motion by means of the steering devices. Nevertheless, these vehicles are reasonably maneuverable because relative to the fluids producing the side forces they are far less dense than an aircraft.

Note that although we could think of each vehicle as a particle in order to predict the net force required to produce the steady turn, we had to examine the shape and orientation of the vehicle to see how the external forces were being produced. Far more detailed models would be required to evaluate the internal load distributions within the structure of these vehicles. ▲

EXAMPLE 3–3. A fundamental aircraft maneuver which illustrates the use of cartesian reference axes is the landing-run deceleration and its relation to runway requirements. If we are again satisfied that a ground observer ① and representation as a particle lead to a reasonable dynamic model, we can draw Fig. 3–5 and write [following Eq. (3–3)] for an aircraft in straight-line motion,

$$\sum F_x = m\frac{dv_x}{dt}, \qquad \sum F_y = 0, \qquad \sum F_z = 0.$$

(The directions taken for the axes XYZ are quite common in aircraft maneuver and stability analysis.) Since a net external force is needed only

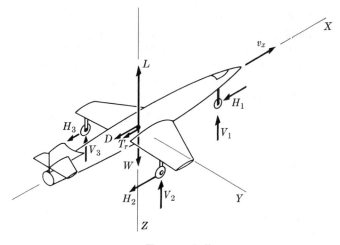

FIGURE 3–5

in the negative X-direction to decelerate the aircraft, it would seem that the use of the other reference directions is unnecessary. That this is not so in the determination of the forces acting may be seen in the free-body diagram (Fig. 3–5). The net aerodynamic force is upward and to the rear. The relative sizes of the lift and drag components depend primarily on the setting of wing flaps, whereas the absolute sizes vary with speed v_x and overall airplane attitude. A nose-high deceleration takes advantage of the large drag force but prevents really effective use of the brakes, because the associated large lift reduces the maximum friction force that the wheels can develop. On the other hand, the low angle of attack ground-run common to tricycle gear designs has lower drag but more effective braking action. If we call any available reverse thrust from the engines T_r, the force expressions become

$$-H_1 - H_2 - H_3 - T_r - D = \frac{dv_x}{dt},$$

$$W - L - V_1 - V_2 - V_3 = 0.$$

Looking at some numbers, suppose an airplane must slow from 120 mi/hr to 20 mi/hr in 3000 ft of runway. Since we are only looking for very rough answers, let's assume for simplicity a constant or average deceleration of magnitude A and get

$$\frac{dv_x}{dt} = -A.$$

Integrating, we obtain

$$v_x = -At + 176, \qquad \text{and} \qquad x = -\tfrac{1}{2}At^2 + 176t.$$

For x of 3000 ft and v_x of 35 ft/sec, the last two equations can be solved to give an A of 5 ft/sec^2 and an elapsed time of 28 sec. Since this deceleration is about $0.16g$, a 200-lb passenger would require an average retarding force of 32 lb while a 50-ton aircraft would need 16,000 lb.

During the higher speed part of the ground-run, the drag could easily be this large, but it drops off very rapidly with speed. Particularly on the turbojets which do not have the large drag of windmilling propellers, reverse thrust or drag chutes are needed when the braking conditions are poor.

By the way, does the centripetal acceleration of about 0.1 ft/sec^2 of our earthbound observer mean our 5 ft/sec^2 answer is inaccurate by one part in 50? ▲

EXAMPLE 3–4. Do you remember the lighthouse keeper and his spiral stairway of Example 2–2? Let's find the loads he exerts on the railing as he slides down at constant speed. We can use the cylindrical coordinates

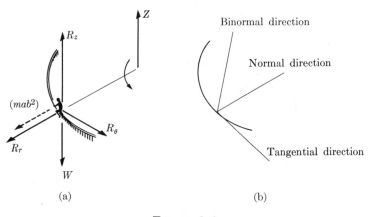

FIGURE 3–6

of Example 2–2 and define the loads the railing exerts on him as R_r, R_θ, R_z shown in the free-body diagram (Fig. 3–6a). His only acceleration is $a_r = -ab^2$, where a is the radius of the spiral and b is the angular velocity of the radius about Z. Using D'Alembert's principle, we can write equations for dynamic equilibrium of the keeper after first applying the inertia force (mab^2) in the positive r-direction.

$$\sum F_r = 0 = R_r + mab^2,$$
$$\sum F_\theta = 0 = R_\theta,$$
$$\sum F_z = 0 = R_z - W.$$

Thus the loads he exerts on the railing are equal and opposite to

$$R_r = -mab^2, \qquad R_\theta = 0, \qquad R_z = W.$$

Note that if we use tangential, normal, and binormal directions as shown in Fig. 3–6(b), all of the inertia force is in the negative normal direction, and the tangential equation relates the friction drag to the tangential component of weight. Note also the similarity between the dynamics of this problem and that of the spirally ascending or descending aircraft, although the forces derive from very different mechanisms. ▲

EXAMPLE 3–5. As another demonstration of the use of D'Alembert's principle in particle dynamics, let's investigate the stress distribution in the helicopter blade of Example 2–8. As shown in Fig. 2–29, points in the blade are moving in horizontal circles at 60 rad/sec about a hub translating at 100 ft/sec. If we assume that each blade is free to flap about a horizontal hinge at the root, the aerodynamic lift will cause the blade to

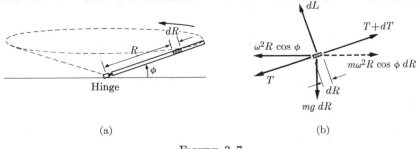

(a)   (b)

FIGURE 3-7

"cone" at a small angle ϕ as shown in Fig. 3-7(a). Of course the lift varies during a revolution because the airspeed relative to a blade section varies considerably, and thus ϕ is not constant. Actually the blade bends as well as flaps, but let's restrict ourselves to the mean stresses accompanying a constant ϕ. Since we are looking for internal loads, we must use a piece of the blade for our particle. Assuming a uniform 10-ft blade of 32 lb, we have a running mass of 0.1 slug/ft of blade. Drawing a free-body diagram for a length dR of the blade in Fig. 3-7(b), we can write the D'Alembert inertia force $0.1\,\omega^2 R \cos\phi\,dR$, the lift dL, the weight $3.2\,dR$, and the tensions on inner and outer blade-section faces. We can assume the tension T changes by only a small amount dT across this infinitesimal section. Summing the forces along and normal to the blade for dynamic equilibrium, we get

$$\sum F_{\text{along}} = 0 = dT + 0.1\,\omega^2 R \cos^2\phi\,dR - 3.2 \sin\phi\,dR,$$
$$\sum F_{\text{normal}} = 0 = dL - 3.2\,dR \cos\phi - 0.1\,\omega^2 R \sin\phi \cos\phi\,dR.$$

Integrating the second equation from root to tip, we get

$$L = 32 \cos\phi - 0.1(60)^2 \left(\frac{10^2}{2}\right) \sin\phi \cos\phi.$$

If we assume that this blade is contributing about 2000 pounds of lift toward supporting the helicopter and that ϕ will be small enough so that $\cos\phi \approx 1$, we can solve for ϕ as

$$\phi = \sin^{-1} 0.11 = 6.5°.$$

Substituting this angle in the first equation indicates that the weight term can easily be neglected, so that

$$dT = -360R\,dR,$$

and, with the idea that the tension must be zero at the tip,

$$T = 18{,}000 - 180R^2 \text{ lb.}$$

The stress can be found by dividing T by the local load-carrying area.

After solving a problem under a set of assumptions, it is often useful, to examine where possible, in the light of the solution, the adequacy of the assumptions. For example, stretching of the blade under this load has been neglected even though the inertia load would increase at each section with the stretching. To estimate this effect, remember that aluminum at 20,000 lb/in^2 elongates only a fraction of one percent. Our original dimensions used in calculating the internal loads are not that accurate. A somewhat different situation exists if we presume that the blade is hollow and ask for the pressure distribution in the air contained in the blade. If we look at the dynamic equilibrium of a volume element dR in length and of cross-sectional area A, we find a significant pressure variation only in the R-direction. If the fluid density is ρ slugs/ft^3, the dynamic equilibrium gives (for $\cos \phi \approx 1$)

$$\sum F_{\text{along}} = 0 = \rho A \omega^2 R \, dR + pA - (p + dp)A,$$

or*

$$dp = \rho \omega^2 R \, dR.$$

If ρ were constant, we could integrate directly, but air is far from incompressible. For an adiabatic compression (no heat transfer through or out of the air) the pressure and density are related as

$$\frac{p}{p_0} = \left(\frac{\rho}{\rho_0}\right)^{1.4}.$$

Alternatively, it is a better assumption here to assume that compression takes place at constant temperature. Here the relation is

$$\frac{p}{p_0} = \frac{\rho}{\rho_0}.$$

Using the latter assumption, we get

$$\int_{p_{\text{root}}}^{p} \frac{dp}{p} = \left(\frac{\rho_0}{p_0}\right) \omega^2 \int_{0}^{R} R \, dR,$$

or

$$\ln\left(\frac{p}{p_{\text{root}}}\right) = \frac{\rho_0}{p_0} \frac{\omega^2 R^2}{2}, \qquad \frac{p}{p_{\text{root}}} = \exp\left[\frac{\rho_0}{p_0} \frac{\omega^2 R^2}{2}\right] \cong e^{0.002R^2}$$

---

* See the more general equations of motion of a fluid continuum in Section 4–2.

using sea-level values of $p_0 = 2100 \, \text{lb/ft}^2$ and $\rho_0 = 0.0024 \, \text{slug/ft}^3$. To better visualize the pressure variation along the blade, let's look at the increment over p_{root}, remembering that e^x can be expanded in the series $1 + x + (x^2/2) + \cdots$, to give

$$\frac{p - p_{root}}{p_{root}} = e^{0.002R^2} - 1 = 0.002R^2 + \frac{(0.002R^2)^2}{2} + \cdots .$$

Thus the pressure increment, like the stress in the blade, varies basically as R^2. The effect of compressibility shows up in the additional terms of the series which are negligible for small R, but at the tip where R is 10 ft, the second term is a full 10% of the pressure increment of 470 lb/ft^2. This indicates that the air is denser near the tip and thus locally increases the centrifugal inertia force. ▲

EXAMPLE 3–6. Next, we will find the motion associated with known forces rather than the reverse as in previous examples. Let's also take the point of view of an accelerated observer. Suppose we are driving to a ball park for a friendly game and you are sitting in the back seat idly tossing a ball vertically a few feet and catching it again. You notice that whenever the car is not in uniform motion the ball deviates from its vertical path. If at the next stoplight our driver accelerates the car from rest at constant acceleration A, in what direction should you toss the ball so that it returns directly to your hand?

It seems reasonable to use an observer ① who stands at the stoplight as our basic inertial reference, and we can be observers ② linearly accelerating with the car. Since the motion will probably be all in the vertical plane, we can use a two-axis cartesian reference system with the origin at the point in the car where you release the ball and to which it will return. Thinking of the ball as a particle and neglecting any air forces exerted on it, we can draw the free-body diagram as in Fig. 3–8(a). Not using D'Alem-

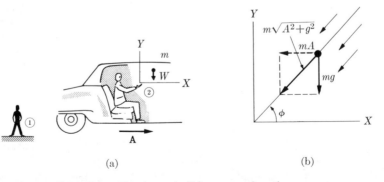

(a)   (b)

FIG. 3–8. Tossing a ball in an accelerating car.

bert's principle this time, the only external force on our particle is its weight W. Setting force equal to mass times absolute acceleration, we have [Eq. (3–7a)]

$$\sum F_x = ma_x + mA = 0, \qquad \sum F_y = ma_y = -mg$$

so that we, as accelerating observers, see

$$a_x = -A, \qquad a_y = -g.$$

Integrating, we obtain

$$v_x = -At + v_{0x},$$
$$v_y = -gt + v_{0y},$$
$$x = -\tfrac{1}{2}At^2 + v_{0x}t + x_0,$$
$$y = -\tfrac{1}{2}gt^2 + v_{0y}t + y_0.$$

Since the ball is released from the origin at $t = 0$, x_0 and y_0 are zero. For it to return to the origin, both x and y must be zero simultaneously at a later time T, where

$$T = \frac{v_{0x}}{\tfrac{1}{2}A} = \frac{v_{0y}}{\tfrac{1}{2}g}.$$

Thus, the initial velocity components must be in the proportion

$$\frac{v_{0x}}{v_{0y}} = \frac{A}{g} = \cotan\,\phi,$$

where ϕ is the elevation of the ball's initial velocity vector.

A D'Alembert type of approach might say that the accelerated observer should apply an inertia force $(-mA)$ to the ball as well as the gravitational force mg and watch the resulting motion. Since A and g are constant, he might visualize an equivalent pseudogravity field of strength $\sqrt{A^2 + g^2}$ at the angle ϕ, as shown in Fig. 3–8(b). In this tilted field, he would naturally throw the ball "up" at the angle ϕ to have it return along a straight line to the origin. Try to plot the trajectory of the ball as seen both in the car and from the ground to see if you really understand the relation between the two points of view. ▲

EXAMPLE 3–7. With the advent of space flight, we must be able to consider problems in which the familiar gravity term does not appear. Suppose we are in a flying saucer out in deep space. To give us some sensation of weight, the saucer is spinning lazily at an angular velocity Ω about its axis of symmetry. Thus if we are standing at radius c, we are accelerated toward the center at a rate $\Omega^2 c$ as we travel in our circular path. (For the reasoning by which we can consider the saucer's center unaccelerated for these purposes, even when we are in a significant external gravity field,

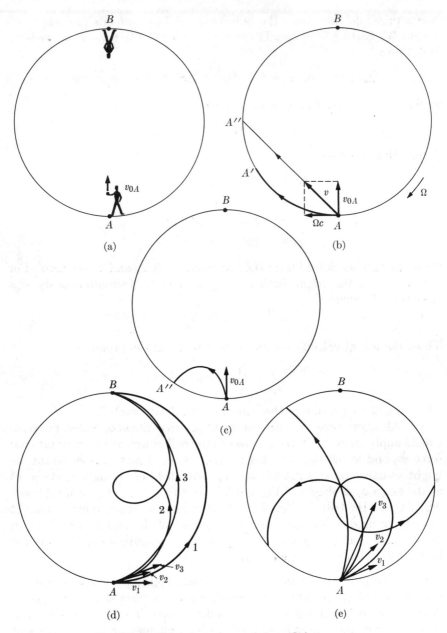

FIG. 3–9. Throwing a wrench in a flying saucer.

see Example 3-1.) If A and B in Fig. 3-9(a) are two plumbers working in the saucer, suppose A has a wrench that B needs. Since B is (to A) directly above him, A can't resist the temptation to toss the wrench straight "up" toward B with an initial velocity v_{0A}. Where does the wrench go?

Let's call the wrench a particle and visualize a free-body diagram for it while it is in mid-air. Neglecting air forces, and in the absence of any effective gravity, we find there are no forces acting on it at all. Since A and B are rotating observers, the vector equation of motion in terms of an origin at the saucer's center is [see Eq. (3-7b)]

$$\sum \mathbf{F} = 0 = m[\mathbf{a}' + 2\mathbf{\Omega} \times \mathbf{v}' + \mathbf{\Omega} \times (\mathbf{\Omega} \times \mathbf{R})].$$

(D'Alembert might say that, since the observers are rotating, they should visualize the motion in response to Coriolis and centrifugal inertia forces. The equation would be written as

$$\mathbf{F}_{\text{Cor}} + \mathbf{F}_{\text{cen}} = (-2m\mathbf{\Omega} \times \mathbf{v}') + [-m\mathbf{\Omega} \times (\mathbf{\Omega} \times \mathbf{R})] = m\mathbf{a}'$$

which is, of course, identical.)

Solving this equation for $\mathbf{R}$ as a function of time is difficult no matter what type of coordinate system A and B decide to use. However, if we realize that the wrench, with no real forces acting, will, according to a nonrotating observer at the saucer's center, simply move at constant speed in a straight line, we will quickly adopt his point of view. To him the wrench's initial velocity is $v_{0A} \leftrightarrow \Omega c$, as shown in Fig. 3-9(b). The wrench travels to A'' while the saucer swings A around through a shorter distance (his speed is only Ωc) to A'. Translating this motion back to A's viewpoint, the wrench appears, as in Fig. 3-9(c), to curve forward and hit the floor in front of him. Possible trajectories from A to B with proper sizes of v_{0A} are sketched in Fig. 3-9(d). A few trajectories which go through the center of the saucer are shown in Fig. 3-9(e). ▲

EXAMPLE 3-8. As a final example in this section on Newton's second law applied to a particle, we will look at a situation which gives rise to an oscillatory motion. Suppose we have a mass m connected by a light spring of overall stiffness k to a fixed wall (Fig. 3-10a). If the mass is constrained by its relatively light wheels to a rectilinear motion, we need only the coordinate x to follow its motion. It is most natural to put the origin for x at the position of the mass reference pointer when the spring is relaxed, because it is then simple to write an expression for the spring force in terms of x. If the spring is assumed to be very nearly linear for reasonable displacements, the force F_s that the spring exerts on the mass is

$$F_s = -kx.$$

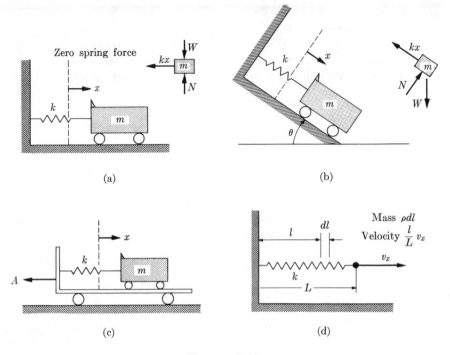

FIGURE 3–10

In the simplest case, we assume the motion of the light wheels and the associated friction can be neglected so that Newton's second law becomes

$$-kx = m\frac{d^2x}{dt^2} = m\frac{dv_x}{dt}.$$

We can either recognize this as a linear homogeneous differential equation of a familiar form and write down the answer, or we can plead ignorance and try to integrate. To integrate, we multiply by dx to get

$$-kx\,dx = -d\left(\frac{kx^2}{2}\right) = m\frac{dv_x}{dt}\,dx = mv_x\,dv_x = d\left(\frac{mv_x^2}{2}\right).$$

Integrating, we get

$$-\frac{kx^2}{2} = \frac{mv_x^2}{2} - c_1.$$

Recognizing $mv_x^2/2$ as the kinetic energy of the particle m and $kx^2/2$ as the work done on the spring in stretching it from equilibrium, we can say that at all times

Elastic energy of spring + kinetic energy of mass = constant.

Replacing v_x with dx/dt and separating the variables x and t, we obtain

$$dt = \frac{dx}{\sqrt{(2c_1/m) - (k/m)x^2}},$$

and

$$x = \sqrt{2c_1/k} \sin (\sqrt{k/m}\, t + \sqrt{k/m}\, c_2),$$

or in terms of different unknown constants c and ϕ, we have

$$x = c \sin (\sqrt{k/m}\, t + \phi).$$

The constants of this sinusoidal oscillation of frequency $(1/2\pi)\sqrt{k/m}$ are dependent on how the motion was started.

Suppose now that somebody has tilted our system as in Fig. 3–10(b). Our dynamical equation for the X-direction becomes

$$-kx + mg \sin \theta = m\frac{d^2x}{dt^2}$$

or

$$\frac{d^2x}{dt^2} + \frac{k}{m}x = g \sin \theta.$$

Note that our previous answer with the constant $(mg \sin \theta)/k$ added seems to satisfy this slightly more complicated equation. Since this constant represents the stretching of the spring under the steady weight component, the full answer

$$x = c \sin (\sqrt{k/m}\, t + \phi) + \frac{mg}{k} \sin \theta$$

represents oscillations about the new equilibrium position.

Looking next at Fig. 3–10(c), in which the entire system is being accelerated at the constant rate A to the left, we get the analogous dynamical equation

$$-kx = m\frac{d^2x}{dt^2} - mA$$

or

$$m\frac{d^2x}{dt^2} + kx = mA.$$

Apparently this will have a solution,

$$x = c \sin (\sqrt{k/m}\, t + \phi) + \frac{mA}{k},$$

which represents oscillations about an equilibrium position proportional to the system's acceleration. This seismic device with a little damping added to minimize the oscillations is called an accelerometer and is very useful for measuring varying accelerations in vehicle-testing problems. Its properties will be further investigated in a later chapter.

Suppose we suddenly realize the mass of the spring in our system is actually a substantial percentage of m, and we wonder about its effect on the frequency of oscillation. Using the reasonable assumption that as the mass moves sinusoidally the not quite massless spring stretches linearly, we can calculate the kinetic energy of the spring when the mass has the velocity v_x (see Fig. 3–10d) as

$$T_{\text{spring}} = \int_0^L \frac{1}{2} (\rho \, dl) \left(\frac{l}{L} v_x \right)^2 = \frac{1}{2} \left(\frac{\rho L}{3} \right) v_x^2 = \frac{1}{2} \left(\frac{m_s}{3} \right) v_x^2.$$

Thus the approximate effect of including the spring's small mass m_s is to add one-third of it to the mass m. The new frequency is

$$\frac{1}{2\pi} \sqrt{\frac{k}{m + (m_s/3)}},$$

so that if $m_s = \frac{1}{10} m$, the frequency is lowered about 1.5%. ▲

3–3 Integrated forms. If we look back over the problems in which we have applied Newton's second law, we may notice that in many cases the mathematical solutions involved integration of our equations. Perhaps we may, in some instances, be able to arrive at our answers more easily and with better understanding if we use Newton's law in a form in which the integration has already been carried out; that is, we may convert the physical problem to the mathematical problem in terms of the integrated law. These integrated forms involve some very useful physical concepts such as work, kinetic energy, impulse, and momentum. In particular the quantities work and energy can be defined in many fields, such as electromagnetism and chemistry, and, through the ideas of thermodynamics, equations interrelating these diverse fields can be written.

In the motion of a particle of mass m under the action of a net external force $\mathbf{F}$ as shown in Fig. 3–11, we have been writing Newton's law in vector form as

$$\mathbf{F} = m\mathbf{a} = m \frac{d\mathbf{v}}{dt} = \frac{d}{dt} (m\mathbf{v}). \tag{3-9}$$

Note that if we multiply both sides by dt, the right-hand side becomes

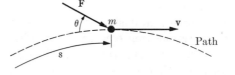

FIG. 3–11. A particle under the action of a net external force **F**.

exactly the differential of the particle's *momentum*. Integrating, we get

$$\int_{t_1}^{t_2} \mathbf{F}\, dt = m\mathbf{v}_2 - m\mathbf{v}_1, \qquad (3\text{–}10)$$

where the integral of force over time is called *impulse*. This impulse change-in-momentum relation can be particularly useful when the applied forces are known as functions of time (or are constant or zero).

In many problems, however, we try to eliminate time because the external forces are known as functions of position or displacement rather than time. Thus we can multiply both sides of Eq. (3–9) by the displacement of m during the time interval dt. This displacement is a vector quantity and, as we shall see, it is the vector dot product that we want to employ.

$$\mathbf{F} \cdot d\mathbf{s} = m\frac{d\mathbf{v}}{dt} \cdot d\mathbf{s} = m\, d\mathbf{v} \cdot \frac{d\mathbf{s}}{dt} = m\mathbf{v} \cdot d\mathbf{v} = \tfrac{1}{2}m\, d(\mathbf{v} \cdot \mathbf{v}).$$

In scalar form, the right-hand side is again a perfect differential, this time of the particle's *kinetic energy*,

$$F\, ds \cos\theta = mv\, dv = d\left(\frac{mv^2}{2}\right),$$

where θ is the angle between the applied force **F** and the direction of **ds** which is along the tangent to the path. Integrating over the particle's displacement gives us

$$\int \mathbf{F} \cdot d\mathbf{s} = \int_{s_1}^{s_2} F\, ds(\cos\theta) = \frac{mv_2^2}{2} - \frac{mv_1^2}{2}, \qquad (3\text{–}11)$$

where $\mathbf{v}_2$ and $\mathbf{v}_1$ are the particle's velocities at s_2 and s_1, respectively.

Observe that if $d\mathbf{s}$ represents the displacement of the particle m, it also represents the displacement of the force **F** *if* the particle does not deform. Thus for rigid particles, the left-hand side of Eq. (3–11) represents the integral over the displacement of the force component in the direction of the displacement. This integral is called the *work* done by the force **F** in moving from s_1 to s_2. Integrating the applied force over space instead of time results in a relationship between work done by the force and change in kinetic energy of the particle. Don't forget, however, that the applied force must have the same displacement as the particle. This is normally not true in collision, impact, and similar problems in which permanent deformations, heat, or composition changes are produced. In these problems the work done does not equal the change in kinetic energy because the energy shifts between other forms as well (see Example 3–13).

An important difference exists between the integrals over time and space. The impulse-momentum equation [Eq. (3–10)] is a vector equation, whereas the work-kinetic energy equation [Eq. (3–11)] is scalar.

Since we have often found it useful to write Newton's law in various coordinate systems, it will be valuable to write our integrated forms in the same manner. Let's see how they look in cartesian axes XYZ which are unaccelerated and nonrotating. In this system, Newton's law [Eq. (3–9)] is written in each direction as

$$F_x = \frac{d}{dt}(mv_x),$$

$$F_y = \frac{d}{dt}(mv_y),$$

$$F_z = \frac{d}{dt}(mv_z).$$

Multiplying by the scalar dt and integrating, we obtain

$$\int_{t_1}^{t_2} F_x\,dt = mv_{x_2} - mv_{x_1},$$

$$\int_{t_1}^{t_2} F_y\,dt = mv_{y_2} - mv_{y_1}, \qquad (3\text{–}12)$$

$$\int_{t_1}^{t_2} F_z\,dt = mv_{z_2} - mv_{z_1},$$

where the left-hand sides represent the components of the resultant impulse [Eq. (3–10)] and the right-hand sides represent the components of the resultant momentum changes.

If instead we multiply by the appropriate components of the displacement $d\mathbf{s}$, we get the scalar relations

$$F_x\,dx = m\frac{dv_x}{dt}\,dx = mv_x\,dv_x = d\left(\frac{mv_x^2}{2}\right),$$

$$F_y\,dy = m\frac{dv_y}{dt}\,dy = mv_y\,dv_y = d\left(\frac{mv_y^2}{2}\right),$$

$$F_z\,dz = m\frac{dv_z}{dt}\,dz = mv_z\,dv_z = d\left(\frac{mv_z^2}{2}\right).$$

On integrating from point 1 to point 2, we have

$$\int_{x_1}^{x_2} F_x \, dx = \frac{mv_{x_2}^2}{2} - \frac{mv_{x_1}^2}{2},$$

$$\int_{y_1}^{y_2} F_y \, dy = \frac{mv_{y_2}^2}{2} - \frac{mv_{y_1}^2}{2}, \tag{3–13}$$

$$\int_{z_1}^{z_2} F_z \, dz = \frac{mv_{z_2}^2}{2} - \frac{mv_{z_1}^2}{2}.$$

Note that since impulse and momentum change are vectors, Eq. (3–10) may be obtained from Eq. (3–12) by vector addition. For example,

$$\mathbf{v}_{x_2} + \mathbf{v}_{y_2} + \mathbf{v}_{z_2} = \mathbf{v}_2.$$

On the other hand, work and kinetic energy change are scalar in nature so Eq. (3–11) must be obtained from Eq. (3–13) by simple algebraic addition. For example,

$$\frac{mv_{x_2}^2}{2} + \frac{mv_{y_2}^2}{2} + \frac{mv_{z_2}^2}{2} = \frac{mv_2^2}{2}.$$

This is also consistent with the properties of the vector dot product since

$$F \, ds \cos \theta = \mathbf{F} \cdot \mathbf{ds}$$
$$= (\mathbf{i}F_x + \mathbf{j}F_y + \mathbf{k}F_z) \cdot (\mathbf{i} \, dx + \mathbf{j} \, dy + \mathbf{k} \, dz)$$
$$= F_x \, dx + F_y \, dy + F_z \, dz.$$

For inertial reference systems in which the coordinate directions change (such as cylindrical and spherical systems), impulse, linear-momentum component equations similar to Eq. (3–12) cannot easily be written down nor can work-energy relations similar to Eq. (3–13), although the overall energy equation (3–11) can be written in such coordinates.

EXAMPLE 3–9. Let's look at a 32,000-lb jet fighter taking off along its runway under the simple assumption that during takeoff the difference between the drag and the thrust is a constant 10,000 lb. If takeoff speed is 135 mi/hr, let's figure the *time* it takes from the start of the takeoff run until the wheels leave the ground. Since time rather than distance is involved, we can use the first of Eqs. (3–12) relating impulse in the X-direction with change in X-momentum. Thus, for the simple case where the net force is constant,

$$\int_0^t F_x \, dt = 10,000t = \left(\frac{32,000}{32}\right)(135 \times 1.47 - 0), \qquad t = 20 \text{ sec.}$$

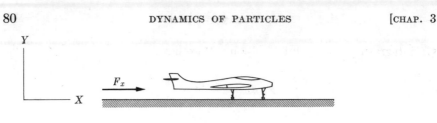

(a)

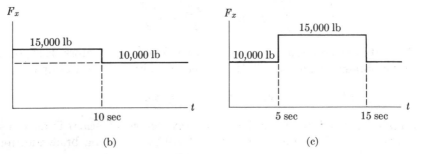

(b)   (c)

FIGURE 3–12

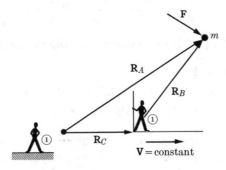

FIG. 3–13. Two unaccelerated observers watching the motion of a particle.

If the fighter uses an auxiliary rocket which produces an additional 5000 lb of thrust for 10 sec during his takeoff run, how long does it take to reach 135 mi/hr? If we interpret the impulse as the area under the curve in a force-time diagram, we can see from Fig. 3–12(b) that

$$\int_0^t F_x \, dt = 5000 \times 10 + 10,000t$$

$$= \frac{32,000}{32}(135 \times 1.47 - 0), \qquad t = 15 \text{ sec.}$$

If we ask now for the *length* of the takeoff run without the rocket assist, we can use the first of Eqs. (3–13) relating work and kinetic energy change to give

$$\int_0^x F_x\,dx = 10{,}000x = \frac{32{,}000}{(2)(32)}\,(135 \times 1.47)^2 - 0, \qquad x = 2000 \text{ ft.}$$

If we try to calculate takeoff distance with the auxiliary rocket, we get into trouble because F_x changes after 10 sec from 15,000 to 10,000 lb (Fig. 3–12b). However, if we use impulse-momentum ideas to determine the velocity at the end of 10 sec as 150 ft/sec, we can do the takeoff run in two stages as

$$\int_0^{x_{10}} F_x\,dx = 15{,}000x_{10} = \frac{32{,}000}{2 \times 32}\,(150)^2,$$

$$\int_{x_{10}}^x F_x\,dx = 10{,}000(x - x_{10}) = \frac{32{,}000}{2 \times 32}\,[(135 \times 1.47)^2 - (150)^2],$$

$$x_{10} = 750 \text{ ft}, \qquad x = 750 + 875 = 1625 \text{ ft.}$$

This is not much of a reduction in takeoff length. A larger reduction can be obtained by firing the rocket during the last 10 sec of takeoff as shown in Fig. 3–12(c). The takeoff time is still 15 sec because the momentum change and thus total impulse must be the same. The takeoff length can be calculated in this case if we first find the velocity after 5 sec to be 50 ft/sec. Then

$$\int_0^{x_5} F_x\,dx = 10{,}000x_5 = \frac{32{,}000}{2 \times 32}\,(50)^2,$$

$$\int_{x_5}^x F_x\,dx = 15{,}000(x - x_5)$$

$$= \frac{32{,}000}{2 \times 32}\,[(135 \times 1.47)^2 - (50)^2],$$

$$x_5 = 125 \text{ ft}, \qquad x = 1250 + 125 = 1375 \text{ ft.} \ \blacktriangle$$

Two inertial observers, moving at different velocities but viewing the same particle motion, will agree explicitly on the applied impulse and change in particle momentum during a given time interval. They will not agree on the work done nor on the particle's kinetic energy change nor even on the size of its displacement. Nevertheless, each will correctly maintain that work done equals the change in kinetic energy. To illustrate this *dependence of work and kinetic energy on reference system velocity*, suppose our second inertial observer has the constant velocity **V** as shown in Fig. 3–13. The two observers agree on the size and direction of the net applied force $\mathbf{F}$ (no D'Alembert ideas here, please) and the particle's mass m. The first observer says, for the time interval t_1 to t_2,

$$\int_1^2 \mathbf{F} \cdot d\mathbf{R}_A = \frac{mv_{A2}^2}{2} - \frac{mv_{A1}^2}{2}. \qquad (3\text{--}14a)$$

Since

$$\mathbf{R}_A = \mathbf{R}_B + \mathbf{R}_C,$$

$$\mathbf{v}_A = \mathbf{v}_B + \mathbf{V},$$

and

$$\mathbf{v}_A \cdot \mathbf{v}_A = v_B^2 + 2\mathbf{v}_B \cdot \mathbf{V} + V^2,$$

we can substitute in Eq. (3–14a) and get

$$\int_1^2 \mathbf{F} \cdot d\mathbf{R}_B + \int_1^2 \mathbf{F} \cdot d\mathbf{R}_C = \frac{mv_{B2}^2}{2} - \frac{mv_{B1}^2}{2}$$
$$+ m\mathbf{v}_{B2} \cdot \mathbf{V} - m\mathbf{v}_{B1} \cdot \mathbf{V} + \frac{mV^2}{2} - \frac{mV^2}{2}.$$

Since

$$\int_1^2 \mathbf{F}\, dt \cdot \frac{d\mathbf{R}_C}{dt} = \mathbf{V} \cdot \int_1^2 \mathbf{F}\, dt = \mathbf{V} \cdot (m\mathbf{v}_{B2} - m\mathbf{v}_{B1}),$$

we can make the second observer happy by showing

$$\int_1^2 \mathbf{F} \cdot d\mathbf{R}_B = \frac{mv_{B2}^2}{2} - \frac{mv_{B1}^2}{2}. \qquad (3\text{--}14b)$$

Apparently their observations of work done as well as kinetic energy change differ by the dot product of their relative velocity and the particle's momentum change.

If our second observer is a linearly accelerating observer ② for whom Newton's second law is

$$\mathbf{F} = m\mathbf{a}_{m/2} + m\mathbf{a}_{2/1}, \qquad (3\text{--}15)$$

we can integrate over time and particle displacement to get the corresponding impulse-momentum and work-energy expressions

$$\int \mathbf{F}\, dt = \Delta m\mathbf{v}_{m/2} + \Delta m\mathbf{v}_{2/1},$$

$$\int \mathbf{F} \cdot d\mathbf{R}_{m/2} = \frac{\Delta mv_{m/2}^2}{2} + m\int \mathbf{a}_{2/1} \cdot d\mathbf{R}_{m/2}, \qquad (3\text{--}16a)$$

which are particularly easy to use when the observer's acceleration $\mathbf{a}_{2/1}$ is a constant. Then

$$\int \mathbf{F}\, dt = \Delta m \mathbf{v}_{m/2} + m \mathbf{a}_{2/1}\, \Delta t,$$

$$\int \mathbf{F} \cdot d\mathbf{R}_{m/2} = \frac{\Delta m v_{m/2}^2}{2} + m \mathbf{a}_{2/1} \cdot \Delta \mathbf{R}_{m/2}.$$

(3–16b)

Note that our inertial and our accelerating observer agree on the impulse but disagree on the amount of work done.

If our second observer is a rotating observer ③, Newton's second law has so many extra kinematic terms [Eq. (3–7b)] for him that general integrated forms cannot be obtained. Even when the observer's angular velocity $\boldsymbol{\Omega}$ is constant, the impulse-momentum expression has the inconvenient form

$$\int \mathbf{F}\, dt = \Delta m \mathbf{v}' + \Delta 2 m \boldsymbol{\Omega} \times \mathbf{R} + m \boldsymbol{\Omega} \times \left(\boldsymbol{\Omega} \times \int \mathbf{R}\, dt \right). \qquad (3\text{–}17a)$$

Note that the impulse seen by observer ③ will differ from that seen by all nonrotating observers because even a force which appears constant to the latter will be rotating at $-\boldsymbol{\Omega}$ for observer ③. Curiously, a rather simple work-energy expression can be obtained for the observer ③ with constant $\boldsymbol{\Omega}$ as

$$\int \mathbf{F} \cdot d'\mathbf{R} = \frac{\Delta m v'^2}{2} - \Delta \frac{m}{2} (\boldsymbol{\Omega} \times \mathbf{R}) \cdot (\boldsymbol{\Omega} \times \mathbf{R})$$

$$= \frac{\Delta m v'^2}{2} - \Delta \frac{m \Omega^2 R_\perp^2}{2},$$

(3–17b)

where $R_\perp$ is the component of $\mathbf{R}$ perpendicular to the constant $\boldsymbol{\Omega}$.

It is interesting to see how the general integrals [Eq. (3–16)] fit into our earlier Example 3–6 of the ball tossed in a uniformly accelerating car. For the constant gravitational force $m\mathbf{g}$, the equations take the form

$$m(\mathbf{g} - \mathbf{a}_{2/1})\, \Delta t = \Delta m \mathbf{v}_{m/2},$$

$$m(\mathbf{g} - \mathbf{a}_{2/1}) \cdot \Delta \mathbf{R}_{m/2} = \frac{\Delta m v_{m/2}^2}{2},$$

where the energy equation implies the same magnitude of initial and final velocity for the ball to return to the origin. The momentum equation shows that all the momentum change takes place in the direction of the equivalent tilted pseudogravity field of strength $\sqrt{g^2 + a_{2/1}^2}$.

EXAMPLE 3–10. To illustrate the direct use of integrated forms of Newton's second law in situations other than constant-speed elevators or roller coasters, let's look at the soaring of birds. In particular, we will recount the trials of a poorly educated baby albatross trying to emulate his elders by soaring near the surface of the ocean.* He could fly well enough by flapping his wings, but he noticed that when a wind was blowing, the more experienced birds hardly ever flapped their wings while slowly wheeling and soaring near the surface.

To discover the essential features of what he learns, let's make some drastic assumptions. Instead of trying to deal with a realistic wind-speed distribution (Fig. 3–14a), we will think of two uniform layers of air, the upper moving faster than the lower (Fig. 3–14b).

If we say that the lowest airspeed at which the baby albatross can maintain flight without flapping his wings, that is, his stalling speed, is 10 mi/hr, let's assume that the upper air layer travels at 20 mi/hr and the lower at 10 mi/hr. We will need the services of three inertial observers: one observer in a rowboat who sees the motions depicted in Fig. 3–14, and two observers in balloons, one of which is drifting at 20 mi/hr with the upper air layer, and the other at 10 mi/hr with the lower air layer. (A balloonist never feels any wind in his face unless the air is very turbulent.)

Our eager learner decides to get a good start, so he flaps up to a generous flightspeed in the upper layer, say 15 mi/hr. Of course, since he is headed downwind, our rowboat observer sees him scooting at 35 mi/hr (Fig. 3–14c). These speeds, his airspeed and groundspeed, are labeled "rel" and "abs" in the picture. From here on, the baby albatross resolves firmly not to flap his wings again until he has learned the secret of unlimited soaring. In soaring configuration, an albatross is a remarkably efficient flying machine. He appears able to achieve lift on his wings even twenty times as large as his drag. Thus, over reasonably short intervals, we should keep in mind that the drag can be held accountable for only small amounts of impulse or work, whereas the portion of the lift not balancing the weight may be the dominating external force.

In any event, our friend soars and wheels with the best of them in the upper layer but soon discovers that the drag has been acting long enough to have slowed him down almost to his stalling speed. He already knows from experience that flying in a gravity field he can always reduce his lift so that the net downward force will accelerate him. After a mild dive, he will be flying at a lower level at a higher airspeed. Conversely, he can lose speed by zooming to a higher altitude. (Try figuring carefully the work done by lift, drag, and weight in these two maneuvers and see if you get the right changes in kinetic energy.)

---

* I can still see my teacher, Manfred Rauscher, flapping and banking across the classroom many years ago. To him goes the credit for this ever-challenging and remarkable example.

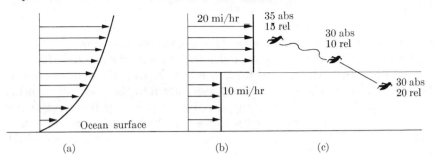

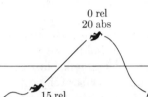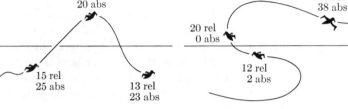

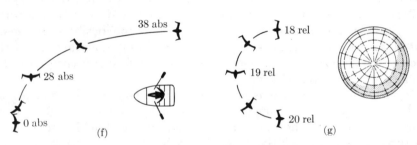

FIG. 3–14.   A baby albatross learning to soar in a wind gradient.

Rather than do anything drastic, the bird glides evenly into the lower layer. As he passes the boundary, he feels a much stronger wind in his face, so he quickly reduces the angle of attack of his wings to keep lift about equal to weight. His drag rises considerably but is still not a very large force. Thus his absolute forward speed remains about the same, as his airspeed goes up sharply. Feeling happy about the gain in airspeed which is a gain in useful kinetic energy, he fritters some of it away before realizing that he cannot gain by going any lower without getting wet but must go up. He zooms recklessly into the upper layer, using 5 mi/hr abs to do it. He is horrified to find that he has no flying speed at all, so he heads down and recovers, somewhat chagrined, to only 23 mi/hr abs (Fig. 3–14d).

(Remember not to shift observers in mid-air while figuring work done or kinetic energy change. Each observer sees different amounts.)

Our discouraged bird banks around a 180° turn in order to start flapping homeward when he decides to give it one last try with his almost marginal flying speed (Fig. 3–14e). He zooms carefully into the upper layer using his last 2 mi/hr abs, and to his surprise, he has plenty of flying speed and thus plenty of kinetic energy with respect to the local air mass. Another 180° turn leaves him zipping along downwind faster than when he started. He is very happy until he discovers that he is a long way downwind from home. He sits in the water until evening when the breeze dies down and then contentedly flies home.

To get this simplified picture of soaring, we admittedly idealized the wind gradient drastically, but the same ideas will hold if we visualize the continuous distribution as a large number of much smaller discrete steps. Observe that in the semicircular banked turns, as seen by the proper drifting observer, the large horizontal component of lift changes the bird's momentum drastically, but his kinetic energy is only slightly reduced. This is because the large lift is perpendicular to his path and only the small drag does work during the turn. The last upper-level turn is shown in (f) and (g) as seen in plan view by the man in the rowboat and the upper balloonist. Conversely, when the bird crosses the boundary between layers his "absolute" momentum and kinetic energy are practically unchanged, but his kinetic energy relative to the local air mass is drastically different because he has changed air masses. It is this relative kinetic energy which is important to continued flight.

It may help you to have as your basic (abs) observer one who travels at 15 mi/hr. To him, the upper wind is 5 mi/hr one way, and the lower wind is 5 mi/hr the other way. It then appears that the bird in making his turns slows down both layers and thus reduces the wind energy seen by this 15 mi/hr observer. Seen from the rowboat, however, the bird tends to reduce the difference between the layers' velocities. That this similarly reduces the translational energy in the wind can be seen by comparing the kinetic energy of two slugs of air, one at 20 mi/hr and the other at 10 mi/hr, with the energy when both are at 15 mi/hr. ▲

3–4 Potentials. In our work-energy expression in the previous section,

$$\int \mathbf{F} \cdot d\mathbf{s} = \frac{\Delta m v^2}{2}, \qquad (3\text{–}11)$$

the right-hand side integrated directly into the kinetic energy. Integration of the left-hand side depends on the nature of the applied force $\mathbf{F}$.

A particularly simple and quite useful type of force is one independent of time or time derivatives of position or velocity; that is, it depends only

on position of the particle on which it is acting. If it has the further property that the work done by the force between initial and final positions is
independent of the path followed by the particle, we call this kind of force
a *conservative force.*

For conservative forces, the quantity $\mathbf{F} \cdot d\mathbf{s}$ is always the perfect differential of some scalar function Φ of the coordinates (Ref. 5, Sokolnikoff and
Redheffer, p. 378), and thus work can always be expressed in terms of this
force function or potential function. Note that if

$$\mathbf{F} \cdot d\mathbf{s} = d\Phi,$$

then, in cartesian coordinates,

$$F_x\, dx + F_y\, dy + F_z\, dz = \frac{\partial \Phi}{\partial x}\, dx + \frac{\partial \Phi}{\partial y}\, dy + \frac{\partial \Phi}{\partial z}\, dz,$$

so that

$$F_x = \frac{\partial \Phi}{\partial x}, \qquad F_y = \frac{\partial \Phi}{\partial y}, \qquad F_z = \frac{\partial \Phi}{\partial z}. \tag{3–18}$$

In more general terms, the partial derivative of Φ with respect to a displacement in any direction is the component of force in that direction. In
cylindrical coordinates, where

$$\mathbf{F} \cdot d\mathbf{s} = F_r\, dr + F_\theta\, r\, d\theta + F_z\, dz$$

and

$$d\Phi = \frac{\partial \Phi}{\partial r}\, dr + \frac{\partial \Phi}{\partial \theta}\, d\theta + \frac{\partial \Phi}{\partial z}\, dz,$$

we get the corresponding relations

$$F_r = \frac{\partial \Phi}{\partial r}, \qquad F_\theta = \frac{1}{r} \frac{\partial \Phi}{\partial \theta}, \qquad F_z = \frac{\partial \Phi}{\partial z}. \tag{3–19}$$

The concept of a potential function is very useful in many instances
besides that of a force potential. In fluid mechanics, much use is made of
velocity potentials as well as acceleration potentials and stream functions.
Similar concepts have proved quite valuable in thermodynamics and
electromagnetic field theory.

It is traditional in dynamics to define the negative of the work done on
a particle by a conservative force as the *potential energy*, V. Thus,

$$-\int_A^B \mathbf{F} \cdot d\mathbf{s} = V_B - V_A,$$

or

$$V = -\int \mathbf{F} \cdot d\mathbf{s} \tag{3–20}$$

within some arbitrary constant depending on the reference from which the integral is figured. This sort of uncertainty is familiar to us in Newtonian dynamics where we have no absolute zero for position or velocity. We have no absolute level for momentum or kinetic energy either. In a given situation, the constant or origin must be taken in a convenient and consistent fashion just as we choose a convenient inertial reference system.

EXAMPLE 3-11. Since we are quite interested in motion in gravitational force fields, let's look at the gravitational potential of the earth. If we consider the earth to be made up of many thin spherical shells each of different density, we have a much better approximation of its gravitational attraction than we have if we assume the earth's density to be constant. Actually the density is not quite spherically symmetric nor is the earth even a perfect sphere. In fact, very precise measurements of the local gravitational field on the earth's surface have been used for years by geophysicists to infer the density variations below the surface.

Remembering Newton's law of gravitation for the attraction between masses m_1 and m_2 as

$$F = -\frac{\gamma m_1 m_2}{R_{12}^2},$$

where γ is the universal gravitational constant, we realize that the work done on m_2 as it moves from A to B is

$$\int_A^B \mathbf{F} \cdot d\mathbf{s} = -\gamma m_1 m_2 \int_A^B \frac{dR}{R_{12}^2}$$

$$= \gamma m_1 m_2 \left(\frac{1}{R_{1B}} - \frac{1}{R_{1A}} \right).$$

Usually the reference point from which the gravitational potential V is calculated is at infinity. Remembering that V is defined as the negative of

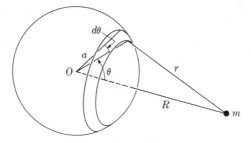

FIG. 3-15. Calculating the gravitational potential of a thin spherical shell.

the work done and with R_{1A} infinite, we see that

$$V = -\frac{\gamma m_1 m_2}{R_{12}}.$$

The potential for mass m in Fig. 3–15 due to the thin ring-shaped element of the spherical shell of density ρ and thickness da is

$$dV = -\gamma m\rho \, da \int_0^\pi \frac{2\pi a^2 \sin\theta \, d\theta}{r}$$

$$= -2\pi\gamma m\rho a^2 \, da \int_0^\pi \frac{\sin\theta \, d\theta}{\sqrt{a^2 + R^2 - 2aR\cos\theta}}$$

$$= -\frac{4\pi\gamma m\rho a^2 \, da}{R} \qquad \text{(for } R > a\text{)}.$$

For the series of concentric shells which make up the earth of outside radius c,

$$V = -\frac{\gamma m}{R} \int_0^c 4\pi\rho a^2 \, da = -\frac{\gamma m}{R} \int_0^{m_e} dm_e$$

$$= -\frac{\gamma m_e m}{R}.$$

Thus the earth's external gravitational potential can be approximated by considering all of the earth's mass to be concentrated at its center. In a later chapter, when we are discussing the mass properties of rigid bodies, we will show that the major effect of the earth's oblateness is to modify the potential as

$$V = -\frac{\gamma m_e m}{R}\left[1 + \frac{B}{R^2}(1 - 3\sin^2\phi)\right],$$

where ϕ is the angle from the equatorial plane to R. In this better approximation, the potential, and therefore the gravitational force, are increased in magnitude for mass m near the equatorial bulge and decreased near the poles. This effect decreases quite rapidly with increasing R, but its influence is quite noticeable on satellite orbits. In fact, the constant B has been verified as 0.000546 (when R is measured in units of the equatorial radius) by observations of satellite orbit precession.

In many references, gravitational potential is deduced for a unit mass rather than a mass m. Calling this potential V^*, we have

$$V^* = -\frac{\gamma m_e}{R}\left[1 + \frac{B}{R^2}(1 - 3\sin^2\phi)\right] \cong -\frac{\gamma m_e}{R}. \quad \blacktriangle$$

When a particle is moving only under the action of conservative forces, the work-energy relation can be very conveniently written in terms of the potential energy V.

$$\int_A^B \mathbf{F} \cdot d\mathbf{s} = -(V_B - V_A) = \tfrac{1}{2}mv_B^2 - \tfrac{1}{2}mv_A^2,$$

$$V_A + \tfrac{1}{2}mv_A^2 = V_B + \tfrac{1}{2}mv_B^2,$$

or

$$V + T = \text{constant.} \tag{3-21}$$

The fact that, for a conservative system, the sum of the potential and kinetic energies is constant is often called the *principle of conservation of mechanical energy*. This energy balance derives for this rather special class of systems from Newton's second law. For a more fundamental understanding of energy in its various forms, we must look to the neighboring field of thermodynamics.

Potential functions for a given force field will generally have different forms for different observers even if they are both inertial. To put it differently, to observers in relative motion only the simplest force fields will appear unchanging with time. Thus a nonrotating observer at the earth's center will certainly see the force field described by the potential (see Example 3–11)

$$V = -\frac{\gamma m_e m}{R}.$$

To an observer moving at constant linear velocity, however, the force at a point in his reference space must be a function of time. Although it is possible to generalize the concept of potential function to this sort of situation, it is preferable to use the observer for whom the force field is constant.

Remember that in limited regions (such as locally on the earth's surface), we are quite willing to call the earth's field uniform and parallel such that[†]

$$V = mgh.$$

It is not difficult to show that any horizontally moving inertial observer will arrive at the same potential function V for this very simple force field.

─────────

[†] For h beyond $R = c$ where $h \ll c$, V becomes

$$V = -\frac{\gamma m_e m}{c + h} = -\frac{\gamma m_e m}{c}\left(1 - \frac{h}{c} + \cdots\right)$$

which, except for a constant, can be written

$$V \cong \frac{\gamma m_e m}{c^2} h = mgh.$$

Similarly, a force field with axial symmetry, such as the earth's gravitational field, looks the same to all observers in simple rotation about the axis of symmetry. Thus it appears stationary to us when we are standing on the surface of the rotating earth, and we would describe it with the potential function

$$V = - \frac{\gamma m_e m}{R}.$$

This does not mean that such rotating observers can blithely use the principle of conservation of mechanical energy because we found that (if their angular velocity Ω is constant) the work-energy expression in their reference space is

$$\int \mathbf{F} \cdot d'\mathbf{R} = \frac{\Delta m v'^2}{2} - \frac{\Delta m \Omega^2 R_\perp^2}{2}. \tag{3–17b}$$

Expressing the work in axially symmetric, potential form, we have

$$V - \frac{m \Omega^2 R_\perp^2}{2} + \frac{m v'^2}{2} = \text{constant}, \tag{3–22}$$

which can be considered the form of the conservation principle for observers rotating at constant Ω about an unaccelerated origin. Note that the first two terms, when considered together as an augmented potential, represent in a D'Alembert view the combined gravitational and centrifugal force field in which we live on the earth's surface. Thus, it may be quite easy for an accelerated or rotating observer to write down a potential function to describe a force field, which to him is stationary, but he cannot in general call it potential energy and use it without modification in a conservation principle.

Even inertial observers must be extremely careful when looking at electric fields. Suppose a stationary observer looks at the uniform electric field between the parallel plates of a stationary condenser. He can easily calculate a potential function for the force exerted on a unit charge between the plates. However, if he moves, even with constant velocity, parallel to the plates he will see the charges in motion and thus a magnetic field whose effect must not be neglected if his velocity is large (see Example 4–4). Whether an observer rotating about the axis of a cylindrical condenser sees a magnetic field as well as an electric one and is thus much less fortunate than the observer watching the gravitational field, I am not sure.

EXAMPLE 3–12. To look at potentials in a familiar situation, we can turn to the simple mass-spring system of Example 3–8. Considering the mass in Fig. 3–10(a) to be our particle, we can represent the influence of the spring by a force field of the form

$$F = -kx$$

which has the potential

$$V_s = -\int F \, dx = \tfrac{1}{2}kx^2.$$

The arbitrary zero for V_s was chosen to correspond to the zero-force position. The conservation of mechanical energy can be written as

$$V_s + T = \tfrac{1}{2}kx^2 + \tfrac{1}{2}mv_x^2 = \text{constant},$$

as derived in Example 3–8.

For the situation of Fig. 3–10(b) the gravity-force field must be included as

$$F_{x_g} = mg \sin \theta,$$

so that

$$V_g = -mgx \sin \theta$$

and, for conservation,

$$V_s + V_g + T = \tfrac{1}{2}kx^2 - mgx \sin \theta + \tfrac{1}{2}mv_x^2 = \text{constant}.$$

Notice that measuring displacement x from a different origin such that

$$x = x_1 + \frac{mg}{k} \sin \theta,$$

we get

$$V_s + V_g = \tfrac{1}{2}kx_1^2,$$

and

$$V_s + V_g + T = \tfrac{1}{2}kx_1^2 + \tfrac{1}{2}mv_{x_1}^2 = \text{constant}.$$

Looking at Fig. 3–10(c) in which the mass-spring system is accelerated at the constant rate A, we can see that, to an observer also accelerating at A, the spring potential V_s and the kinetic energy of m have the same form. Using D'Alembert's idea of replacing the additional term $(-mA)$ in Newton's law with an inertia force $(+mA)$, we can write a potential V_A for this inertia force and have a conservation principle modified for the observer's constant negative linear acceleration A.

$$V_S + V_A + T = \tfrac{1}{2}kx^2 - mAx + \tfrac{1}{2}mv_x^2 = \text{constant}. \;\blacktriangle$$

EXAMPLE 3–13. At times it is not easy to see when mechanical energy is conserved and when it is not. One such area deals with collisions between bodies which may be "perfectly elastic," "perfectly plastic," or somewhere in between. Often the concept of coefficient of restitution is introduced to

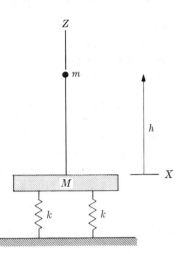

FIG. 3–16. Mass m bouncing on elastically supported block M.

handle simple cases of the in-between variety, but here, let's stick to the extreme cases.

Suppose a mass m is released a height h above a spring-supported block M as shown in Fig. 3–16 so that it falls and strikes the center of M. To what height will m rebound, and what is the subsequent motion of M? To answer this, we must know more about the details of the collision. We don't want to look too closely at it because it involves very complicated local deformations of both m and M. Yet we know that if m and M are very elastic, we can expect to lose very little mechanical energy into other forms such as heat and permanent plastic deformations of the contact surfaces.

One extreme is the perfectly elastic collision in which it is assumed that no mechanical energy is lost in the collision, so the mechanical energy just before equals that just after. The collision itself is assumed to take place in a negligibly short interval of time by a detailed process we need not examine.† Thus we can write conservation of mechanical energy for m up to the collision as

$$mgz + \tfrac{1}{2}mv^2 = mgh,$$

so that the velocity v_1 just before collision at $z = 0$ is

$$v_1 = -\sqrt{2gh}.$$

---

† This treatment is quite similar to the handing of shock waves in the high-speed flow of gases. Even in the perfectly elastic collision, some energy would go into internal elastic vibrations of m and M. See also the relaxation oscillations of Section 7–5 and Figs. 7–21 and 7–22.

If we assume that during the collision neither m nor M changes vertical position appreciably, they will have no change in potential energy caused by gravity or spring forces, and we can say simply that kinetic energy must be conserved as $T_1 = T_2$ and

$$\tfrac{1}{2}mv_1^2 = \tfrac{1}{2}mv_2^2 + \tfrac{1}{2}MV_2^2.$$

We can also say that during such a collision the impulse m exerts on M just equals the one exerted in return. Since the external spring and gravity forces just cancel and thus exert no impulse, the total momentum must be conserved as

$$mv_1 = mv_2 + MV_2.$$

Solving the three equations for v_2 gives, after some manipulation,

$$v_2 = \sqrt{2gh}\,\frac{M - m}{M + m},$$

which indicates that m will rebound upward only if it is smaller than M. With this velocity v_2 it will subsequently rise to height h_2 as

$$h_2 = \frac{v_2^2}{2g} = h\left(\frac{M - m}{M + m}\right)^2.$$

If we solve instead for V_2, we get

$$V_2 = -\sqrt{2gh}\,\frac{2m}{M + m},$$

and the subsequent motion of M is a sinusoidal oscillation about the initial static equilibrium position at a frequency $\omega = \sqrt{2k/M}$ (see Example 3–8). If we measure t from the time of collision, the motion of M has no initial displacement but has an initial velocity V_2, so its time history becomes

$$z = \sqrt{M/2k}\,V_2 \sin \sqrt{2k/M}\,t.$$

Alternatively, if the collision is perfectly plastic, so that m sticks to M, we cannot say that mechanical energy is conserved, because some of it must go into heat and permanent deformations of the plastic materials. In this extreme case, however, we can ignore the details of the collision and say simply that immediately after the collision

$$v_2 = V_2.$$

Since momentum is still conserved during the collision because the impulses are all internal and still equal and opposite, we have

$$mv_1 = mv_2 + MV_2.$$

Thus,

$$v_2 = V_2 = -\frac{m}{m + M} \sqrt{2gh}.$$

To obtain the subsequent motion of $(m + M)$ it is convenient to define displacement z^* from the new static equilibrium position of $(m + M)$, where

$$z^* = z + \frac{mg}{2k}.$$

The combined mass then performs a sinusoidal oscillation in z^* with initial position (immediately after the collision) as $mg/2k$ and initial velocity V_2. After some manipulation as in Examples 3–8 and 3–12, we can get

$$z^* = \sqrt{\frac{m^2}{m + M} \frac{2gh}{2k} + \frac{m^2g^2}{4k^2}} \sin\left(\sqrt{\frac{2k}{m + M}}\, t + \phi\right),$$

where

$$\phi = \tan^{-1}\left(-\frac{g}{\sqrt{2gh}} \sqrt{\frac{m + M}{2k}}\right). \quad \blacktriangle$$

The concept of energies is not only fundamental to the interdisciplinary views of thermodynamics but also plays a central role in much of classical analytical dynamics. Although its significance can best be understood by looking at minimum principles similar to those of minimum potential energy and minimum strain energy in elasticity, as we will do carefully and in detail in Chapter 11, we can arrive here at a way of expressing Newton's second law in terms of energies in a very limited class of situations by the following reasoning. We know that the components of applied force for a conservative system can be expressed as partial derivatives of the force potential V [Eqs. (3–18) and (3–19)]. We may then wonder whether the other side of Newton's law, the mass times acceleration term, is not also derivable from a potential of some sort, possibly the kinetic energy itself. The situation is bound to be more complex because time as well as spatial coordinates are involved. The equations which we will obtain are often called *Lagrange's equations*.

Without immediately and carefully outlining the limits of applicability, we note that in cartesian coordinates the kinetic energy T, in the very simple case of a particle, is

$$T = \tfrac{1}{2}m(\dot{x}^2 + \dot{y}^2 + \dot{z}^2),$$

where, as usual, the dot signifies derivative with respect to time. In terms of an alternative set of three† independent coordinates q_1, q_2, q_3, let us suppose we can write the transformation relations

$$x = \phi_1(q_1, q_2, q_3),$$

$$y = \phi_2(q_1, q_2, q_3),$$

$$z = \phi_3(q_1, q_2, q_3).$$

The velocity components can be represented by

$$\dot{x} = \frac{\partial \phi_1}{\partial q_1} \frac{dq_1}{dt} + \frac{\partial \phi_1}{\partial q_2} \frac{dq_2}{dt} + \frac{\partial \phi_1}{\partial q_3} \frac{dq_3}{dt}$$

and similar expressions for $\dot{y}$ and $\dot{z}$ so that the kinetic energy becomes

$$T = \tfrac{1}{2}m \sum_{i=1}^{3} \left(\frac{\partial \phi_i}{\partial q_1} \dot{q}_1 + \frac{\partial \phi_i}{\partial q_2} \dot{q}_2 + \frac{\partial \phi_i}{\partial q_3} \dot{q}_3 \right)^2. \tag{3-23}$$

Note that we can establish a useful identity for this homogeneous quadratic function of the $\dot{q}_i$'s by multiplying $\partial T/\partial \dot{q}_1$ by $\dot{q}_1$.

$$\frac{\partial T}{\partial \dot{q}_1} \dot{q}_1 = m \sum_{i=1}^{3} \left[\left(\frac{\partial \phi_i}{\partial q_1} \dot{q}_1 + \frac{\partial \phi_i}{\partial q_2} \dot{q}_2 + \frac{\partial \phi_i}{\partial q_3} \dot{q}_3 \right) \frac{\partial \phi_i}{\partial q_1} \right] \dot{q}_1.$$

Adding similar equations for $\dot{q}_2$ and $\dot{q}_3$, we get

$$\sum_{j=1}^{3} \frac{\partial T}{\partial \dot{q}_j} \dot{q}_j = m \sum_{i=1}^{3} \left(\frac{\partial \phi_i}{\partial q_1} \dot{q}_1 + \frac{\partial \phi_i}{\partial q_2} \dot{q}_2 + \frac{\partial \phi_i}{\partial q_3} \dot{q}_3 \right)^2 = 2T.$$

Hence, we have

$$T = \frac{1}{2} \sum_{j=1}^{3} \frac{\partial T}{\partial \dot{q}_j} \dot{q}_j, \tag{3-24}$$

even though T is generally a function of both the q_j's and the $\dot{q}_j$'s. Remember that an added form of Newton's second law for a particle in cartesian coordinates is

$$d\left(\frac{mv_x^2}{2} + \frac{mv_y^2}{2} + \frac{mv_z^2}{2} \right) = F_x \, dx + F_y \, dy + F_z \, dz$$

_____

† As we will see later in Chapters 5 and 11, in more complicated situations, the number of independent coordinates is usually much less than the number of cartesian coordinates for all the particles making up the system under study. The transformation to independent coordinates thus usually casts the problem in its simplest form.

or, more generally,

$$dT = dW$$

where, we already know, for a conservative system

$$dW = -dV = -\left(\frac{\partial V}{\partial q_1}\,dq_1 + \frac{\partial V}{\partial q_2}\,dq_2 + \frac{\partial V}{\partial q_3}\,dq_3\right).$$

Using Eq. (3–24), we can express dT as

$$2\,dT = \sum_{i=1}^{3}\left[\frac{\partial T}{\partial \dot{q}_i}\,d\dot{q}_i + d\left(\frac{\partial T}{\partial \dot{q}_i}\right)\dot{q}_i\right]$$

$$= \sum_{i=1}^{3}\left[\frac{\partial T}{\partial \dot{q}_i}\,d\dot{q}_i + \frac{d}{dt}\left(\frac{\partial T}{\partial \dot{q}_i}\right)dq_i\right].$$

Alternatively, since T is in general a function of the q_i's and $\dot{q}_i$'s, we get

$$dT = \sum_{i=1}^{3}\left(\frac{\partial T}{\partial \dot{q}_i}\,d\dot{q}_i + \frac{\partial T}{\partial q_i}\,dq_i\right).$$

Subtracting this from the previous expression, we obtain

$$dT = \sum_{i=1}^{3}\left[\frac{d}{dt}\left(\frac{\partial T}{\partial \dot{q}_i}\right) - \frac{\partial T}{\partial q_i}\right]dq_i.$$

Combining the above with the expression for dW, we get

$$dT + dV = \sum_{i=1}^{3}\left[\frac{d}{dt}\left(\frac{\partial T}{\partial \dot{q}_i}\right) - \frac{\partial(T - V)}{\partial q_i}\right]dq_i = 0.$$

Since V is a function only of the q_i's, this can be written as

$$\sum_{i=1}^{3}\left[\frac{d}{dt}\left(\frac{\partial(T - V)}{\partial \dot{q}_i}\right) - \frac{\partial(T - V)}{\partial q_i}\right]dq_i = 0.$$

Remembering that the q_i's are independent and also remembering that we have been rearranging an added form of Newton's law, we can deduce that the equations

$$L = T - V$$

$$\frac{d}{dt}\left(\frac{\partial L}{\partial \dot{q}_i}\right) - \frac{\partial L}{\partial q_i} = 0 \qquad (i = 1, 2, 3)$$

(3–25)

are equivalent to the usual form of Newton's second law for conservative systems, at least for a particle. The far more general applicability of these equations, called *Lagrange's equations*, will be established later in Chapter 5 for rigid bodies (and in Chapter 11 for very general situations).

EXAMPLE 3–14. Suppose we have a body of mass m attracted toward an unaccelerated origin as though connected to it by a spring of stiffness k. If we study the possible motions of the body in the horizontal XY-plane, we can write

$$L = T - V = \tfrac{1}{2}mv_x^2 + \tfrac{1}{2}mv_y^2 - \tfrac{1}{2}kx^2 - \tfrac{1}{2}ky^2.$$

Substitution into Lagrange's equations (Eq. 3–25) for $x = q_1$ and $y = q_2$ gives

$$\frac{d}{dt}\left(\frac{\partial L}{\partial v_x}\right) - \frac{\partial L}{\partial x} = ma_x + kx = 0,$$

and

$$\frac{d}{dt}\left(\frac{\partial L}{\partial v_y}\right) - \frac{\partial L}{\partial y} = ma_y + ky = 0.$$

Since x and y both have sinusoidal solutions of frequency $(1/2\pi)\sqrt{k/m}$ (see Example 3–8), the motion of the mass will be elliptical, centered at the origin.

Note that we could have written L in terms of polar coordinates as

$$L = T - V = \tfrac{1}{2}m\dot{r}^2 + \tfrac{1}{2}mr^2\dot{\theta}^2 - \tfrac{1}{2}kr^2.$$

With $r = q_1$, $\theta = q_2$, Lagrange's equations then become

$$\frac{d}{dt}\left(\frac{\partial L}{\partial \dot{r}}\right) - \frac{\partial L}{\partial r} = m\ddot{r} - mr\dot{\theta}^2 + kr = 0,$$

and

$$\frac{d}{dt}\left(\frac{\partial L}{\partial \dot{\theta}}\right) - \frac{\partial L}{\partial \theta} = mr^2\ddot{\theta} + 2m\dot{r}r\dot{\theta} = rm(r\ddot{\theta} + 2\dot{r}\dot{\theta}) = 0.$$

The first equation sets the radial force $(-kr)$ equal to mass times the absolute acceleration in the r-direction. The second equation indicates the absence of an applied force in the θ-direction and sets the absolute θ acceleration component equal to zero. Note that in this case q_2 does not have the dimensions of length so that the second equation has the dimensions of moment of force. This is quite consistent with the idea that the work done in the θ-direction is the integral of $F_\theta r \, d\theta$ and that F_θ is $-(1/r)\,\partial v/\partial\theta$ [Eq. (3–19)].

Although Lagrange's equations and subsequent developments in analytical mechanics have been basic to the physicist's view of elementary particles, their main application for most engineers has been the actual derivation of equations of motion for complex dynamical systems. ▲

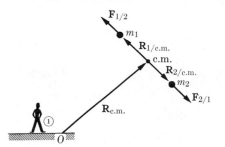

FIG. 3–17.   The interaction of two isolated particles.

3–5 Central forces. Fundamental to many problems in dynamics is the motion of a pair of particles under the influence of a mutual central force, the origin of which may be in gravitational, electric, or even nuclear phenomena. Let's examine the way in which such motion can be reduced to motion of a single particle around a fixed force center without specifying the nature of the force except that it always acts along the line joining the two particles.

Using the services of an inertial observer at the origin O of Fig. 3–17 and remembering that by definition the positions of m_1 and m_2 with respect to their center of mass* are related as

$$m_1 \mathbf{R}_{1/\text{c.m.}} = -m_2 \mathbf{R}_{2/\text{c.m.}},$$

we can write the position of m_1 with respect to m_2 as

$$\mathbf{R}_{1/2} = \mathbf{R}_{1/\text{c.m.}} - \mathbf{R}_{2/\text{c.m.}} = \frac{m_1 + m_2}{m_2} \mathbf{R}_{1/\text{c.m.}} = \frac{m_1}{\mu} \mathbf{R}_{1/\text{c.m.}},$$

or

$$\mathbf{R}_{1/2} = -\frac{m_2}{\mu} \mathbf{R}_{2/\text{c.m.}},$$

where

$$\mu = \frac{m_1 m_2}{m_1 + m_2}.$$

Relating the force exerted on m_1 by m_2 to m_1's absolute acceleration, we get

$$\mathbf{F}_{1/2} = m_1(\ddot{\mathbf{R}}_{1/\text{c.m.}} + \ddot{\mathbf{R}}_{\text{c.m.}}) = \mu\ddot{\mathbf{R}}_{1/2} + m_1\ddot{\mathbf{R}}_{\text{c.m.}}.$$

Similarly, for m_2,

$$\mathbf{F}_{2/1} = -\mathbf{F}_{1/2} = m_2(\ddot{\mathbf{R}}_{2/\text{c.m.}} + \ddot{\mathbf{R}}_{\text{c.m.}}) = -\mu\ddot{\mathbf{R}}_{1/2} + m_2\ddot{\mathbf{R}}_{\text{c.m.}}.$$

---

* See Section 4–1 for a careful definition of center of mass of a finite group of particles.

Adding these equations gives

$$\ddot{\mathbf{R}}_{c.m.} = 0, \tag{3-26}$$

which is the usual result that the center of mass is unaccelerated in the absence of any external forces (see Chapter 4). The motion of m_1 can now be written as

$$\mathbf{F}_{1/2} = m_1 \ddot{\mathbf{R}}_{1/c.m.}, \tag{3-27a}$$

or

$$\frac{m_1}{\mu} \mathbf{F}_{1/2} = \frac{m_1 + m_2}{m_2} \mathbf{F}_{1/2} = m_1 \ddot{\mathbf{R}}_{1/2}. \tag{3-27b}$$

Similarly, for m_2,

$$\mathbf{F}_{2/1} = m_2 \ddot{\mathbf{R}}_{2/c.m.}, \tag{3-27c}$$

$$\frac{m_1 + m_2}{m_1} \mathbf{F}_{2/1} = m_2 \ddot{\mathbf{R}}_{2/1}, \tag{3-27d}$$

or

$$\mathbf{F}_{1/2} = \mu \ddot{\mathbf{R}}_{1/2}. \tag{3-27e}$$

Equations (3–27a) and (3–27c) show that we could have used an inertial observer riding on the unaccelerated center of mass. However, these forms are not too useful because the forces are usually known in terms of $\mathbf{R}_{1/2}$, the separation of the masses, rather than their respective distances from the center of mass. The more useful forms (b) and (d) show that if we use an augmented force, we can, in this special case, set it equal to mass times relative acceleration. Alternatively, in Eq. (3–27e) we can relate the actual force to a reduced mass times the relative acceleration. Note that in either the augmented-force or reduced-mass form, the equation of motion looks just as though it were written for particle motion around a fixed force center. Consequently, if we study such fixed-center motion, it can be quickly interpreted in terms of the motion of two particles about their center of mass.

Looking now at a single particle of mass m moving about an unaccelerated force center, we can see that, if its velocity is known at one instant, the plane in which the entire motion takes place is determined by the velocity vector and the force center. Since the force is always in this plane and has no component perpendicular to it, there can be no stretching or swinging of the velocity vector except in this plane. It thus seems reasonable to use polar coordinates in this plane with the origin O and a non-rotating unaccelerated observer ① at the force center.

Our equations of motion in polar coordinates

$$F_r = ma_r = m(\ddot{r} - r\dot{\theta}^2),$$
$$F_\theta = ma_\theta = m(r\ddot{\theta} + 2\dot{r}\dot{\theta}) \tag{3-28}$$

have two immediate integrals. If we multiply the second by r to form the moment of F_θ, the other side becomes the rate of change of moment of momentum H (or angular momentum).

$$rF_\theta = \frac{d}{dt}(mr^2\dot{\theta}).$$

Since F_θ is zero in this central force problem, the moment of momentum is a constant

$$mr^2\dot{\theta} = H, \tag{3–29}$$

where $H/2m$ is readily seen in Fig. 3–18 to be the rate at which the radius vector r sweeps out area. Thus Kepler's law for planetary motion, that the area within the orbit is swept over at a uniform rate, is generally applicable to any central force problem.

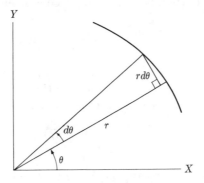

FIG. 3–18. Calculating the rate at which r sweeps out area.

The second integral is the work-energy integral written in polar coordinates. If we assume that our force is conservative and has the potential V, a function only of r, this integral takes the form of Eq. (3–21):

$$V + T = V(r) + \tfrac{1}{2}mv_r^2 + \tfrac{1}{2}mv_\theta^2 = \text{constant},$$

or

$$V(r) + \tfrac{1}{2}m\dot{r}^2 + \tfrac{1}{2}mr^2\dot{\theta}^2 = E, \tag{3–30}$$

which we called the principle of conservation of mechanical energy E. Note that the angle coordinate can be eliminated by combining Eqs. (3–29) and (3–30) so that

$$V(r) + \tfrac{1}{2}m\dot{r}^2 + \frac{1}{2}\frac{H^2}{mr^2} = E. \tag{3–31}$$

In principle, we can obtain r as a function of time from the integral of

$$dt = \frac{dr}{\sqrt{\dfrac{2}{m}\left(E - V - \dfrac{H^2}{2mr^2}\right)}}$$

and then obtain θ as a function of time from

$$d\theta = \frac{H}{mr^2}\, dt.$$

These integrals are often unmanageable and alternative techniques may be used depending on the form of $V(r)$. Of the four necessary constants of integration, H and E are perhaps the most useful and interesting, as we shall see.

In order to make an enlightening interpretation of Eq. (3–31), let's recall that the conservation of energy could be written as

$$V - \frac{m\Omega^2 R_\perp^2}{2} + \frac{mv'^2}{2} = \text{constant} \tag{3-22}$$

for an observer rotating about an unaccelerated origin at the constant rate Ω. We can make this look like conservation of mechanical energy in the rotating space by defining the augmented potential

$$V_{\text{aug}} = V - \frac{m\Omega^2 R_\perp^2}{2}.$$

In a similar fashion, we can say that since an observer rotating with the radius vector r as it sweeps area at the rate $H/2m$ sees only the kinetic energy $\frac{1}{2}m\dot{r}^2$, we can think of an augmented potential for him as

$$V_{\text{aug}} = V + \frac{1}{2}\frac{H^2}{mr^2}. \tag{3-32a}$$

In this fashion, Eq. (3–31) can be thought of as expressing energy conservation

$$V_{\text{aug}} + \tfrac{1}{2}m\dot{r}^2 = E \tag{3-32b}$$

for this observer whose angular velocity is

$$\Omega = \dot{\theta} = \frac{H}{mr^2}. \tag{3-32c}$$

He visualizes straight-line motion of total energy E in a force field represented by V_{aug}. From this familiar relationship, Eq. (3–32b), we can deduce some of the characteristics of the actual planar motion.

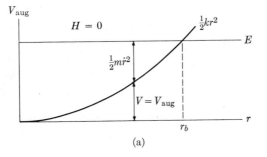

(a)

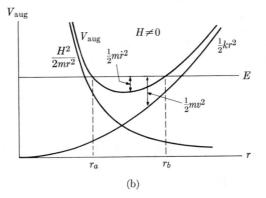

(b)

FIGURE 3–19

EXAMPLE 3–15. To illustrate these ideas, let's return to the mass-spring system that we encountered in Example 3–14. We will assume that the mass is attracted to the force center by a force proportional to the distance r,

$$\mathbf{F} = -k\mathbf{r}.$$

Then

$$V = \tfrac{1}{2}kr^2, \qquad V_{\text{aug}} = \tfrac{1}{2}kr^2 + \frac{1}{2}\frac{H^2}{mr^2},$$

$$E = V_{\text{aug}} + \tfrac{1}{2}m\dot{r}^2.$$

Looking first at the case where the angular momentum H is zero, we see the motion is actually along a straight line, as shown in Fig. 3–19(a). For a given total energy E, the amplitude never exceeds r_b for which V equals E because that would correspond to negative kinetic energy and thus to imaginary velocity. As we have seen in Example 3–8, m oscillates sinusoidally between $\pm r_b$.

For a given constant angular momentum H, the plot for V_{aug} is shown in Fig. 3–19(b). For the total energy E as shown, r is limited to the range between r_a and r_b. Thus the planar motion is limited by circles of radius r_a and r_b at which the radial velocity $\dot{r}$ is zero. Since the angular momentum is the constant H, the θ-component of velocity can be found to be [Eq. (3–32c)]

$$v_\theta = r\dot{\theta} = \frac{H}{mr}.$$

Alternatively, the magnitude of the resultant velocity at any r can be found from the difference between the actual potential V and E. This picture of an orbit limited between r_a and r_b with smaller velocity at the larger values of r corresponds exactly to the elliptical orbits predicted in Example 3–14. ▲

We are often more interested in the relation between r and θ, that is, *the equation of the orbit* or trajectory, than we are in knowing each of them as functions of time. We can eliminate time by solving Eq. (3–29) for dt

$$dt = \frac{H}{mr^2}\, d\theta$$

and substituting in the energy equation [Eq. (3–31)], to get

$$V(r) + \frac{H^2}{2mr^4}\left(\frac{dr}{d\theta}\right)^2 + \frac{1}{2}\frac{H^2}{mr^2} = E.$$

Solving for $d\theta$ and integrating, we obtain

$$\theta = \int_{r_0}^{r} \frac{dr}{r^2\sqrt{(2m/H^2)[E - V(r)] - (1/r^2)}} + \theta_0. \qquad (3\text{–}33a)$$

If we change the variable of integration to $u = 1/r$, we get the simpler looking integral

$$\theta = \theta_0 - \int_{u_0}^{u} \frac{du}{\sqrt{(2m/H^2)[E - V(u)] - u^2}}. \qquad (3\text{–}33b)$$

This integral can be expressed in terms of well-known functions for a variety of force laws, a favorite topic in many of the older treatises on dynamics.

For the important power-law case where the force varies with the nth power of r,

$$V = Kr^{n+1} = Ku^{-n-1} \qquad (3\text{–}34a)$$

and

$$\theta = \theta_0 - \int_{u_0}^{u} \frac{du}{\sqrt{(2mE/H^2) - (2mK/H^2)u^{-n-1} - u^2}}. \qquad (3\text{–}34b)$$

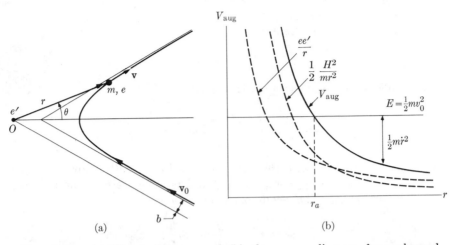

FIG. 3–20. (a) The trajectory, and (b) the energy diagram for a charged particle in a repulsive inverse-square field.

This integrates into circular functions for $n = -2, -3$, and, with proper change of variable, for $n = 1$ (Example 3–14). We get elliptic functions for $n = 5, 3, 0, -4, -5, -7$, and also for some fractional exponents (Ref. 2, Goldstein).

EXAMPLE 3–16. Despite the fact that quantum effects are usually large in considering particle motion on the atomic scale, let's consider the historically important problem of the scattering of a stream of charged particles by the coulomb or electrostatic field of another charged particle. Many of the results of a classical analysis can be very useful even though the uniqueness of the classical trajectory of a given particle differs from the probability ideas of the quantum approach. Limiting ourselves in this example, but not in the problems at the end of the chapter, to watching one of the particles in the incident stream, we have a two-body central force problem which we can quickly transform into the equivalent one-body, fixed force center problem.

Using this latter viewpoint, we will consider a fixed charge e' and an approaching mass m with charge e and initial velocity v_0 at very large distance as shown in Fig. 3–20(a). The force on the moving particle follows a repulsive inverse-square law so that in the proper units

$$F = \frac{ee'}{r^2},$$

and

$$V = \frac{ee'}{r}, \qquad V_{\text{aug}} = \frac{ee'}{r} + \frac{1}{2}\frac{H^2}{mr^2}.$$

The particle's constant moment of momentum H can be figured when it is remote from the force center as [Eq. (3–29)]

$$H = mv_0 b,$$

and, similarly, its total energy E is [Eq. (3–31)]

$$E = \frac{ee'}{r} + \frac{1}{2}\frac{H^2}{mr^2} + \tfrac{1}{2}m\dot{r}^2 = \tfrac{1}{2}mv_0^2.$$

A comparison of V_{aug} with total energy E in Fig. 3–20(b) shows that the radial velocity r is always less than v_0 and becomes zero at the point of closest approach r_a. The θ-component of velocity,

$$v_\theta = r\dot{\theta} = \frac{H}{mr} = v_\theta \frac{b}{r},$$

increases as the particle approaches until $r = r_a$, when it represents the entire resultant velocity.

The differential equation for the particle's trajectory is, from Eq. (3–34b),

$$\theta = \theta_0 - \int_0^u \frac{du}{\sqrt{(2mE/H^2) - (2mee'/H^2)u - u^2}},$$

so that

$$\theta = \theta_0 - \cos^{-1}\frac{u + (mee'/H^2)}{\sqrt{1 + (2EH^2/me^2e'^2)}},$$

and

$$u = \frac{1}{r} = -\frac{mee'}{H^2}(1 - \epsilon \cos \theta),$$

where

$$\epsilon = \sqrt{1 + (2EH^2/me^2e'^2)} = \sqrt{1 + (mv_0^2 b/ee')^2}$$

and θ_0 was made zero by the symmetrical choice of axes in Fig. 3–20(a). Notice that ϵ is always positive and greater than unity so that θ is limited to the range $\cos \theta > 1/\epsilon$. If we delve into our knowledge of analytical geometry, we find that the trajectory is a hyperbola with the force center at a focus and asymptotes Θ

$$\Theta = \pm\cos^{-1}\frac{1}{\epsilon} = \pm\cos^{-1}\left(\frac{1}{\sqrt{1 + (mv_0^2 b/ee')^2}}\right).$$

Thus, the larger the initial kinetic energy and offset, and the smaller the electric field strength, the larger the angle between asymptotes. Conversely, the same effects mean less scattering; that is, less deviation from the initial straight-line path. Geometrically the scattering angle Φ is related to Θ as

$$\Phi = 180° - 2\Theta,$$

or

$$\cos \Theta = \sin\left(\frac{\Phi}{2}\right) = \frac{1}{\epsilon},$$

which is equivalent to

$$\tan\left(\frac{\Phi}{2}\right) = \frac{ee'}{mv_0^2 b} = \frac{ee'}{2Eb}.$$

The interpretation of this result in terms of scattering cross-section and scattering seen from stationary coordinates is postulated in problems at the end of the chapter. ▲

3–6 Velocity-dependent forces. Most of the forces we have encountered so far have been functions of position or time or, in the case of D'Alembert inertia forces, acceleration. However, it is not at all unusual when studying the motion of bodies moving through fluids to encounter forces dependent on relative velocity. Similar forces act on charged particles in magnetic fields and are characteristic of plastic deformations of materials where forces are related to strain rates rather than to strains themselves.

You probably already know that the resistance or drag of ship hulls is proportional to varying powers of velocity in different speed ranges. At extremely low speeds, we can use the first power, at moderate speeds the square, and when wave-making becomes dominant, the cube. For submerged bodies at the very low speeds where viscous forces dominate (low Reynolds number), the first power is appropriate. For vehicles such as submarines and aircraft, speed squared is a good approximation up to limiting speeds such as sonic speeds for aircraft where wave-making again becomes important.

EXAMPLE 3–17. As an example of viscous flow at a very low Reynolds number, let's look at Millikan's famous oil-drop experiment for determining the charge on the electron. Suppose we have very small drops of oil sprayed into the air between the horizontal plates of a condenser. Because of our knowledge of surface tension, we can be sure the drops are quite spherical, and we can use the relation called Stoke's law (see your physics text or Ref. 6, p. 273) relating the retarding force D to the velocity v and radius R of the sphere, and to the air's viscosity μ, as

$$D = 6\pi\mu Rv.$$

If the air is ionized so that one or more ions may attach themselves to a particular drop, that drop can be given an upward force by charging the condenser to a potential Φ. For a plate separation d, the electric field strength E is

$$E = \frac{\Phi}{d}.$$

The force on the oil drop with n electron charges e is

$$F = neE.$$

If we adjust the potential so that the drops which have one charge e remain stationary under the microscope because of the force balance between weight, buoyancy, and electric force,

$$\tfrac{4}{3}\pi R^3 (\rho_{\text{oil}} - \rho_{\text{air}})g = eE,$$

the drops with more charges will rise and the drops without charge will fall. Thus for an unbalanced drop

$$neE - \tfrac{4}{3}\pi R^3 (\rho_{\text{oil}} - \rho_{\text{air}})g - 6\pi\mu Rv = \tfrac{4}{3}\pi R^3 \rho_{\text{oil}} \dot{v}.$$

This can be integrated by solving for dt, thus leaving a function of v on the other side, or it can be recognized as a nonhomogeneous first-order linear differential equation* whose solution is

$$v = \frac{2R^2(\rho_{\text{oil}} - \rho_{\text{air}})g}{9\mu}\left[(n-1) - ne^{-(9/2)\,(\mu/R^2\rho_{\text{oil}})\,t}\right]$$

for the initial condition that the drop is falling at its terminal velocity when the electric field is suddenly applied. The subsequent motion of a drop is shown in Fig. 3–21 for various values of n. The charge e could be determined from a drop with one charge, if the drop size were known, because E, ρ_{oil}, and ρ_{air} are easily measured. In the experiment, R is determined by measuring the terminal velocity V of the drop after the field is removed. From this, we find

$$R = \sqrt{\frac{9}{2}\frac{\mu V}{g(\rho_{\text{oil}} - \rho_{\text{air}})}},$$

so that

$$e = \frac{4\pi}{3}\sqrt{\frac{1}{g(\rho_{\text{oil}} - \rho_{\text{air}})}}\frac{(\tfrac{9}{2}\mu V)^{3/2}}{E}.$$

------

* See Section 7–3, especially Example 7–3.

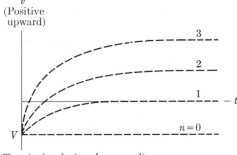

v
(Positive upward)

3

2

1

$-t$

$n=0$

V

(Terminal velocity downward)

FIGURE 3–21

Actually Millikan found that e determined in this way depended somewhat on the air pressure and drop radius. Attributing this to the fact that the drops are so close to molecular dimensions that the Stokes assumption of a continuous fluid structure is not good enough, he successfully introduced a correction factor based on the ratio of the mean free path of the air molecules to the drop radius. ▲

EXAMPLE 3–18. As an example of force dependence on the square of the speed, we can take a simplified look at the dynamic disturbance of an aircraft from steady level flight. We can make a fair approximation of the low-frequency phugoid oscillation relating change in speed to change in height by assuming that the angle of attack of the aircraft relative to the instantaneous direction of its velocity remains constant during the disturbed motion. It was this sort of approach by early investigators such as Lanchester which led to current, far more complex and complete theories of aircraft dynamic stability. The real justification of such crude approximations is in their favorable comparison with experimental evidence.

The integrated reaction of the surrounding air on the aircraft in steady flight at speed V can be represented as the lift and drag (defined as the components perpendicular and parallel to the velocity),

$$L = \alpha C_{L\alpha}\rho \frac{V^2}{2} S = K_L V^2,$$

and

$$D = C_D\rho \frac{V^2}{2} S = K_D V^2.$$

Note that they are just proportional to V^2 for constant angle of attack α and air density ρ (S is the wing area, and $C_{L\alpha}$ and C_D are dimensionless constants depending on aircraft geometry and the basic character of the

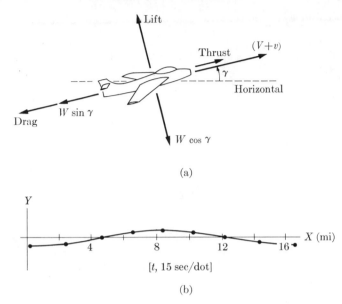

(a)

(b)

FIG. 3–22. The poorly damped phugoid oscillation of a jet transport.

external air flow). We also have the external forces of engine thrust T and aircraft weight W, where for steady level flight $W = L$ and $T = D$.

If we assume the airplane is disturbed slightly as shown in Fig. 3–22(a) so that its speed is $V + v$ along a flight path inclined at the small angle γ, the force equation normal to the flight path is

$$K_L(V + v)^2 - W \cos \gamma = m(V + v)\frac{d\gamma}{dt},$$

where $d\gamma/dt$ is the rate of swinging of the velocity vector. The force equation along the flight path (assuming no significant change of thrust with v or γ) is

$$T - K_D(V + v)^2 - W \sin \gamma = m\frac{d}{dt}(V + v).$$

Remembering that γ is small so that $\cos \gamma \approx 1$ and $\sin \gamma \approx \gamma$, setting $W = K_L V^2$ and neglecting terms involving products or powers of the perturbation quantities v and γ, we derive the equations

$$2K_L Vv = mV\frac{d\gamma}{dt},$$

and

$$-2K_D Vv - K_L V^2\gamma = m\frac{dv}{dt},$$

where the equilibrium equations have been subtracted.

This pair of simultaneous, homogeneous, first-order differential equations can be solved in a number of ways (see Chapter 7). If we differentiate the second equation and substitute it into the first to eliminate $d\gamma/dt$, we have

$$m\ddot{v} + 2K_D V\dot{v} + \frac{2K_L^2 V^2}{m} v = 0.$$

This has the solution

$$v = Ae^{-(K_D V/m)t} \sin(\omega_n t + \phi),$$

where A and ϕ are constants of integration and

$$\omega_n = \frac{K_D V}{m} \sqrt{2(K_L/K_D)^2 - 1}.$$

Remembering that lift-to-drag ratios are much larger than unity, we obtain

$$\omega_n \cong \sqrt{2}\frac{K_L V}{m} = \sqrt{2}\frac{W}{mV} = \sqrt{2}\frac{g}{V}.$$

Substitution of the solution for v into the second of our differential equations gives the corresponding solution for γ as

$$\gamma = -\sqrt{2}\frac{A}{V} \exp\left[-\frac{K_D V}{m} t\right] \sin(\omega_n t + \phi + \psi),$$

where

$$\psi = \tan^{-1} \sqrt{2}\frac{K_L}{K_D},$$

which is almost 90°. As shown in Fig. 3–22(b), the motion of the aircraft along the oscillatory flight path resembles that of a roller coaster in that kinetic energy is traded for potential energy in the gravitational field as the aircraft's height changes. The mechanical energy in the oscillation is not conserved but is slowly dissipated due to the presence of a drag term in the equations of motion. For $K_D = 0$, the disturbance would not die out ($e^0 = 1$). (For a more complete treatment of aircraft stability, see Section 6–6 and the end of Chapter 9. ▲

Two techniques used in this illustration deserve further comment. In the rather common situation in which we are interested in small deviations or perturbations from an equilibrium condition, it is very useful to write the equations in terms of the equilibrium quantities plus their perturbations. After subtracting the equilibrium equations, we are left with relatively convenient equations in the perturbation quantities. The second technique, linearization, further simplifies the problem by the additional assumption that since the perturbation quantities are quite small, we can neglect the terms involving their powers and products. Since we retain only the linear terms, we have approximated the problem with a set of linear differential equations which are generally far easier to solve. Although this linearization procedure can be a powerful ally in attacking many problems, it represents an additional level of approximation and must be used with caution. (See Chapter 7 for further discussion of perturbation techniques and linearity.)

3–7 Gravitational orbits. In this age of satellites and space flight, there is a strong motivation to look a little closer than our fathers did at particle motion in gravitational fields. In even earlier days, many of the great men of dynamics were deeply involved in the development of celestial mechanics, and much of their work is of considerable use to us now. Of course we can no longer always make the assumptions that our dynamical system is conservative and that angular momentum is conserved even in the two-body problem. Our modern, man-made heavenly bodies are not passive but may generate their own thrust. They also may spend considerable lengths of time in an appreciable atmosphere, and if they are of very low density, they may even be affected substantially by the pressure of radiation from the sun.

Celestial mechanics, which has always had an innate beauty and simplicity, has never been characterized by elegant closed-form solutions, but has been the spawning ground of many of the techniques of numerical analysis. These have been invaluable in recent years as engineers and scientists have endeavored to learn to use the high-speed computer. Nevertheless, the simple concepts of orbital motion which we can easily

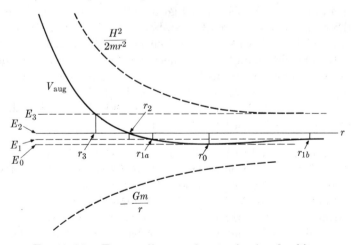

Fig. 3–23. Energy diagram for gravitational orbits.

derive analytically in the case of two bodies give us a sound basis of experience and intuition from which we can approach the more complicated problems numerically.

Remembering from Section 3–5 that the two-body problem can always be reduced to an equivalent one-body problem about a fixed force center, let's integrate the equations of motion of a mass m in a gravitational field whose potential is

$$V(r) = -\frac{Gm}{r},\tag{3–35}$$

where G for the earth is γm_e (see Example 3–11). Rather than write Newton's second law, we can write the two integrals we have derived for any conservative central force as the conservation of angular momentum

$$mr^2\dot{\theta} = H\tag{3–29}$$

and the conservation of mechanical energy

$$V(r) + \tfrac{1}{2}m\dot{r}^2 + \tfrac{1}{2}mr^2\dot{\theta}^2 = E.\tag{3–30}$$

These can be combined to eliminate $\dot{\theta}$ and obtain

$$-\frac{Gm}{r} + \frac{H^2}{2mr^2} + \tfrac{1}{2}m\dot{r}^2 = E.$$

If we think of the first two terms as an augmented potential V_{aug}, we can find bounding values of r from the energy plot in Fig. 3–23 by noting where V_{aug} equals the total energy E. [Compare this with the plot in Fig. 3–20(b) for electrostatic repulsion.] Apparently the particle always has a minimum approach distance for every value of total energy E but is unbounded for energies larger than E_2. For E_1, the motion must be between r_{1_a} and r_{1_b}, and for E_0, it is always at r_0 and thus is circular. "Escape" orbits must have $E > 0$. Notice that Fig. 3–23 is drawn for a given value of angular momentum H.

Although Eqs. (3–35, 29, 30) cannot be integrated explicitly to give r and θ as functions of time, we can get a simple relation between r and θ if we eliminate time as we did in Eq. (3–33b) where we use the dummy variable u for $1/r$. Thus, the proper combination gives

$$\theta = \theta_0 - \int_{u_0}^{u} \frac{du}{\sqrt{(2mE/H^2) + (2m^2Gu/H^2) - u^2}}$$

$$= \theta_0 + \cos^{-1}\left[\frac{u - (m^2G/H^2)}{\sqrt{(m^4G^2/H^4) + (2mE/H^2)}}\right]\Bigg|_{u_0}^{u}.$$

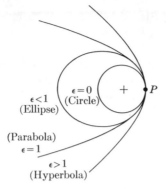

FIG. 3–24. Conic sections as simple gravitational trajectories.

If we combine θ_0 and the u_0-term into one constant of integration α, we can write

$$u = \frac{1}{r} = \frac{m^2 G}{H^2} [1 + \sqrt{1 + (2EH^2/m^3 G^2)} \cos(\theta + \alpha)]$$

or

$$r = \frac{H^2/m^2 G}{1 + \epsilon \cos(\theta + \alpha)}, \tag{3–36a}$$

where

$$\epsilon = \sqrt{1 + (2EH^2/m^3 G^2)}. \tag{3–36b}$$

Referring to analytical geometry, we might recognize Eq. (3–36) as the equation of conic sections with focus at the origin. The dimensionless eccentricity ϵ determines the character of the conic sections as shown in Fig. 3–24, and the constant $H^2/m^2 G$ determines the size. Note that this constant is actually independent of m because H^2 contains m^2 and is more simply thought of as the ratio of the square of the angular momentum per unit mass to the attracting body's gravitational constant G. The constant α is zero when the ($\theta = 0$)-line bisects the trajectory symmetrically.

Since we are basically interested in flight around the earth or around the sun, we are concerned primarily with elliptical orbits. Inasmuch as an orbit represents the integration of three scalar second-order differential statements of Newton's second law in three perpendicular directions, there should in general be six constants of integration for a particular orbit. These could be the three scalar components of the particle's initial position and velocity but are usually far more conveniently expressed in other forms. As shown in Fig. 3–25, we can use two constants to determine the orientation of the orbit plane with respect to a reference XY-plane. Thus i represents the inclination of the orbit plane, and Ω the angle from the reference X-axis to the line of nodes or intersection. More specifically, Ω is

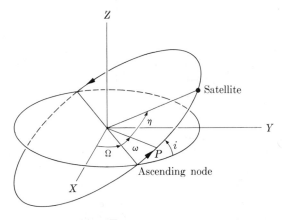

FIGURE 3–25

positive about Z and extends to the ascending node when the satellite crosses from below the reference plane. The XY-plane is usually either the plane of the earth's orbit around the sun, called the ecliptic, or the earth's equatorial plane. The X-axis is usually aligned with the line of intersection of these planes, which is the direction of the sun at the vernal (spring) equinox.

In the orbital plane, the orientation of the ellipse can be designated by the angle ω to the closer intersection P of the ellipse with its own major axis. This angle ω is called the longitude of the perifocus.* The shape of the ellipse is determined by the eccentricity ϵ and its size by the numerator of Eq. (3–36a) or simply by the semimajor axis a. The sixth constant must relate an origin in time to the orbital motion and is often specified as the initial time of passage through the perifocus P.

Besides these six parameters, known as the orbital elements, there are a few other quantities that should be mentioned. An ephemeris is a table of locations of the satellite on the celestial sphere. The angular location of the satellite from the perifocus is the true anomaly η. A useful measure of time is the mean anomaly M, which is the angle to a fictitious body that orbits in the same period but at constant rate. The eccentric anomaly E is still another angle related to the motion of the satellite, which has prominence in the calculation procedures for finding the true anomaly.

When the orbiting body is subject to small disturbances from another body, atmospheric drag, or thrust, it no longer follows exactly a conic

---

* For sun-centered orbits the perifocus is called the perihelion and for earth-centered orbits, the perigee. The more distant ends of the major axes are called aphelion and apogee, respectively.

section. Its path may be close to a slightly different conic section at each instant, and a very useful way of describing such a perturbed orbit is to find or specify the six elements as slowly varying functions of time. Of course if the disturbances are large, such as with substantial thrust, entirely different procedures are required.*

EXAMPLE 3–19. An earth satellite (see Fig. 3–26) on a rather eccentric orbit may, as it goes through perigee P, come close enough to the earth to feel momentarily the retarding effects of atmospheric drag. If we assume that the drag acts over a short enough part of the path near P, its primary effect is to reduce **v** slightly at each passage. Although successive orbits will come very near P, they will fall successively shorter and shorter of A because the energy and angular momentum are both reduced by each pass through the atmosphere at P. From Eq. (3–36b), we can see that the eccentricity is becoming smaller, and quite obviously, the semimajor axis is shrinking. Thus the orbit becomes more circular and, curiously enough, the period becomes shorter because the average velocity during each orbit is increasing.

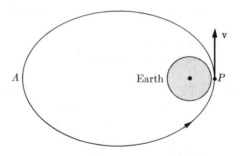

FIG. 3–26. An earth satellite grazing the atmosphere at perigee P.

This effect of a nearly impulsive drag force can be reversed and extended to predict the effect of nearly impulsive thrusts at perigee and apogee. Thus a satellite circling the earth at the radius of P could, by applying a substantial impulsive thrust at P, transfer to the eccentric elliptical orbit and reach A. It would be going too slowly to stay in a circular orbit through A but the application of an impulsive thrust at A could bring the velocity up to the required circular velocity. This would increase both angular momentum and total energy (per unit mass) and could thus be thought to increase the eccentricity to zero.

---

* For further information and other specific references, see Ehricke, Ref. 7, and Siefert, Ref. 8.

Note that it is impossible to achieve a specific orbit by application of thrust unless the last part of the thrust is applied during the last instants, as the rocket's motion becomes locally coincident with that of the desired orbit. One cannot shift from one orbit to a nonintersecting one with only one impulsive application of thrust. There must be at least an initial thrust to achieve a transfer orbit and a terminal thrust to achieve the desired orbit. ▲

EXAMPLE 3–20. So far, all of our discussion of orbits has been from the point of view of an inertial observer located at the fixed force center. As observers standing on the earth's surface, we are rotating at earth rate and see the same satellite motion as would a similarly rotating observer at the earth's center who would appear stationary to us (and vice versa). A so-called equatorial twenty-four-hour satellite (see Example 2–12) moving in a circular path will appear to us to be stationary right over a point on the equator in our (rotating) space.

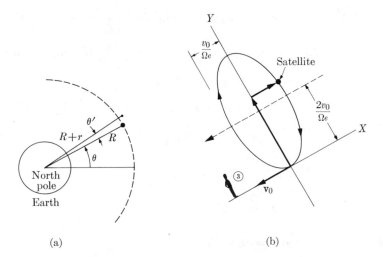

FIG. 3–27. Perturbation of a 24-hr satellite in equatorial orbit, as seen from the earth.

Suppose a steering rocket is accidentally fired, which suddenly gives the satellite a small velocity directly inward. What does the subsequent motion look like to us on the earth? If we assume that the disturbance is small, we can say that the radius is the original constant R plus a small change r. The small motion in the θ-direction can be represented by the very small incremental angle θ' (Fig. 3–27a). The nonrotating observer at the earth's center sees $R + r$ and $\theta + \theta'$, where $\dot{\theta} = \Omega$. The fellow rotating with the earth at its center at Ω_e sees $R + r$ and θ'. Writing the equations of motion for the nonrotating observer in polar coordinates, we have

$$-\frac{Gm}{(R+r)^2} = m\left\{\frac{d^2(R+r)}{dt^2} - (R+r)\left[\frac{d}{dt}(\theta+\theta')\right]^2\right\},$$

and

$$0 = m\left\{\frac{1}{(R+r)}\frac{d}{dt}\left[(R+r)^2\frac{d}{dt}(\theta+\theta')\right]\right\}.$$

Expanding these equations, we have

$$-\frac{G}{R^2}\left(1 - \frac{2r}{R} + \cdots\right) = \ddot{r} - (R+r)(\dot\theta+\dot\theta')^2,$$

$$(R+r)^2(\dot\theta+\dot\theta') = \text{constant} = R^2\dot\theta.$$

Canceling $-(G/R^2)$ against $-R\dot\theta^2$ and dropping terms in products and powers of the small quantities r and θ', we get

$$\frac{2rG}{R^3} = \ddot{r} - r\dot\theta^2 - 2R\dot\theta\dot\theta', \qquad \text{and} \qquad R^2\dot\theta' + 2R\dot\theta r = 0$$

Eliminating $\dot\theta'$ between equations and replacing $\sqrt{G/R^3}$ and $\dot\theta$ with Ω_e, we obtain

$$\ddot{r} + \Omega_e^2 r = 0$$

with the initial conditions that at $t = 0$, $r = 0$, $\dot{r} = -v_0$. The solution for r can be verified as

$$r = \frac{-v_0}{\Omega_e}\sin\Omega_e t.$$

From the second equation above, we can obtain

$$\dot\theta' = -2\frac{\Omega_e}{R}r = +2\frac{v_0}{R}\sin\Omega_e t.$$

Thus, with $\theta' = 0$ at $t = 0$, we have

$$\theta' = \frac{2v_0}{R\Omega_e} = 1 - \cos\Omega_e t.$$

If we think, as rotating observers, of a fixed XY-system with origin at the original satellite position, the coordinates x and y will correspond to r and $R\theta'$ for these small perturbations. Thus,

$$x = -\frac{v_0}{\Omega_e}\sin\Omega_e t,$$

and

$$y = \frac{2v_0}{\Omega_e}(1 - \cos\Omega_e t),$$

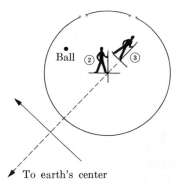

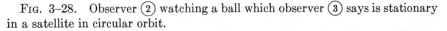

To earth's center

FIG. 3–28. Observer ② watching a ball which observer ③ says is stationary in a satellite in circular orbit.

which corresponds to an elliptical motion centered at $y = 2v_0/\Omega_e$, as shown in Fig. 3–27(b), with a period of twenty-four hours. Can you see what all this looks like to the nonrotating earth-centered observer? If not, try plotting the motion every six hours. Can you estimate the result if the steering rocket had been fired tangentially instead of inward? (See Example 3–19.)

We might compare in an even simpler case the motion seen by non-rotating and rotating observers when both are themselves in circular orbit at the center of mass of a satellite as shown in Fig. 3–28. Suppose the rotating fellow ③, who is always standing vertically according to the local rules, releases a ball several feet in front of him with no relative velocity as he sees it. Since it is in the same orbit as the satellite although slightly ahead of it, the ball will remain stationary to ③. Our nonrotating but accelerated observer ② will claim the ball is traveling around him in a circle having a radius of two feet at a period equal to that of the satellite around the earth. Notice that a nonrotating observer in "free fall" can thus observe locally another object in "free fall" and have it appear to move uniformly in a circular path about him. ▲

PROBLEMS

3–1. Suppose you want to weigh packages while enroute in a mail-sorting truck. You have a choice of a simple spring scale or a balance-arm scale with a movable weight. (a) Which would you choose and why? (b) How much would a one-pound package appear to weigh on each of the scales as you rounded a curve of 600 ft radius at 30 mi/hr?

3–2. A rescue helicopter hovers over a floating man while he fastens the hoist-ing line under his arms. The helicopter then accelerates steadily at 10 ft/sec² up along a path inclined at 45° with the horizontal while reeling in the hoisting line at 3 ft/sec. Assuming that there is no pendulumlike swinging of the man, (a) what is the tension in the hoisting line if the man weighs 160 lb, and (b) what is the angle between the hoisting line and the vertical?

3–3. To use an atomic source of power in a space station, it has been suggested that the power plant be enclosed in a sphere connected by a long cable to another sphere containing the living quarters. If the spheres are made to move in circular paths about a point of the cable midway between them, the people have the sensation of a gravity field. If each sphere has a mass of 1000 slugs and the cable length is 2000 ft, (a) what should the angular velocity of the cable be to give the effect of a $\frac{1}{2}$-g gravity field in each sphere? (Neglect the force of gravitational attraction between the spheres.) (b) What is the tension in the cable for this value of angular velocity? (c) Including the effect of gravitational attraction between the spheres, what is the tension in (b)?

3–4. In the early days of flying, a long-range airplane A was mounted on top of a powerful flying boat B which helped it to take off and reach cruising speed. Just before B released A, they were in level flight with a vertical tension force of 1600 lb holding them together. If A weighed 16,000 lb, B weighed 48,000 lb, and A was suddenly released from B, at what initial rate did they accelerate away from each other? Approximately how much did they separate in the first second?

3–5. How much torque must be transmitted to the cable through pulley A (Fig. 3–29) to accelerate the partially counterbalanced elevator upward at $\frac{1}{4}$ of a g? The diameters of A and B are both 3 ft, and their masses are negligible. Use the D'Alembert point of view in setting up your equations.

3–6. Both an automobile and an airplane make a steady horizontal turn in Example 3–2. If we follow the ideas developed in the example, should the automobile make a wide high-speed turn or a slow sharp turn to achieve a high rate of turn (angular velocity of the radius vector)? What limits its rate of turn? What about the airplane?

3–7. Suppose an aircraft is in a steady climbing turn at 200 mi/hr such that its rate of climb is 1000 ft/min and the radius of its helical path is 1000 ft. Assuming that the thrust and drag forces are parallel to the flight path and the lift is per-

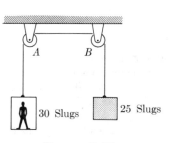

FIGURE 3–29

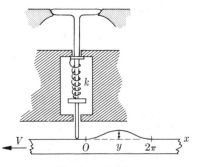

FIGURE 3–30

pendicular to it, find the magnitude of lift and thrust required for this maneuver. Use D'Alembert's principle and estimate the drag as 10% of the 100,000-lb weight of the aircraft. (Note the similarity to the spiral stairway of the lighthouse of Examples 2–2 and 3–4.)

3–8. A valve weighing 0.1 lb (Fig. 3–30) is about to be lifted by a bump on a cam moving at speed V. To an observer on the cam, the bump extends over a distance of 2π inches and has the shape $y = \frac{1}{2}(1 - \cos x)$ measured in inches. If the spring has a constant k of 1 lb/in, how much preload or initial compression must the spring have to keep the valve from leaving the cam momentarily as the bump goes by at a V of 50 ft/sec?

3–9. A large flying saucer is coasting through space in a quiet unaccelerated fashion while spinning slowly about its axis of symmetry in order to maintain inside an "artificial gravity field." A crewman is leaving an air lock on the rim in order to travel to a neighboring saucer. Assume that he leaves the saucer merely by letting go and does not use his personal rocket until he is several diameters away.

(a) After he lets go, does he have any absolute acceleration? Explain.

(b) A friend looks out of a saucer window after it has turned one radian. What does he see for the crewman's velocity and acceleration?

(c) Sketch your idea of the crewman's path as seen by the friend during the first revolution of the saucer.

3–10. A boy sitting in the back of a pick-up truck traveling at 20 mi/hr throws a snowball at a friend standing 20 ft to the side. If the boy throws the snowball at 40 ft/sec just as he passes the friend, in what direction (azimuth and elevation) must he throw it to hit the friend?

3–11. A wooden block is sitting at a radius R_0 on a rotating horizontal platform whose angular velocity Ω is *very gradually* increasing. If the coefficient of friction is μ between block and platform, (a) find the Ω at which the block will begin to slide, and (b) write Newton's second law for the block after it has begun to slide. (Don't try to integrate it—just write it down carefully and explicitly.) (c) As a rotating observer using the D'Alembert approach, write the equation for the sliding block and compare it with (b).

3–12. Two wooden blocks, one resting on top of the other (Fig. 3–31), are connected by a rope around a fixed pulley. The weights of the large and small blocks are 90 and 10 lb, respectively, and the coefficient of friction μ between sliding surfaces is 0.2.

(a) If a force F of 50 lb is applied to the lower block, what is the resulting acceleration of each block? Neglect the inertia of the pulley.

(b) Is the acceleration larger or smaller if the force F is reversed?

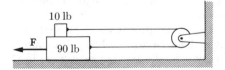

FIGURE 3–31

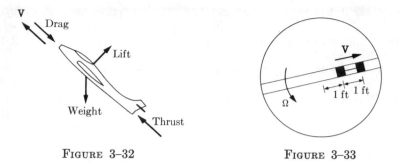

FIGURE 3–32   FIGURE 3–33

3–13. (a) Use D'Alembert's principle to find the variation in pressure in a spherical fuel tank being accelerated vertically at 2 g's. The density of the liquid fuel is 1 slug/ft³. (b) Is the pressure gradient any different if the tank is being accelerated horizontally at 2 g's?

3–14. In early aeromedical experiments on "weightlessness," some Air Force pilots flew their jets on paths in a vertical plane (Fig. 3–32) in such a way that their passengers had the sensation of being weightless; that is, they felt no forces from the floor or seat or seat belt and were in "free fall." (a) Describe an airplane path which satisfies these requirements for as long a time as possible. (b) What values of lift and thrust are required in the maneuver? Are they constant? (Assume drag $\sim V^2$.)

3–15. In Problem 2–34, a crewman on a flying saucer hovering over Boston walks from one rim observation window to another 60° away while the saucer rotates counterclockwise. Use the D'Alembert point of view to determine (a) how he must lean, as he walks, in order to keep from falling over, and (b) whether it makes any difference if the saucer rotates clockwise.

3–16. A large horizontal turntable (Fig. 3–33) rotating at the constant rate Ω has a frictionless slot cut along a diameter. Two equal masses joined by a fine wire are sliding along the slot at a velocity $\mathbf{V}$ at the instant shown. Find the tension in the wire at this instant.

*3–17. We have all seen a batter hit a home run. To understand some of the mechanics of the feat, let's take some basic data and make some rough calculations. Suppose the baseball weighs 9 ounces and is traveling about 100 ft/sec when it reaches the batter. Let's assume the fence is 15 ft high and is 400 ft away from the batter and that the bat weighs about 2½ lb. We might also observe that a baseball dropped from 6 ft onto a hard floor rebounds to only 1½ ft.

(a) Estimate the speed of the bat when it strikes the ball. Carefully state all of the assumptions you make with an estimate of their relative influence on the accuracy of your answer.

(b) Estimate the range of heights at which the batter can swing the bat at a pitch of given height without having the ball fall within the field and be caught by the fielder as an easy out. Assume the swings are in parallel planes.

---

* Starred problems are more difficult.

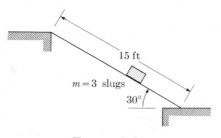

FIGURE 3-34

3–18. Suppose a crewman of a flying saucer in deep space hangs a ball on a string attached to a point in the saucer midway between center and rim.

(a) If the saucer rotates slowly about its axis of symmetry at the rate Ω, what is the equilibrium position for the ball?

(b) If the ball is displaced slightly in a plane perpendicular to the axis, will it swing like a pendulum? If so, what will be its period?

*3–19. If you are in an airplane making a steady horizontal turn of radius R at speed V and you have a simple pendulum hanging from the roof of the cabin, pull the mass to one side and let it go. Try to describe the motion of the pendulum mass as you see it. (Remembering that you are rotating with the airplane, will the pendulum swing in one plane or not?) Can you write down correct equations of motion?

3–20. Suppose a box slides down a chute as shown in Fig. 3–34. The coefficient of friction μ is 0.3, and the box has an initial velocity of 10 ft/sec.

(a) Find, by work-energy ideas, the velocity of the box when it has traveled to the bottom of the chute.

(b) Looking now at the chute rather than the box, note that the friction force appears to do work on the chute but yet the chute experiences no change in kinetic energy. Explain carefully.

3–21. Show that an unaccelerated observer rotating at the constant rate Ω can write the work-energy relation for a particle of mass m,

$$\int \mathbf{F} \cdot d'\mathbf{R}' = \frac{\Delta m v'^2}{2} - \frac{\Delta m \Omega^2 R'^2_\perp}{2},$$

where $R'_\perp$ is the component of $\mathbf{R}'$ perpendicular to the vector Ω.

3–22. A launching mechanism for aircraft exerts a force which can be closely approximated by $F = 5000$ lb for 1 sec and then $F = K(t - 1)^{7/3}$ for the rest of the launching operation. The constant K has a value of 10^5 with F given in pounds, and time t given in seconds. How much time will it take for a 10,000-lb aircraft to attain a velocity of 100 ft/sec? The time after starting from rest is t. Use impulse and momentum ideas directly.

3–23. A 10,000-lb fighter lands on an aircraft-carrier at a relative velocity of 60 mi/hr parallel to the deck. It is immediately caught by an arrester gear which exerts a decelerating force directly proportional to the travel of the airplane along the deck, the constant of proportionality being 100 lb/ft. When it has been slowed to 15 mi/hr, the arrester releases the airplane and the pilot brings it to a stop with a constant 1000-lb braking force. What is the total landing distance measured from point of contact with the arrester gear? Use work and kinetic energy ideas directly.

3–24. An airplane of weight W is descending with a vertical velocity v; then it meets the deck of a carrier that has, at the time, a downward velocity w. The airplane's shock absorber is a spring with a restoring force $F = kx$. To what maximum deflection x_{max} will the spring deflect, and what will be the maximum spring force if we assume that the aerodynamic lift remains equal to the weight during this short time? Do your equations indicate these quantities to be greater or less than they would be if the landing were made on a fixed platform? Do your conclusions seem reasonable?

3–25. A 10-ton airplane is to be launched at 90 mi/hr from a catapult whose carriage run is 60 ft. The launching mechanism is such that the net accelerating force changes linearly with the displacement of the carriage from an initial value F to a final value $F/2$. Find F.

3–26. The gravitational potential of a unit point mass can be written as $V = -G/R$. Plot some surfaces of constant potential and indicate the direction and magnitude, at several points, of the force for which V is the potential.

3–27. (a) Show that the gravitational force inside a thin homogeneous spherical shell is zero. (b) Considering the earth to be made up of concentric layers of such shells, show that the gravitational potential inside the earth drops off linearly with decreasing radius if the density is assumed to be constant.

3–28. With the idea that ϕ represents the velocity potential of a flowing fluid such that the fluid velocity components are

$$v_x = \frac{\partial \phi}{\partial x}, \qquad v_y = \frac{\partial \phi}{\partial y}, \qquad v_z = \frac{\partial \phi}{\partial z}$$

or

$$v_r = \frac{\partial \phi}{\partial r}, \qquad v_\theta = \frac{1}{r}\frac{\partial \phi}{\partial \theta}, \qquad v_z = \frac{\partial \phi}{\partial z},$$

find the flows corresponding to the following potentials by plotting some equipotential surfaces and indicate velocity vectors at several points:

(a) $\phi = x$, (b) $\phi = \ln r$, (c) $\phi = \theta$.

3–29. A particle of mass m and charge e is moving in the empty space between the parallel plates of a condenser. If the electric potential is given by $V = ay$, and the force components on a charge e are given by

$$F_x = -Ke\frac{\partial V}{\partial x}, \qquad F_y = -Ke\frac{\partial V}{\partial y},$$

find the equations of motion for the particle. If it is moving with velocity v_0 in the X-direction midway between the plates at $t = 0$, find its subsequent motion.

3–30. The electric potential in a condenser consisting of a long wire surrounded by a charged circular cylinder is $V = V_0 \ln r$. (a) Noting the expressions for cartesian components of electric force in the previous problem, what are the force components, in cylindrical coordinates, for this potential acting on a particle of mass m and charge e? (b) What are the equations of motion for the particle in differential form? in integrated form? (c) Can you visualize initial conditions which permit the particle to follow a steady spiral path?

3–31. Remembering that the force on a particle of charge e in a magnetic field of strength $\mathbf{H}$ is $\mathbf{F} = e\mathbf{v} \times \mathbf{H}$, (a) write the equations of motion if the particle has mass m, and (b) show that if the particle has a component of initial velocity perpendicular to $\mathbf{H}$ it will spiral about a line parallel to $\mathbf{H}$.

3–32. A ball of mass m rests in a deep radial slot in a horizontal disk rotating at the constant vertical angular velocity Ω. At $t = 0$ it is released with zero radial velocity at a point halfway to the rim. (a) Use the concepts of augmented potential and conservation of mechanical energy for a rotating observer [Eq. (3–22)] to find the resultant velocity of the ball at the instant it leaves the slot at the rim of the wheel. (b) What are the components of force applied by the disk to the ball just before it leaves the slot?

3–33. A perfectly elastic $\frac{1}{4}$-lb ball (Fig. 3–35) is shot up a 60° incline by a spring gun with spring constant $k = 5 \, \text{lb/ft}$. If the distance from the tip of the un-strained spring to the vertical wall is 2 ft and the slope is nearly frictionless, to what height h will the ball go if the spring is compressed 1 ft and released? At what distance from the vertical wall will it reach height h?

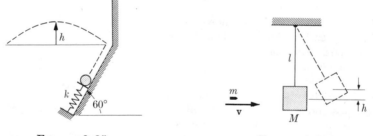

FIGURE 3–35   FIGURE 3–36

3–34. The striking power of a bullet is often measured by using a "ballistic pendulum" as shown in Fig. 3–36. The bullet embeds itself in the mass M and the combination swings to a height h. (a) Show how the initial kinetic energy of the bullet is related to the height h. (b) Will the temperature of the bullet increase or decrease during the impact? Explain. (c) If a typical bullet weighs 0.1 lb and travels at 2500 ft/sec, what would be reasonable sizes for l and M?

3–35. A particle has an initial velocity $\mathbf{v}_0$ in a fluid of the same density as the particle. If the force exerted by the fluid in resisting the motion is opposite to the particle's velocity, (a) show that the particle will always move in a straight line, and describe its motion if the resisting force is proportional to (b) the particle's velocity, and (c) the square of the velocity.

3–36. A particle of mass m and density ρ_p is given an initial horizontal velocity $\mathbf{v}_0$ in a tank of fluid of lower density ρ_f. If the particle hits the bottom at a 45°

path angle, find the height h at which it started. Assume the fluid resistance proportional to particle velocity.

3–37. A hapless construction worker finds himself sliding down a large spherical radome. He inadvertently started at the top with a small horizontal velocity v_0. At what latitude, neglecting friction, does he lose contact with the surface? (a) Set up the equation(s) of motion using Lagrange's equation(s) and solve. (b) Use an energy conservation principle to immediately write down an integral of the equation(s) of motion. (c) If the coefficient of friction $\mu = 0.1$, can you find the latitude at which contact is lost?

3–38. Two large masses of sizes m and $2m$ resting on a frictionless table are connected by a long but light spring of constant k. If the masses are separated such that the spring has been stretched a distance s and then are released, find their relative velocity at the instant the spring force becomes zero by (a) first using Lagrange's equations to find their equations of motion in two different sets of independent coordinates, and (b) by conserving both momentum and energy.

3–39. Use Lagrange's equations to find the equations of motion of a particle of mass m sliding around on the inside of a frictionless spherical bowl in a uniform gravity field. Solve the equations for a few simple motions.

3–40. Derive the equations of motion in Problems 3–29 and 3–30 by using Lagrange's equations.

3–41. Derive the equations of large amplitude pendulum motion in the flying saucer of Problem 3–18 by using Lagrange's equations.

3–42. The double pendulum shown in Fig. 3–37 is made up of two point masses connected by nearly massless rods. Find the "small amplitude" equations of planar motion by using Lagrange's equations and the coordinates θ and ϕ.

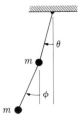

*3–43. We have studied the motion of a mass on a weightless spring. Now let's look at an actual uniform spring without a mass. If the spring is of

FIGURE 3–37

unstrained length l, has running mass of m slugs/ft, and the stiffness of a unit length is k lb/ft, show that the motion x of a segment dl long is governed by the equation

$$(m\,dl)\,\frac{\partial^2 x}{\partial t^2} = \left(T + \frac{\partial T}{\partial l}\,dl\right) - T,$$

where the local tension T is related to the elongation dx of the segment dl as $T = k\,\partial x/\partial l$. The partial differential equation is then

$$m\,\frac{\partial^2 x}{\partial t^2} = k\,\frac{\partial^2 x}{\partial l^2}$$

and can be solved by assuming that the time and position parts of x appear in product form as $x(l, t) = x_l(l)x_t(t)$. Can you show that a spring fixed at one end has many frequencies of sinusoidal oscillation which satisfy the equation of motion? Can you find the lowest frequency and the mode of deformation associated with it?

3–44. With reference to the 24-hr satellite perturbation of Example 3–20, (a) what does the perturbation look like to a nonrotating earth-centered observer, and (b) what would the perturbation have appeared to be from the surface if the accidental firing had been tangential rather than inward?

3–45. A ball of mass m, which moves on a smooth table, is attached to a rubber band, that goes through a hole in the middle of the table and is fastened to the floor. The length of the rubber band is such that its pull on the ball is proportional to the distance between the ball and the hole.

The ball is now held at a point x_0 away from the hole and released at time $t = 0$ with a velocity v_0 perpendicular to the rubber band. (a) Compute the subsequent motion of the ball and find its trajectory. (b) Is there an escape velocity $v_0 = v_{0escape}$? (c) Is the area swept over by the rubber band per second constant?

3–46. The differential equations of central force motion in polar coordinates for a general radial force $\mathbf{F}(r)$ can be combined to eliminate time. (a) Show that with the substitution $u = 1/r$ and the identity

$$\frac{1}{r^2} \frac{dr}{d\theta} = - \frac{d(1/r)}{d\theta},$$

the equation for the orbit can be written in the form

$$\frac{d^2u}{d\theta^2} + u = - \frac{m}{H^2u^2} F\left(\frac{1}{u}\right).$$

(b) Solve this equation for the special case of a gravitational field and check your result with Eq. (3–36). (Notice the similar differential equation in Example 3–8.)

3–47. We derived [Eq. (3–32a)] the relationship $V_{aug} = V(r) + \frac{1}{2}(H^2/mr^2)$ for an observer rotating at the angular velocity $\dot{\theta}$ which corresponds to both constant areal velocity and constant angular momentum. Show by differentiation that V_{aug} represents for this observer the potential of the gravitational and centrifugal forces.

3–48. Demonstrate the relationship between Eq. (3–27b), derived for the isolated two-mass problem, and the first correction term in the expression for the moon's acceleration as seen from the earth's center in Example 3–1.

3–49. If we think of a horizontal stream (Fig. 3–38) of uniformly distributed similar particles approaching our fixed force center in Example 3–16 on coulomb scattering, the scattering angle Φ depends for each particle on b and its total energy E as

$$\tan (\Phi/2) = \frac{ee'}{2Eb}.$$

Show that if I represents the uniform number of approaching particles per unit area and $\sigma(\Phi)I$ represents the number of scattered particles per unit area, then

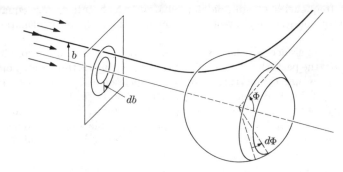

FIGURE 3–38

from the geometry of the problem

$$\sigma(\Phi) = -\frac{b}{\sin \Phi}\frac{db}{d\Phi}.$$

We can then derive Rutherford's famous result for scattering cross section:

$$\sigma(\Phi) = \frac{1}{4}\left(\frac{ee'}{2E}\right)\frac{1}{\sin^4 (\Phi/2)}.$$

3–50. The scattering in Example 3–16 and Problem 3–49 has been handled as a one-body problem in a fixed inverse-square force field. Actually the scattering involves two bodies m_1 and m_2, and the originally stationary particle m_2 recoils as shown in Fig. 3–39. Use the ideas of Section 3–5 to show that (a) the angle Φ of Problem 3–49 is identical with the angle shown here as the limiting value of the direction of the line of centers, and (b) that the scattering angle α in unaccelerated "laboratory coordinates" is related to Φ as

$$\tan \alpha = \frac{\sin \Phi}{\cos \Phi + m_1/m_2}.$$

3–51. Suppose a space ship in a circular polar orbit at 200-mi altitude transfers to a circular orbit at 500-mi altitude by applying tangential thrust over the

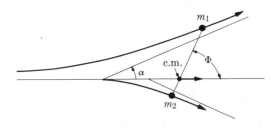

FIGURE 3–39

North Pole and then again over the South Pole. What is the transfer orbit, and how much change in momentum per unit mass is required over each pole?

3–52. A space ship in a circular earth orbit inclined 10° to the equator suddenly changes course into an equatorial orbit. As a function of orbit radius, find the change in momentum per unit mass needed to switch orbits. At what place must this change be made?

3–53. If you are in a closed space ship in "free fall" in a gravitational field, can you detect by internal measurements or experiments that you are accelerating (a) if the field is of the radial $1/r^2$ type, or (b) if it is a uniform parallel field? [*Note:* See the end of Example 3–20.]

CHAPTER 4

GROUPS OF PARTICLES

In our applications of Newton's second law up to this point, we have been able to consider each body as though it were a particle; that is, we have been willing to think of the body's mass as concentrated at a point and of the external forces as acting at the same point. This simplification of actual physical problems has often given us very useful results, but it cannot serve even as a rough approximation in many other situations. For example, it can give no information concerning the rotational motion of rigid or flexible bodies and by itself is useless in an attempt to study the dynamics of fluids.

In this chapter we will look first at the dynamics of a *finite grouping of particles*, leading primarily to the study of the general motion of rigid and nonrigid bodies. Next we will derive some of the basic dynamical relations for large, relatively unbounded groups of similar particles, primarily *fluids and gases*. Finally we will look at the "variable-mass" problems in which our attention is concentrated on continuously changing groupings of particles such as rocket engines spewing forth great quantities of gases.

4–1 The finite group. Let's consider the motions of a large number of bodies each small enough to be considered a particle but together making up a group which is of particular interest to us. As illustrated in Fig. 4–1, we can think of the large but finite number of particles as moving in an arbitrary fashion with each particle characterized by its mass and acted upon by a set of forces. If with the aid of our inertial observer ①, we write

$$\mathbf{F} = m\mathbf{a} \tag{4–1}$$

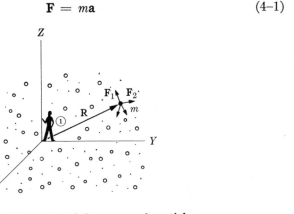

Fig. 4–1. A large but finite group of particles.

for each particle, we find ourselves with a large cumbersome set of equations. Since many of the forces acting on each of the particles undoubtedly originate with other particles in the group, our set of equations is usually, in mathematical terms, a set of simultaneous differential equations.

Fortunately, we can often satisfy the needs of our physical problem by finding the characteristics of the general motion of the group rather than the detailed motion of the individual particles. In order to get this overall look at the group, we might try adding all the Eqs. (4–1) to obtain

$$\sum \mathbf{F} = \sum (m\mathbf{a}).$$

In summing all the forces, we will observe, if we look carefully, a good deal of cancellation occurring. Investigating further, we will usually find it very useful to separate the forces acting on the particles into *external forces* originating outside of the group and *internal forces* representing the actions of one particle on another within the group. Almost all such internal forces have the very convenient characteristic that they occur in pairs of collinear, equal, and opposite forces. We must be wary, however, of internal forces of electromagnetic origin because they do not ordinarily have this nice property, as we will see in Example 4–4. However, in the usual applications involving, for example, rigid or elastic bodies, it is an excellent assumption that all the internal forces occur in pairs such that in a summation over the group, only the external forces remain.

$$\sum \mathbf{F} = \sum (\mathbf{F}_i + \mathbf{F}_e) = \sum \mathbf{F}_e. \qquad (4\text{–}2)$$

Apparently we can almost always say that the group as a whole is influenced only by forces external to the group. Thus the general or average motion of the group should be directly related only to these external forces. This average motion might well be that of a representative point at the "center" of the group. Our determination of this "center" should probably involve not only the position of the particles but also their relative importance as measured by their mass. A possible definition of such an average point might be

$$\mathbf{R}_{\text{c.m.}} = \frac{\sum m\mathbf{R}}{\sum m}, \qquad (4\text{–}3)$$

where the coordinate of each particle is "weighted" by the particle's mass. Of course this is the definition of the familiar *center of mass*, which is often called *center of gravity* by engineers.* Note that if Eq. (4–3) is multiplied

---

* In principle, the centers of mass and gravity coincide only for a group of particles in a uniform gravitational field. In a nonuniform field, they will not generally coincide, and in the case of earth satellites, their separation may be associated with an appreciable gravity moment on the satellite (see Chapter 6).

by $\sum m$ and differentiated twice with respect to time, it can be combined with Eq. (4–2) to give

$$\sum \mathbf{F}_e = (\sum m)\mathbf{a}_{\text{c.m.}}. \tag{4–4}$$

Thus, the center of mass proves to be a useful concept as defined by Eq. (4–3) because the motion of the center of mass of a group can be very simply related to just the external forces acting on the group. Of course, Eq. (4–4) does not really tell us much about what the particles in the group are doing. It merely says that, on the average, they are responding to the net external force. To realize the significance of this result, however, we can see in retrospect that it is really the basis of the idealization process, used in Chapter 3, of replacing a body or group of particles with a single particle of the same total mass and applying the external forces to it.

If we notice that Eq. (4–4) concerns the average translational motion of the group, we might be inspired to look for a relation concerning the group's general rotational motion. To put it differently, Eqs. (4–1) represent many independent relationships which we are not usually interested in solving explicitly. We would often prefer just a few independent equations formed from the set of Eq. (4–1) that tell us something of the general character of the motion. Equation (4–4) represents the simplest possible combination, a summation. For further combinations, we can look at summations of moments of the equations about a suitable origin. The more such independent equations we write, the more we know about the details of the particles' motions without having to solve the original complete set [Eqs. (4–1)]. On the assumption that our next most useful summation involves taking moments about the origin in Fig. 4–1, we might write the *moment of the momentum* of our typical particle of mass m as

$$\mathbf{H} = \mathbf{R} \times m\dot{\mathbf{R}}$$

and for the entire group as

$$\sum \mathbf{H} = \sum (\mathbf{R} \times m\dot{\mathbf{R}}).$$

The rate of change of total moment of momentum is then

$$\frac{d}{dt}\sum \mathbf{H} = \sum (\dot{\mathbf{R}} \times m\dot{\mathbf{R}}) + \sum (\mathbf{R} \times m\ddot{\mathbf{R}}),$$

where the first term vanishes. In the second term, $m\ddot{\mathbf{R}}$ can be equated, by means of Eqs. (4–1) and (4–2), to $\mathbf{F}_i + \mathbf{F}_e$. In the summation, the moments of the internal forces cancel if they occur in equal, opposite, and collinear-force pairs, so that we can write, for the entire group,

$$\sum (\mathbf{R} \times \mathbf{F}_e) = \frac{d}{dt}\sum (\mathbf{R} \times m\dot{\mathbf{R}}). \tag{4–5a}$$

In words, the moment about the unaccelerated origin of observer ① of the forces external to the group is equal to the rate of change seen by ① of the total moment of momentum* of the group.

In many situations the taking of moments about an unaccelerated origin while viewing the motion as an observer ① is not convenient. To obtain alternative forms for Eq. (4–5a), we note that the expressions we have been writing down for moment of momentum could just as well pertain to the motion seen by a linearly accelerating observer ② about his origin. The only difference comes in relating $m\ddot{\mathbf{R}}$ to the external forces because in this case $\ddot{\mathbf{R}}$ does not represent absolute acceleration. This time we must write for a single particle

$$\mathbf{F}_i + \mathbf{F}_e = m(\ddot{\mathbf{R}} + \mathbf{a}_0),$$

where $\mathbf{a}_0$ is the linear acceleration of the origin and thus of observer ②. Assuming again that the moments of the internal forces cancel, we get

$$\sum(\mathbf{R} \times \mathbf{F}_e) = \sum(\mathbf{R} \times m\ddot{\mathbf{R}}) + \sum(\mathbf{R} \times m\mathbf{a}_0).$$

Recognizing that $\mathbf{a}_0$ may be taken outside the summation because it does not vary as different particles are considered, we can write the general form

$$\sum(\mathbf{R} \times \mathbf{F}_e) = \frac{d}{dt}\sum(\mathbf{R} \times m\dot{\mathbf{R}}) + \left(\sum m\right)\mathbf{R}_{\text{c.m.}} \times \mathbf{a}_0. \qquad (4\text{–}5b)$$

Note that the last term vanishes, as it should when the origin is unaccelerated ($\mathbf{a}_0 = 0$). It also vanishes when our accelerated observer moves right with the center of mass ($\mathbf{R}_{\text{c.m.}} = 0$) as well as in the unusual instance where the origin's acceleration has no moment about the center of mass. Usually we will use an observer and origin such that the last term is zero and the expression is just that of Eq. (4–5a). Occasionally a less orthodox choice of origin may be convenient.

Usually it is not particularly fruitful to try to describe the moment of momentum of the group in terms of average rotational motion. For the rigid body, however, we can relate the body's angular velocity $\boldsymbol{\omega}$ directly to its moment of momentum $\mathbf{H}$. Here let's replace the summations over particles of mass m with integrals over the rigid body of elements of mass dm. Equation (4–5b) becomes

$$\sum(\mathbf{R} \times \mathbf{F}_e) = \frac{d}{dt}\int \mathbf{R} \times \dot{\mathbf{R}}\, dm + \left(\int dm\right)\mathbf{R}_{\text{c.m.}} \times \mathbf{a}_0.$$

_____

* The term "angular momentum" is sometimes used in place of "moment of momentum," particularly for rigid bodies.

If the origin is taken to be a particular point in the rigid body, we can (following Sections 2–3 and 2–4) write the velocity of any point in the rigid body relative to the observer ② moving with the origin as

$$\dot{\mathbf{R}} = \boldsymbol{\omega} \times \mathbf{R}. \tag{4–6}$$

The moment of momentum $\mathbf{H}$ of the rigid body about that point in it which was taken as origin is, thus,

$$\mathbf{H} = \int \mathbf{R} \times (\boldsymbol{\omega} \times \mathbf{R}) \, dm, \tag{4–7}$$

and the moment equation is

$$\sum (\mathbf{R} \times \mathbf{F}_e) = \frac{d}{dt} \int \mathbf{R} \times (\boldsymbol{\omega} \times \mathbf{R}) \, dm + m(\mathbf{R}_{\text{c.m.}} \times \mathbf{a}_0). \tag{4–8}$$

The evaluation of Eq. (4–7) in terms of the moments of inertia of the rigid body will be carried out for general rotational motion in Chapter 5. The special case of rotation about an axis fixed in direction can be very simply handled here. This is essentially the case of planar motion (Section 2–3) in which we have usually taken Z to be the axis about which the rotation takes place. The angular velocity $\boldsymbol{\omega}$ is thus entirely ω_z, and Eq. (4–7) becomes about Z,

$$H_z = \int \sqrt{x^2 + y^2} \, \omega_z \sqrt{x^2 + y^2} \, dm$$

$$= \omega_z \int (x^2 + y^2) \, dm = I_z \omega_z.$$

The moment equation (4–8) becomes, about Z,

$$M_{z_e} = \sum (x F_{y_e} - y F_{x_e}) = I_z \alpha_z + m(x_{\text{c.m.}} a_{y_0} - y_{\text{c.m.}} a_{x_0}), \tag{4–9}$$

where M_{z_e} and I_z are, respectively, moments of external force and inertia about the Z-axis, and α_z is the angular acceleration. As we will see in Chapter 5, the concept of a rigid body implies many equations concerning the relative fixity of the particles making up the body. Thus the planar motion of a rigid body is completely specified by only two component force equations (4–4) for the center-of-mass translation and the single moment equation (4–9), together with the implied rigidity relationships. To put it differently, the group of particles making up a rigid body in planar motion has only three degrees of freedom (three independent coordinates) left to it and thus requires only three independent equations of motion.

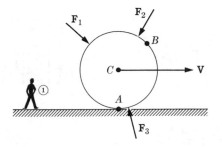

FIG. 4–2. A rolling wheel.

EXAMPLE 4–1. To illustrate the use of various origins for writing the moment equation (4–8) for a rigid body, let's look at the wheel in Fig. 4–2, rolling under the action of some external forces. The average linear motion is given by Eq. (4–4) relating the external forces to the absolute acceleration of the center of mass.

$$\Sigma \mathbf{F}_e = m\mathbf{a}_{\text{c.m.}}$$

For the rotational motion, we must find an origin about which we can conveniently apply the moment equation (4–8) or (4–9); that is, an origin which makes the last term vanish. There is no obviously stationary point in the wheel, nor even one moving at constant velocity, that we could use to make $\mathbf{a}_0$ zero. Of course, if $\mathbf{V}$ happens to be constant, C is unaccelerated and would serve nicely. Actually, so would any other point such as B because, although it is accelerated, the acceleration is in this special case directed at C, the center of mass ($\mathbf{R}_{\text{c.m.}} \times \mathbf{a}_0 = 0$). If $\mathbf{V}$ is not constant, the point A on the wheel in contact with the ground has an acceleration with no moment about C, and thus appears to be a convenient origin, at least for the instant in which it is in contact. (A will not do if the wheel is slipping, will it? What if the center of mass is not exactly at C?)

An advantage in using A as an origin is that the bothersome ground-reaction force does not appear in the moment equation. It would even seem desirable to use an observer who moves with the "point of contact" and thus would have the velocity V and the acceleration $\mathbf{a}_c$ of C. For him, we can't use Eq. (4–8) directly because this fellow's origin does not have the motion of a point in the body; that is, Eq. (4–6) does not hold. Instead,

$$\dot{\mathbf{R}} = \boldsymbol{\omega} \times \mathbf{R} - \mathbf{V},$$

$$\mathbf{H} = \int \mathbf{R} \times (\boldsymbol{\omega} \times \mathbf{R})\, dm - m(\mathbf{R}_{\text{c.m.}} \times \mathbf{V}),$$

and, in this planar case,

$$\mathbf{M}_{z_e} = I_A \alpha_z - m \frac{d}{dt} (\mathbf{R}_{\text{c.m.}} \times \mathbf{V}) + m\mathbf{R}_{\text{c.m.}} \times \mathbf{a}_0.$$

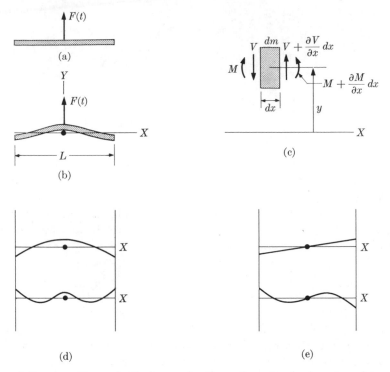

FIG. 4–3.   A uniform elastic bar under the action of a single external force.

To this observer always at the point of contact, $\mathbf{R}_{\text{c.m.}}$ does not change with time and $d\mathbf{V}/dt$ is just $\mathbf{a}_0$, so we still get the simple form

$$M_{z_e} = I_A \alpha_z.$$

Of course, even this fellow would have to include some correction terms if the wheel were slipping. (If you are somewhat confused by these special cases, it is comforting to remember that the correction terms are always zero for an origin moving with the center of mass of a rigid body.) ▲

It is important to remember that *the rigid body is an idealized concept,* as is the particle. No group of particles is actually interconnected in such a way that absolutely no relative displacement ever takes place. The rigid-body idea is very valuable, nevertheless, for groups where the relative displacement is small and where it does not significantly affect the character of the applied forces. The wheel in Example 4–1 is represented quite accurately by a rigid body in many situations. However, if it happens to be a low-pressure balloon tire subjected to large varying vertical forces, the rigid-body approximation can lead to very misleading results. Similarly, airplanes can be treated as rigid bodies for many purposes, but anyone who has watched the flexing of a jet transport wing in turbulent air will be very careful when and how he makes the rigid-body approximation.

EXAMPLE 4–2. To gain some insight into the applicability of the rigid-body assumption, we can look at the uniform flexible bar shown in Fig. 4–3(a) with a single time-varying force applied at its center. If we think of it as a rigid body, we come to the immediate conclusion that all parts of it accelerate upward at the rate $\mathbf{F}(t)/m$. It does not rotate because no moment is applied by $\mathbf{F}(t)$ about the center of mass.

If we think of $\mathbf{F}(t)$ as an abruptly applied force, our experience suggests that in the first few instants the tips lag behind the center (Fig. 4–3b), even though the acceleration of the body on the average ($\mathbf{a}_{\text{c.m.}}$) is still $\mathbf{F}(t)/m$. To study the elastic deformation more closely, let's set up a non-rotating axis system with origin at the center of mass. If we assume that the elastic deformations y are essentially due to simple bending of the beam,* we can conveniently think of the beam as made up of many elements (Fig. 4–3c) of mass dm and length dx sliced from the beam. The vertical motion of the element shown can be written in terms of the net vertical force applied by neighboring elements and the absolute acceleration as

$$V + \frac{\partial V}{\partial x}\,dx - V = dm\left(\frac{\partial^2 y}{\partial t^2} + \frac{F}{m}\right).$$

(We use $\partial^2 y/\partial t^2$ because y is also a function of x.) With dm equal to $(m/L)\,dx$, this becomes

$$\frac{\partial V}{\partial x} = \frac{m}{L}\frac{\partial^2 y}{\partial t^2} + \frac{F}{L}.$$

Making the usual assumption that the rotary inertia of the element is small, we can write a moment balance on the element as

$$M + \frac{\partial M}{\partial x}\,dx - M + V\,dx \cong 0,$$

or

$$V = -\frac{\partial M}{\partial x},$$

where M is the bending moment. Simple beam theory relates the bending moment to the local curvature $\partial^2 y/\partial x^2$ through the bending stiffness EI,

---

* The theory of simple beams is treated in all elementary texts on structures. The dynamic behavior is handled in an elegant manner in Chapter 3 of Bisplinghoff, Ashley, and Halfman, Ref. 9.

where E is Young's modulus and I is the area moment of inertia of the cross-section.

$$M = EI \frac{\partial^2 y}{\partial x^2}.$$

Eliminating M and then V for this uniform beam, we have the partial differential equation* for the elastic deformations as

$$EI \frac{\partial^4 y}{\partial x^4} + \frac{m}{L} \frac{\partial^2 y}{\partial t^2} = -\frac{F(t)}{L}.$$

Although the solution of this equation is rather complicated, especially for a time-varying applied force $\mathbf{F}(t)$,† the beam will respond in a superposition of "rigid-body" translation in Fig. 4–3(a) and deformation modes like the ones in Fig. 4–3(d). Since each elastic deformation mode has a characteristic frequency of oscillation associated with it (see Chapter 7, and also Chapter 9), the response of the beam will depend on the way in which $\mathbf{F}$ varies with time. If $\mathbf{F}$ varies slowly and evenly, the rigid-body motion will be dominant. If $\mathbf{F}$ is essentially sinusoidal at a frequency near $22\sqrt{EI/mL^3}$, the beam response will almost entirely be a vibration in the upper mode of Fig. 4–3(d). In a similar fashion, if the force $\mathbf{F}(t)$ is applied to the right of the center of mass, it can give rise to a rigid-body rotation as well as anti-symmetrical modes of deformation as in Fig. 4–3(e). ▲

4–2 The infinite group or continuum. Many times we find that we would like to study a local dynamical situation in a medium which is relatively infinite in extent. Examples include the motion of vehicles through fluids and the propagation of disturbances, such as sound waves. Whereas many of the problems involving solids are similar to the deforming beam of Example 4–2 in that they can be treated as rigid or deformable bodies of finite extent, an important group of fluid flow problems requires the concept of an extended *continuous medium*. Despite the discrete nature of both solids and fluids on a microscopic scale, the idealization of assuming mathematically continuous properties, such as density and pressure, is very useful on a macroscopic scale; in this sense a continuum is analogous to our previous idealized models, the particle and the rigid body.

Keeping track of our physical variables is somewhat more complex for a continuum than for a group of n particles. Instead of having n distinct velocities to deal with, we have a whole field of velocities; instead of writing

---

* See Section 11–3 for a similar equation derived from Hamilton's principle and Lagrange's equations.

† See Chapters 3 and 6 of Bisplinghoff, Ashley, and Halfman, Ref. 9.

$\mathbf{v}_i(t)$ for all i from 1 to n, we must write

$$\mathbf{v}(\mathbf{R}, t);\tag{4–10a}$$

$$
\begin{aligned}
v_x(x, y, z, t),\\
v_y(x, y, z, t),\\
v_z(x, y, z, t).
\end{aligned}
\tag{4–10b}
$$

Thus the physical variables must be functions of the spatial coordinates as well as time. If, in a particular flow, $\mathbf{v}$ at each point is not dependent on t, we say that we have a steady flow. However, even in a steady flow, the particles will usually be changing their velocities as they move from one point to the next and are thus accelerated. We must be careful to distinguish between the behavior of the velocity field as a whole and the time histories of the motions of individual particles.

Suppose we do want to find the acceleration of a single particular fluid particle. Its velocity can be written $\mathbf{v}(x, y, z, t)$ in terms of its identifying coordinates and time. In the time interval dt it will have the linear displacements dx, dy, and dz. If we divide the change in its velocity

$$d\mathbf{v} = \frac{\partial \mathbf{v}}{\partial x}\, dx + \frac{\partial \mathbf{v}}{\partial y}\, dy + \frac{\partial \mathbf{v}}{\partial z}\, dz + \frac{\partial \mathbf{v}}{\partial t}\, dt$$

by dt, we will have its acceleration $\mathbf{a}$ in two forms (after substituting v_x for dx/dt, etc.)

$$\mathbf{a} = \frac{d\mathbf{v}}{dt} = \left[v_x \frac{\partial \mathbf{v}}{\partial x} + v_y \frac{\partial \mathbf{v}}{\partial y} + v_z \frac{\partial \mathbf{v}}{\partial z} \right] + \frac{\partial \mathbf{v}}{\partial t}.\tag{4–11}$$

Such a derivative of a field variable following a given particle is often called the *substantial or total derivative*. It is sometimes denoted by the special symbolism D/Dt. The part of Eq. (4–11) in the brackets is called the convective acceleration, which may exist even in steady flow. The last term $\partial \mathbf{v}/\partial t$ represents the unsteadiness of the flow as a whole and is called the local acceleration.

EXAMPLE 4–3. In the radially symmetric flow of Fig. 4–4, let's assume that the pattern is the same in all planes above and below the XY-plane; that is, we have a two-dimensional flow. Since the flow is everywhere away from the origin, we must have a source of fluid there. If we don't want to lose or gain any fluid elsewhere in the flow, a little thought indicates that, for a steady flow of an incompressible fluid, the velocity $\mathbf{v}$ must be inversely proportional to the distance from the origin:

$$v_r = \frac{A}{r}.$$

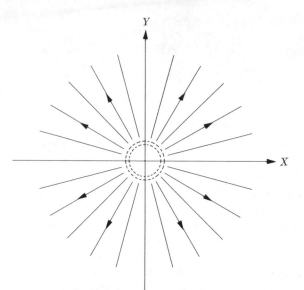

FIG. 4–4.   An axially symmetrical radial flow of an incompressible fluid.

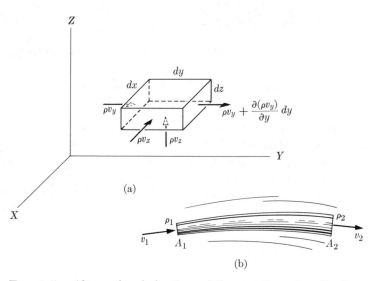

FIG. 4–5.   Alternative derivations of the equation of continuity.

Along the X-axis,

$$v_x = \frac{A}{x}, \qquad v_y = 0, \qquad v_z = 0.$$

Note that even though the flow pattern looks the same from instant to instant, a particle moving along the X-axis is decelerating. This comes from the convective part of the substantial derivative [Eq. (4–11)] as

$$a_x = v_x \frac{\partial v_x}{\partial x} = -\frac{A^2}{x^3}, \qquad \frac{\partial v_x}{\partial t} = 0.$$

If our source begins to put ever-increasing amounts of fluid into the flow, A is no longer a constant, and the velocity expression might be like

$$v_r = \frac{A}{r} = \frac{Bt}{r}.$$

For the same point on the X-axis, we still have the convective acceleration, but it is modified by the local acceleration indicating the general speeding up of the flow. Thus

$$v_x \frac{\partial v_x}{\partial x} = -\frac{B^2 t^2}{x^3} \qquad \text{(convective)},$$

$$\frac{\partial v_x}{\partial t} = \frac{B}{x} \qquad \text{(local)},$$

$$a_x = -\frac{B^2 t^2}{x^3} + \frac{B}{x} \qquad \text{(total)}.$$

Are there components of acceleration in other directions for this particle? Try visualizing this flow from a source for various forms of time dependence. What does the flow look like if A is negative? How about a three-dimensional source flow entirely symmetrical about the origin? ▲

In trying to arrive at a "reasonable" velocity-distance relation in the source flow of Example 4–3, you may have discovered the difficulty of keeping track of all the particles in a flow, particularly if their density is changing. In particle and rigid-body problems, it was hard to lose inadvertently some of the mass. In fluid flow problems it is very helpful to have mathematical relations which express this idea of *conservation of mass*. If we look at the small stationary element of volume in Fig. 4–5(a), we would like to say mathematically that the mass which flows in, either flows out again or accumulates inside.

The mass flow in across the left-hand face can be due only to v_y and is equal to $\rho v_y \, dx \, dz \, dt$ in time dt, where ρ is the density (mass per unit volume). The flow out of the opposite face during the same interval dt will generally be different because both ρ and v_y are not constant throughout the flow. Working with their product, we can say the outflow is

$$\left[\rho v_y + \frac{\partial(\rho v_y)}{\partial y}\, dy\right] dx\, dz\, dt.$$

Including the other directions in a similar fashion, we can write the net inflow as equal to the accumulation inside.

$$\rho v_x\, dy\, dz\, dt + \rho v_y\, dx\, dz\, dt + \rho v_z\, dx\, dy\, dt$$

$$-\left[\rho v_x + \frac{\partial(\rho v_x)}{\partial x}\, dx\right] dy\, dz\, dt$$

$$-\left[\rho v_y + \frac{\partial(\rho v_y)}{\partial y}\, dy\right] dx\, dz\, dt$$

$$-\left[\rho v_z + \frac{\partial(\rho v_z)}{\partial z}\, dz\right] dx\, dy\, dt$$

$$= \left(\rho + \frac{\partial \rho}{\partial t}\, dt\right) dx\, dy\, dz - \rho\, dx\, dy\, dz.$$

Or, canceling terms and then the common differential factors, we get

$$\frac{\partial(\rho v_x)}{\partial x} + \frac{\partial(\rho v_y)}{\partial y} + \frac{\partial(\rho v_z)}{\partial z} + \frac{\partial \rho}{\partial t} = 0. \tag{4--12a}$$

This is called the *equation of continuity* for unsteady compressible flow. For a steady flow, the density ρ will not change with time at a particular location (although it may change from point to point) and the continuity equation becomes

$$\frac{\partial(\rho v_x)}{\partial x} + \frac{\partial(\rho v_y)}{\partial y} + \frac{\partial(\rho v_z)}{\partial z} = 0. \tag{4--12b}$$

In liquid flows and some low-speed gas flows, it is reasonable to make the assumption that the fluid density is essentially constant. In this case, even if this incompressible flow is unsteady,

$$\frac{\partial v_x}{\partial x} + \frac{\partial v_y}{\partial y} + \frac{\partial v_z}{\partial z} = 0. \tag{4--12c}$$

You may be more familiar with the continuity equation when it is written for a streamtube such as shown in Fig. 4–5(b). In this steady flow, we can look at a thin tube of fluid whose sides are made up of streamlines of the

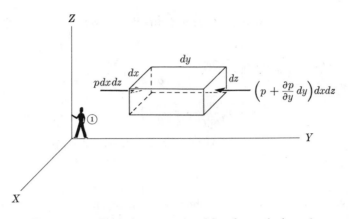

FIG. 4–6.   Forces on a fluid element caused by the variation of pressure with position.

flow. Thus, the only flow of fluid across the boundaries of the streamtube must be at the ends. If we assume that v and ρ represent the average fluid properties over the cross-sectional area A, the inflow is $\rho_1 A_1 v_1$. This must equal the outflow $\rho_2 A_2 v_2$. More generally, along a streamtube in steady flow,

$$\rho A v = \text{constant}. \tag{4–12d}$$

To see how Newton's second law can be written for a fluid, let's look at a single fluid element (Fig. 4–6) and equate the forces acting on it with its mass times its absolute acceleration. Suppose at the instant t we choose an infinitesimal element of fluid which is rectangular. As it moves it will distort if we insist on not letting any fluid cross its boundaries. Perhaps it will help to think of painting all the fluid in the element red so that it will be easier to watch. Assuming the internal forces cancel each other, we can relate the external forces in the element to its total acceleration. Thus,

$$d\mathbf{F}_e = (\rho \, dx \, dy \, dz) \frac{d\mathbf{v}}{dt}.$$

These external forces may be due to gravitational or electromagnetic causes or may be pressure and shear forces on the faces of the element due to the neighboring fluid. To look at a simple case, we might just consider the gravitational and pressure terms usually dominant in a relatively non-viscous fluid. In component form, the Y-force is

$$dF_{y_e} = \left[p - \left(p + \frac{\partial p}{\partial y} dy \right) \right] dx \, dz + \rho g_y \, dx \, dy \, dz.$$

With similar expressions for X- and Z-directions, we get *Euler's dynamical equations:*

$$\frac{dv_x}{dt} = \left(v_x \frac{\partial v_x}{\partial x} + v_y \frac{\partial v_x}{\partial y} + v_z \frac{\partial v_x}{\partial z} \right) + \frac{\partial v_x}{\partial t} = \frac{1}{\rho} \frac{\partial p}{\partial x} - g_x,$$

$$\frac{dv_y}{dt} = \left(v_x \frac{\partial v_y}{\partial x} + v_y \frac{\partial v_y}{\partial y} + v_z \frac{\partial v_y}{\partial z} \right) + \frac{\partial v_y}{\partial t} = \frac{1}{\rho} \frac{\partial p}{\partial y} - g_y, \qquad (4\text{--}13)$$

$$\frac{dv_z}{dt} = \left(v_x \frac{\partial v_z}{\partial x} + v_y \frac{\partial v_z}{\partial y} + v_z \frac{\partial v_z}{\partial z} \right) + \frac{\partial v_z}{\partial t} = \frac{1}{\rho} \frac{\partial p}{\partial z} - g_z,$$

where g_x, g_y, g_z are the components of the gravitational attraction per unit mass. Note that we can write either the total acceleration or its alternative form in terms of convective and local accelerations.

Even if we assume that g is a known function, the three dynamical equations and the continuity equation contain five scalar variables, v_x, v_y, v_z, ρ, p. To complete the mathematical statement of a fluid flow problem, we need another equation. This usually takes the form of a relationship between pressure and density according to the appropriate equation of state for the fluid involved.* However, this equation usually involves the temperature T and, in the case of the ideal gas,† is of the form

$$p = \rho RT, \qquad (4\text{--}14)$$

where R is a constant. To deal with the new variable, temperature, we usually must introduce the first and second laws of thermodynamics.

In some situations, we can make simplifying assumptions which effectively eliminate temperature from our dynamical problem. The simplest assumption is that ρ is a constant and unrelated to p. This works well in many liquid flows such as water and in low-speed gas flows. If the fluid maintains a constant temperature, then Eq. (4–14) indicates that p is directly proportional to ρ for this "isothermal" case.‡ If instead we assume at the other extreme no appreciable flow of heat between fluid elements, the thermodynamic laws and the equation of state (4–14) tell us that in such an "adiabatic" flow

$$\frac{p}{\rho^\gamma} = \text{constant},$$

---

* For the elastic solid in Example 4–2, we introduced, as an equation of state, the stress-strain relationship through $M = EI(\partial^2 y/\partial x^2)$, which is derived from Hooke's law for simple beam bending.

† See your physics or chemistry text.

‡ See Example 3–5 for the treatment of air compression in a rotating helicopter blade.

where γ is the ratio of specific heats and is about 1.4 for air. If our fluid problem involves electromagnetic effects such as in magnetohydrodynamics, we must also include appropriate relationships such as Maxwell's equations.

EXAMPLE 4–4. To illustrate some of the analogies between fluid fields and electromagnetic fields, and at the same time try to gain a little insight into the difficulties of applying classical Newtonian mechanics to the motion of charged particles, let's look at two charged particles in relative motion. We have already studied the interaction of such particles (in Example 3–16 and in problems at the end of the chapter) in coulomb scattering where we assumed that the particles each exhibited a simple electrostatic inverse-square field. With this assumption, the forces of interaction were central, that is, along the line joining the particles, and we were able to use all the results of our preceding study of central force motion.

Perhaps, in your study of electromagnetism, you have encountered the idea that a moving charge has a magnetic field as well as an electric field associated with it and have wondered at the assumption, in Example 3–16, of a simple electrostatic interaction between moving charges. To investigate these ideas at least qualitatively, we can examine the interaction of two identical but oppositely charged bodies moving as shown in Fig. 4–7(a). To take advantage of the symmetry of the situation, we have adopted the viewpoint of a nonrotating observer at the center of mass.

If we think first of only the positively charged moving particle in terms of the moving charge representing essentially an electric current, we can expect* to have an associated magnetic field with axial symmetry of the sort indicated in Fig. 4–7(b) in which the field strength **H** drops off in intensity in an inverse-square manner as we look out along a radius from the particle. If we actually calculate the strength of this magnetic field at a representative point, we find that it becomes significant compared with the electric field only when the particle's velocity **v** is appreciable compared with the speed of light c. (This explains why we were able to neglect the magnetic field in studying coulomb scattering in Example 3–16.) At such a velocity the electric field is also distorted, as shown in Fig. 4–7(c). Instead of the familiar spherically symmetric electrostatic field, we find the field lines somewhat "bunched" toward the plane normal to the direction of motion. These complementary electric and magnetic fields can be derived directly from Maxwell's equations.

If we now visualize the forces on the second particle in the field of the first, we can deduce that the electric part of the force on the second particle

---

* See, for example, Page, Ref. 6, Sections 159 and 161, for considerable substantiating background material of a quantitative nature.

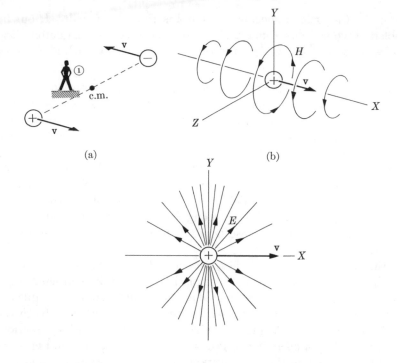

(a) (b)

(c)

FIG. 4–7. Isolated charged particles in motion.

is along the line joining the particles but the magnetic part is not. Remembering the basic symmetry of this problem, we realize the mutual interaction between the particles would appear to consist of resultant *forces which are not collinear although equal and opposite.* Thus in the absence of any external forces, the total linear momentum of the particles presumably remains constant but their angular momentum does not. Note that we seem to have a situation where the moments of the internal forces on the particles do not sum to zero so that their angular momentum must change even in the absence of external forces.

Although this picture is oversimplified, it suggests a cautious approach to applying Newtonian ideas to the motion of charged particles, particularly when moving at high relative speed. In Chapter 12 we will look at the way in which traditional "low-speed" Newtonian mechanics must be modified to be compatible with the relativistic ideas already inherent in electromagnetic-field theory as represented by Maxwell's equations.

Before leaving this example, however, we can take a few more steps in a very qualitative fashion. Actually both particles in Fig. 4–7(a) not only have a velocity **v** but also are accelerating as well. Acceleration of a charged

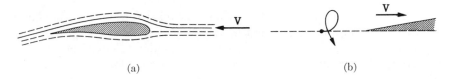

FIG. 4–8. The motion of a fluid particle over a wing seen (a) from the wing, and (b) from the ground.

particle modifies the associated electromagnetic field sketched in Figs. 4–7(b) and (c) for an unaccelerated particle and also is accompanied by a radiation of energy as the field changes. This radiation of energy, you may have learned, is associated with the Poynting vector and the cross product of the electric and magnetic fields. These ideas can in turn be related to momentum per unit volume of the electromagnetic field. This association, even in "empty space," of energy and momentum with the field itself is fundamental to electromagnetic theory and is illustrated by the influence of radiation pressure on very light satellites and its possible use in solar sailing of space ships.

Returning to our two particles whose angular momentum seems to be changing with time, we can now suspect that there is also angular momentum in the associated fields, which is changing with time in a compensating fashion. We were "too Newtonian" in looking for momentum just by watching the particles. The newer relativistic equivalence between mass and energy leads to momentum associated with the fields as well as the particles. ▲

In studying fluid flows, it is often very helpful to look for a viewpoint from which the flow appears least complex. I think we would all agree that the flow around an airplane in steady flight looks fairly smooth and stable to an observer in the airplane. By comparison, a ground observer sees a very unsteady motion despite the fact that both observers are unaccelerated and can apply Newton's second law in the same form [Eq. (4–13)]. Observe the motion of a fluid particle along the streamline over the wing section of Fig. 4–8(a). We can assume it is a steady flow with the velocity far upstream of magnitude V. In Fig. 4–8(b), we adopt the viewpoint of an observer to whom the distant stream is stationary (our ground observer if there is no wind). To this fellow the wing suddenly comes along, sweeps by, and disappears. The same fluid particle has the motion shown in getting out of the way of the wing. The residual downward and forward momentum of the particle indicates the presence of lift and drag on the wing section. This process of converting flows from unsteady to steady is somewhat analogous to reducing general motion of a rigid body to pure rotation about a fixed point by merely assuming the motion of a point in the body. If that point is unaccelerated or is the center of mass, you can use the moment equations in simple form.

As you can see for the idealized continuum model, the mathematics can get extremely complicated even for relatively simple flows involving only pressure and gravity forces. If other effects must be introduced such as viscosity and perhaps the chemical properties of the fluid, we sometimes may not even be able to write enough adequate equations between the variables because our basic knowledge may be inadequate. The pertinent problem may thus occasionally not be the solving of a complex mathematical set of equations, but rather a simple-minded and elementary look at which of many variables may be important and in what combinations the important variables may be expected to occur. The decision as to which variables are important must come from experience usually coupled with exploratory experimentation in the laboratory. The matter of finding proper combinations of the important variables can be handled systematically by merely analyzing their dimensions. This process of *dimensional analysis* can be very valuable to a scientist or engineer making an exploratory investigation into an unfamiliar area.

In looking at the dimensions of physical quantities, we soon notice that some dimensions are made up of others appearing as products to various powers. In dynamics, we find that the dimensions of all the pertinent physical quantities can be formed in this manner from any set of three independent dimensions. Usually it is most convenient to use as the "primary" set either force, length, and time (F, L, T) or mass, length, and time (M, L, T) and then build up the secondary quantities from the chosen primary as

$$S = CP_1^{d_1}P_2^{d_2}P_3^{d_3}, \tag{4-15}$$

where C is a pure number and d is an integer for the usual sets of primary quantities. If we arbitrarily choose M, L, T as primary, then force is expressible as $CM^1L^1T^{-2}$. Similarly, density is CM^1L^{-3}, pressure $CM^1L^{-1}T^{-2}$, and velocity CL^1T^{-1}. For the usual consistent sets of units, C is unity. It is not unity for force if we use pounds, slugs, feet, and minutes nor for velocity in knots with length and time in miles and hours, respectively.

In other fields, such as thermodynamics, it is necessary to have a fourth primary quantity usually taken as temperature (θ). Likewise, in electromagnetic phenomena, we use electric charge (Q) as a fourth primary quantity. In statics, however, only two primary quantities, such as force and length (F, L), are needed to form the dimensions of quantities like stress, bending moment, axial load, and area moment of inertia.

In the relationships that we are seeking between the physical quantities of importance in our typical exploratory investigation, we can be sure that the two sides of each equation must be dimensionally the same. Thus, in the kinematic relationship between position and time for a point in uniform motion,

$$s = s_0 + v_0 t,$$

and each term has the dimensions of length. Note that if we divide by s_0 so that

$$\left[\frac{s}{s_0}\right] = 1 + \left[\frac{v_0 t}{s_0}\right],$$

we can think of the expression as a relationship between the two bracketed, dimensionless ratios. Thus a relation among four physical quantities appears in terms of only two dimensionless combinations of these quantities.

Suppose, in more general terms, that we are interested in how a physical quantity q_1 is related in a given problem to other quantities $q_2, q_3, q_4 \ldots q_n$ in a field in which there are N primary quantities. Without losing much generality, we can suppose that q_1 is expressible in a power series form as

$$q_1(q_2 \ldots q_n) = C_1 q_2^{a_1} q_3^{b_1} q_4^{c_1} + C_2 q_2^{a_2} q_3^{b_2} q_4^{c_2} + \cdots$$

$$+ C_r q_2^{a_r} q_3^{b_r} q_4^{c_r} + \cdots.$$

For dimensional homogeneity, we know that each term, such as the typical rth term, must have the same dimensions as q_1, even though we may know nothing at all about the specific form of the series in the given problem. Since the dimensions of q_1 and the other q's can be written in terms of the N primary quantities to known powers, each of the primary quantities must appear in both q_1 and the rth term to the same power. If we write this equality for each primary quantity, we will have N algebraic equations in the n unknowns $a_r, b_r, c_r \ldots$, which represent N restrictions on the generality of the exponents. That this procedure leads us directly and simply to a set of independent dimensionless ratios, which can be viewed as the basic parameters of the problem, is illustrated in the following example.

EXAMPLE 4–5. Let's assume that we know very little about a simple and familiar problem in dynamics, the swinging of a simple pendulum, and see how much we can learn from dimensional analysis. Suppose that we are wondering how the period A of a pendulum depends on the pendulum and its environment. We may innocently (and intuitively) guess that the period is influenced by the length l of the pendulum, its mass m, its weight which can be characterized by the gravitational constant g (since we already have m), and perhaps the linear amplitude a (an angular amplitude is dimensionless and surely cannot be useful here). Thus we can write the period as

$$A(l, m, g, a) = C_1 l^{a_1} m^{b_1} g^{c_1} a^{d_1} + C_2 l^{a_2} m^{b_2} g^{c_2} a^{d_2}$$
$$+ \cdots + C_r l^{a_r} m^{b_r} g^{c_r} a^{d_r} + \cdots .$$

Since we have a problem in dynamics, we will take as a principal set mass, length, and time (M, L, T). The dimensions of the various quantities are

$$A = M^0 L^0 T^1,$$
$$l = M^0 L^1 T^0,$$
$$m = M^1 L^0 T^0,$$
$$g = M^0 L^1 T^{-2},$$
$$a = M^0 L^1 T^0.$$

Comparing A dimensionally with the typical rth term

$$M^0 L^0 T^1 = L^{a_r} M^{b_r} (L^1 T^{-2})^{c_r} L^{d_r},$$

we can write, for the exponents of M, $0 = b_r$, and for L and T

$$0 = a_r + c_r + d_r, \qquad 1 = -2c_r.$$

Thus, we find

$$b_r = 0, \qquad c_r = -\tfrac{1}{2}, \qquad a_r = \tfrac{1}{2} - d_r.$$

Putting these findings into the typical rth term,

$$C_r l^{1/2 - d_r} m^0 g^{-1/2} a^{d_r},$$

it appears that we should never have included m to begin with because dimensionally it cannot fit. Also, we do not have enough equations to solve for either a_r or d_r explicitly. Nevertheless, the power series can now be condensed to the form

$$A(l, m, g, a) = \sqrt{\frac{l}{g}} \left[C_1 \left(\frac{a}{l} \right)^{d_1} + C_2 \left(\frac{a}{l} \right)^{d_2} + \cdots \right]$$
$$= \sqrt{\frac{l}{g}} f\left(\frac{a}{l} \right),$$

where the common factor $\sqrt{l/g}$ can be factored out of each term, leaving only an unknown function of a/l.

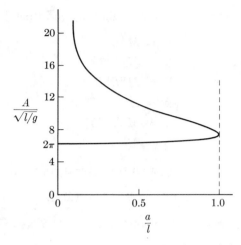

FIG. 4–9. The nondimensional period of a simple pendulum as a function of nondimensional amplitude of oscillation.

Thus we find from dimensional arguments only that m was unrelated to the other quantities and that $A/\sqrt{l/g}$ is a function of dimensionless amplitude a/l. This quite properly reduces the five original parameters to two dimensionless parameters for $N = 3$. Of course, with a different original intuitive choice of influential quantities, we would have obtained a different set of dimensionless parameters. The superiority of one selection over another is the purpose of a selected set of experiments. Such a set of experiments on different simple pendulums might well give rise to the plot in Fig. 4–9 which checks with our simple analysis at small a/l and throughout the entire range with the well-known extended solution in terms of elliptic rather than circular functions. ▲

EXAMPLE 4–6. As a second example of dimensional analysis which is far less familiar, we might look quickly at the problem of the drag or retarding force F on a body moving in a fluid. Because the force is expected to depend on the body's shape, let's restrict ourselves to spheres of diameter D moving at uniform velocity V. We can presume that other important variables are the fluid density ρ, and its coefficient of viscosity μ. Since wave-making drastically influences the drag of ships, we can also include the wave speed or speed of sound a.

Writing the drag force F in series form, we get

$$F(D, V, \rho, \mu, a) = \cdots + C_r D^{a_r} V^{b_r} \rho^{c_r} \mu^{d_r} a^{e_r} + \cdots .$$

Again we are dealing in a problem in dynamics in which all the dimensions can be written in terms of mass M, length L, and time T as

$$F = M^1 L^1 T^{-2},$$
$$D = M^0 L^1 T^0,$$
$$V = M^0 L^1 T^{-1},$$
$$\rho = M^1 L^{-3} T^0,$$
$$\mu = M^1 L^{-1} T^{-1},$$
$$a = M^0 L^1 T^{-1}.$$

Comparing F dimensionally with the typical rth term

$$M^1 L^1 T^{-2} = L^{a_r}(L^1 T^{-1})^{b_r}(M^1 L^{-3})^{c_r}(M^1 L^{-1} T^{-1})^{d_r}(L^1 T^{-1})^{e_r},$$

we can equate separately the exponents of M, L, T as

$$1 = c_r + d_r,$$
$$1 = a_r + b_r - 3c_r - d_r + e_r,$$
$$-2 = -b_r - d_r - e_r.$$

With some manipulation, we can find a_r, b_r, c_r in terms of d_r, e_r as

$$a_r = 2 - d_r,$$
$$b_r = 2 - d_r - e_r,$$
$$c_r = 1 - d_r.$$

The typical term becomes

$$C_r D^{2-d_r} V^{2-d_r-e_r} \rho^{1-d_r} \mu^{d_r} a^{e_r},$$

and the power series can be condensed to the form

$$F(D, V, \rho, \mu, a) = \rho V^2 D^2 \left[C_1 \left(\frac{\mu}{\rho V D} \right)^{d_1} \left(\frac{a}{V} \right)^{e_1} + \cdots \right]$$

$$= \rho V^2 D^2 f\left(\frac{\rho V D}{\mu}, \frac{V}{a} \right).$$

Thus the dimensionless force $F/\rho V^2 D^2$ can be thought of as a function of just two dimensionless variables, which have become known as Reynolds number and Mach number, respectively, after two pioneers in the field. Of course dimensional analysis can tell us nothing about the form of the functional relationship, but it does enable us to use most fruitfully data on spherical bodies in many different fluids because the apparent set of variables, F, D, V, ρ, μ, a, has been reduced to just three in dimensionless form. ▲

4–3 Bodies of variable mass. There are many situations in which we prefer to look not at a finite group of particles, not at an extensive continuum, but rather at a body or closed surface which has a significant flow of mass through its boundary. In this category are diversion of fluid streams, propulsion systems for vehicles, and, especially, the rocket engine. When a rocket vehicle takes off, as shown in Fig. 4–10(a), with its engines discharging tremendous streams of gas, we are primarily interested in where the vehicle goes. We do not care where the discharged gas ends up nor are we particularly interested in the motion of the center of mass of vehicle and expended fuel. Even though the mass of the vehicle is decreasing rapidly, we are interested in what the vehicle itself is doing.

In our study of particles and rigid bodies, we have found it useful to identify carefully the particular mass to which we are applying Newton's second law. We used the free-body diagram to aid us. In variable-mass problems, we must be even more careful because with mass continually crossing the boundaries of our system, we have a difficult bookkeeping problem. A useful concept here is the *control volume*, a closed volume containing exactly that mass at any instant whose motion we are studying. The control volume which is particularly suited to the study of rocket vehicles is sketched in Fig. 4–10(b), where the solid line indicates the control surface. Note that part of the enclosed mass makes up the rigid structure of the vehicle, part is moving machinery such as pumps, and part is complicated internal gas flow resulting in a high-speed jet of exhaust across the control surface.

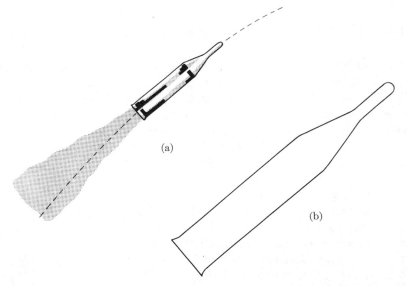

(a)

(b)

FIG. 4–10.   (a) A rocket vehicle, and (b) the corresponding control volume.

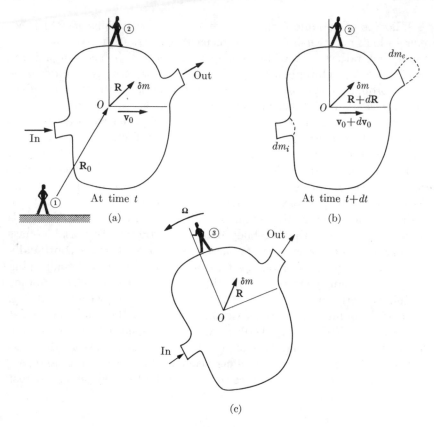

FIG. 4–11. Nonrotating and rotating control surfaces of variable mass.

To write Newton's second law for such a continually changing aggregate of particles, we can look at the fairly general control volume in Fig. 4–11(a). We will indicate only one point of inflow and one of outflow although more can easily be added. Although we must use accelerations as seen by our inertial observer ①, we will also use the services of linearly accelerating ② and, later, rotating ③ because in many cases these latter observers will be able to see essentially steady flow inside the control volume. As we have seen in the previous section on fluids, steady flow is relatively easy to work with analytically.

Looking first at the bookkeeping problem of identifying the total mass m inside the control surface at any time t, we can see in Fig. 4–11(b) that in the time interval dt, three things happen. A small aggregate dm_e moves across the boundary at the outlet, another aggregate of new particles dm_i moves into the inlet, and much of the internal mass changes relative position. The change dm in the total mass m contained within the control surface is simply the difference between what comes in and what goes out. Thus,

$$dm = dm_i - dm_e.$$

Dividing by the time interval, we have a *continuity equation:*

$$\frac{dm}{dt} - \frac{dm_i}{dt} + \frac{dm_e}{dt} = 0. \tag{4-16}$$

This equation looks the same to all observers.

If we look now at a typical particle* δm within the control surface (see Fig. 4–11a), we can write

$$d\mathbf{F} = \delta m \frac{d}{dt}(\dot{\mathbf{R}}_0 + \dot{\mathbf{R}}) = \delta m \frac{d}{dt}(\mathbf{v}_0 + \mathbf{v}) = \mathbf{a}_0\, \delta m + \delta m \frac{d\mathbf{v}}{dt},$$

where the subscript "$_0$" refers to motion of observer ② which is normally chosen to be that of the control volume itself. Here we are following a particle of fixed mass δm for an interval dt, so we are, from a fluid point of view, using a substantial derivative. In summing over all the δm's making up m at time t, we must watch carefully what we do at inlet and exhaust. Thus, for the summation

$$\mathbf{F} = m\mathbf{a}_0 + \int_m \frac{d\mathbf{v}}{dt}\, \delta m,$$

the last term is the tricky one. The first term on the right-hand side just represents a transfer of viewpoint from ① to ②.

The troublesome term really represents the net change in momentum seen by ② of all the δm's. This can be represented from a field point of view by the change in total momentum enclosed by the control surface, less the momentum of the new particles dm_i, plus the momentum of the outgoing aggregate dm_e. Using $\mathbf{P}$ for momentum, we can write this piece of bookkeeping as

$$\int_m \frac{d\mathbf{v}}{dt}\, \delta m = \int_m \frac{d}{dt}(\mathbf{v}\, \delta m) = \frac{d\mathbf{P}_{c.v.}}{dt} - \frac{d\mathbf{P}_i}{dt} + \frac{d\mathbf{P}_e}{dt},$$

where

$$d\mathbf{P}_i = \sum_{dm_i} \mathbf{v}\, \delta m, \qquad d\mathbf{P}_e = \sum_{dm_e} \mathbf{v}\, \delta m. \tag{4-17}$$

---

* We use δm here for a single particle to distinguish from dm, the change in total mass m in time dt. In other words, the momentum at $t + dt$ within the original control volume includes the momentum of the group dm_i at the inlet, which should not be included in this integration over the particles making up m at time t. Similarly, it does not include the momentum of the group dm_e just outside the exhaust, which should be part of the integral.

To visualize the change $d\mathbf{P}_{\text{c.v.}}$ of momentum within the control volume, we must change from following a given δm to watching the change in momentum in an element of the control volume. During the interval dt, new particles replace the old ones in the volume element, and the difference in momentum in the volume element contributes to $d\mathbf{P}_{\text{c.v.}}$. Note that if the flow in the control volume appears steady to observer ②, there is no change in $\mathbf{P}_{\text{c.v.}}$.

If we now make the usual assumption that all of the internal forces occur in mutually canceling pairs, we get, for *the linear motion of a body of variable mass*,

$$\sum \mathbf{F}_e = m\mathbf{a}_0 + \frac{d\mathbf{P}_{\text{c.v.}}}{dt} - \frac{d\mathbf{P}_i}{dt} + \frac{d\mathbf{P}_e}{dt} \qquad (4\text{--}18\text{a})$$

in terms of the motion $\mathbf{a}_0$ of observer ② and his observations of the various momenta. If observer ② is able to adopt a motion such that he sees only steady flow inside of a fixed control volume, we get the simpler expression

$$\sum \mathbf{F}_e = m\mathbf{a}_0 - \frac{d\mathbf{P}_i}{dt} + \frac{d\mathbf{P}_e}{dt}. \qquad (4\text{--}18\text{b})$$

For the special case, useful in flow diversion and streamtube problems, where the control volume is unaccelerated and the internal flow is steady,

$$\sum \mathbf{F}_e = -\frac{d\mathbf{P}_i}{dt} + \frac{d\mathbf{P}_e}{dt}. \qquad (4\text{--}18\text{c})$$

The external forces in any part of Eq. (4–18) may be distant acting forces like gravity or they may be contact forces on the surface of the control volume. In summing the surface forces do not forget those acting on the portions of the control surface across the inlet and exhaust.

EXAMPLE 4–7. As the first illustration of a variable-mass problem, let us look at a solid-fuel rocket engine bolted to a test stand (Fig. 4–12) so as to fire downward. With a stationary observer ($\mathbf{a}_0 = 0$) and no inflow through the control surface, Eq. (4–18a) becomes

$$\sum \mathbf{F}_e = \frac{d\mathbf{P}_{\text{c.v.}}}{dt} + \frac{d\mathbf{P}_e}{dt}.$$

The outflow momentum rate is simply $c \, (dm_e/dt)$ if we think of $\mathbf{c}$ as the exhaust velocity at the boundary (if it varies slightly across the nozzle, let $\mathbf{c}$ be the average exhaust velocity). The internal flow is not quite steady because the powder grain is being used up, and more and more of the chamber is full of hot gas. However, the additional hot gas has little momentum compared with that of the flow through the nozzle. Thus it is

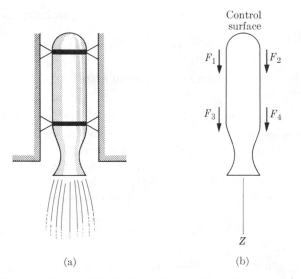

Control surface

F_1 F_2

F_3 F_4

Z

(a)   (b)

FIG. 4–12. A solid-fuel rocket motor in a test stand.

a good approximation to say that $\mathbf{P}_{c.v.}$ is a constant. The external forces are those of the attachment bolts, gravity, and the integral $\mathbf{F}_p$ of the fluid pressure and the tangential shear around the entire surface of the rocket engine. We can write, in the Z-direction,

$$F_1 + F_2 + F_3 + F_4 + mg + F_p = c\frac{dm_e}{dt} = -c\frac{dm}{dt}.$$

Note that F_p is zero if the pressure across the nozzle is the same as the atmospheric pressure on the rest of the control surface. (The shear forces are negligible.)

If the bolts break so that the engine accelerates upward, we must write, in the Z-direction,

$$mg + F_p = ma_0 + c\frac{dm_e}{dt} = ma_0 - c\frac{dm}{dt}$$

or

$$a_0 = \frac{c}{m}\frac{dm}{dt} + g + \frac{F_p}{m}.$$

Here we have assumed that observer ② riding on the engine still sees essentially steady flow in the nozzle despite its upward acceleration. We should also recognize that F_p changes with flight speed and contains the force that we normally designate as drag. There are many ways in which $[F_p + c\,(dm/dt)]$ can be divided into thrust and drag, and we should use these terms carefully.

If we neglect F_p and call g and c constant, we can integrate to get

$$v_0 = - \left(c \ln \frac{m_{\text{initial}}}{m} - gt \right),$$

where the minus sign indicates an upward velocity because Z was taken positive down. ▲

EXAMPLE 4–8. As another type of situation, which we can now easily analyze, we might look at a closed return wind tunnel. Suppose we want to find the horizontal forces which must be absorbed by the bolts attaching the end section to the rest of the tunnel. Let's isolate this section and indicate the control surface with a heavy outline in Fig. 4–13. Since the observer is stationary and we have steady flow, we can write [Eq. (4–18c)]

$$\sum \mathbf{F}_e = - \frac{d\mathbf{P}_i}{dt} + \frac{d\mathbf{P}_e}{dt}.$$

Since dm_e/dt equals dm_i/dt, this becomes, in the X-direction,

$$\sum F_e = (v_i + v_e) \frac{dm_i}{dt}.$$

We can relate the mass flow to some of the flow variables by noting that the continuity equation insists [Eq. (4–12d)] that

$$\frac{dm_i}{dt} = \rho_i A_i v_i = \rho_e A_e v_e.$$

Also, the pressure and shear integral, with p_0 as atmospheric pressure, gives

$$F_p = -A_i(p_i - p_0) - A_e(p_e - p_0).$$

If we further assume approximately adiabatic flow (Section 4–2) in this part of the tunnel, we have a relation among pressure, density, and velocity, as

$$\frac{p_i}{p_e} = \left(\frac{\rho_i}{\rho_e} \right)^{1.4} = \left(\frac{A_e v_e}{A_i v_i} \right)^{1.4}.$$

In any event, the final result can be written as

$$\sum F_{\text{bolts}} = A_i(p_i - p_0) + A_e(p_e - p_0) + (v_i + v_e) \frac{dm_i}{dt}. \quad \blacktriangle$$

If our rocket motor of Example 4–7 had happened to be rotating, or if we were studying an ordinary lawn sprinkler, our nonrotating observer ② would not have been able to see steady flow. To analyze situations such as these, we must generalize Eq. (4–18) to permit a rotating control surface and a companion rotating observer ③ who might often be able to see a

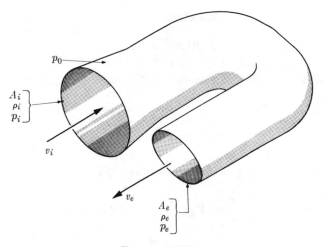

$$\text{Figure } 4\text{–}13$$

reasonably steady internal flow. Perhaps we should also write a moment equation as well as a force equation. In the case of the lawn sprinkler, for example, the steady swirling motion can be looked at as a moment balance (see Example 4–10).

Starting with the same equation for an internal particle δm as before,

$$d\mathbf{F} = \mathbf{a}_0 \, \delta m + \delta m \, \frac{d\mathbf{v}}{dt},$$

we must convert the $d\mathbf{v}/dt$ seen here by the nonrotating observer ② to that seen by ③ who has the same linear motion as ② but is rotating at the angular velocity $\boldsymbol{\Omega}$. [See Fig. 4–11(c).] Designating observations of ③ with primes as before (Section 2–4), we have

$$\mathbf{v} = \mathbf{v}' + \boldsymbol{\Omega} \times \mathbf{R}, \qquad (2\text{–}54c)$$

$$\mathbf{R} = \mathbf{R}',$$

and

$$\frac{d\mathbf{v}}{dt} = \frac{d'\mathbf{v}'}{dt} + \frac{d\boldsymbol{\Omega}}{dt} \times \mathbf{R}' + 2\boldsymbol{\Omega} \times \mathbf{v}' + \boldsymbol{\Omega} \times (\boldsymbol{\Omega} \times \mathbf{R}'). \qquad (2\text{–}56)$$

Summing over all particles δm which make up m at time t and canceling internal forces in pairs as usual, we have

$$\sum \mathbf{F}_e = m\mathbf{a}_0 + \frac{d\boldsymbol{\Omega}}{dt} \times \int_m \mathbf{R}' \, \delta m + \boldsymbol{\Omega} \times \left(\boldsymbol{\Omega} \times \int_m \mathbf{R}' \, \delta m \right)$$

$$+ 2\boldsymbol{\Omega} \times \int_m \mathbf{v}' \, \delta m + \int_m \frac{d'}{dt} (\mathbf{v}' \, \delta m).$$

We can quickly write, by definition,

$$\int_m \mathbf{R}' \, \delta m = \mathbf{R}'_{\text{c.m.}} m.$$

If we designate the momenta seen by ③ with a prime, we can rewrite the last term,

$$\int_m \frac{d'}{dt} (\mathbf{v}' \, \delta m) = \frac{d'\mathbf{P}'_{\text{c.v.}}}{dt} - \frac{d'\mathbf{P}'_i}{dt} + \frac{d'\mathbf{P}'_e}{dt},$$

just as before. Thus, *the force expression for our observer* ③ *watching an accelerating and rotating control volume* becomes

$$\sum \mathbf{F}_e = m \left[\mathbf{a}_0 + \frac{d\mathbf{\Omega}}{dt} \times \mathbf{R}'_{\text{c.m.}} + \mathbf{\Omega} \times (\mathbf{\Omega} \times \mathbf{R}'_{\text{c.m.}}) \right]$$

$$+ 2\mathbf{\Omega} \times \mathbf{P}'_{\text{c.v.}} + \frac{d'\mathbf{P}'_{\text{c.v.}}}{dt} - \frac{d'\mathbf{P}'_i}{dt} + \frac{d'\mathbf{P}'_e}{dt}. \qquad (4\text{--}19a)$$

If the rotating observer ③ sees a stationary control surface with steady flow inside, $\mathbf{P}'_{\text{c.v.}}$ is constant, and the position $\mathbf{R}'_{\text{c.m.}}$ of the center of mass appears fixed so that we have

$$\sum \mathbf{F}_e = m\mathbf{a}_{\text{c.m.}} + 2\mathbf{\Omega} \times \mathbf{P}'_{\text{c.v.}} - \frac{d'\mathbf{P}'_i}{dt} + \frac{d'\mathbf{P}'_e}{dt}. \qquad (4\text{--}19b)$$

The companion moment equation can be quickly formed by multiplying both sides by $\mathbf{R}'$ to get

$$\mathbf{R}' \times d\mathbf{F} = \mathbf{R}' \times \mathbf{a}_0 \, \delta m + \mathbf{R}'$$

$$\times \left[\frac{d'\mathbf{v}'}{dt} + \frac{d\mathbf{\Omega}}{dt} \times \mathbf{R}' + 2\mathbf{\Omega} \times \mathbf{v}' + \mathbf{\Omega} \times (\mathbf{\Omega} \times \mathbf{R}') \right] \delta m$$

and then summing to get

$$\int (\mathbf{R}' \times \mathbf{F}_e) = m\mathbf{R}'_{\text{c.m.}} \times \mathbf{a}_0 + \int_m \mathbf{R}' \times \left(\frac{d\mathbf{\Omega}}{dt} \times \mathbf{R}' \right) \delta m$$

$$+ \int_m \mathbf{R}' \times [\mathbf{\Omega} \times (\mathbf{\Omega} \times \mathbf{R}')] \, \delta m + \int_m \mathbf{R}' \times (2\mathbf{\Omega} \times \mathbf{v}') \, \delta m$$

$$+ \int_m \mathbf{R}' \times \frac{d'}{dt} (\mathbf{v}' \, \delta m).$$

The first term is our familiar correction term for an accelerated moment center not at the center of mass.

The next two terms are just those we would have obtained for rate of change of moment of momentum if we had been dealing with a rigid body of the same mass distribution. Looking back to Section 4–1, we had, for a rigid body,

$$\mathbf{H} = \int_m \mathbf{R} \times (\boldsymbol{\omega} \times \mathbf{R}) \, dm. \qquad (4\text{–}7)$$

Note that $d\mathbf{H}/dt$, when expanded, becomes

$$\frac{d\mathbf{H}}{dt} = \int_m \frac{d\mathbf{R}}{dt} \times (\boldsymbol{\omega} \times \mathbf{R}) \, dm + \int_m \mathbf{R} \times \left(\frac{d\boldsymbol{\omega}}{dt} \times \mathbf{R} \right) dm$$

$$+ \int_m \mathbf{R} \times \left(\boldsymbol{\omega} \times \frac{d\mathbf{R}}{dt} \right) dm.$$

With

$$\frac{d\mathbf{R}}{dt} = \boldsymbol{\omega} \times \mathbf{R},$$

the first term vanishes, and the last two are just the two terms in the variable mass relation. If we define, at any instant, a "solidified body" with the mass distribution of our actual control volume, we can call its moment of momentum $\mathbf{H}_s$ and treat it in the normal rigid-body terms; that is, in terms of moments of inertia, etc. (This will be particularly useful for general rotational motions to be taken up in the next chapters.)

If we observe that

$$\mathbf{R}' \times \frac{d'\mathbf{v}'}{dt} \, \delta m = \frac{d'}{dt} (\mathbf{R}' \times \mathbf{v}' \, \delta m),$$

we can rewrite the last term of our expression as

$$\int_m \mathbf{R}' \times \frac{d'}{dt} (\mathbf{v}' \, \delta m) = \frac{d'}{dt} \int_m \mathbf{R}' \times \mathbf{v}' \, \delta m = \frac{d'\mathbf{H}'_{\text{c.v.}}}{dt} - \frac{d'\mathbf{H}'_i}{dt} + \frac{d'\mathbf{H}'_e}{dt},$$

where $d'\mathbf{H}'_{\text{c.v.}}$ is the change in moment of momentum seen by ③ within the control surface in the interval dt. The intake and exhaust terms are defined as

$$d'\mathbf{H}'_i = \sum_{dm_i} \mathbf{R}' \times \mathbf{v}' \, \delta m, \qquad d'\mathbf{H}'_e = \sum_{dm_e} \mathbf{R}' \times \mathbf{v}' \, \delta m.$$

Putting all this together gives us a *moment equation in terms of the motion of a rotating and accelerating observer* ③ *watching the moving control surface.* Thus, we have

$$\sum (\mathbf{R}' \times \mathbf{F}_e) = m\mathbf{R}'_{\text{c.m.}} \times \mathbf{a}_0 + \frac{d\mathbf{H}_s}{dt} + \int_m \mathbf{R}' \times (2\boldsymbol{\Omega} \times \mathbf{v}') \, \delta m$$

$$+ \frac{d'\mathbf{H}'_{\text{c.v.}}}{dt} - \frac{d'\mathbf{H}'_i}{dt} + \frac{d'\mathbf{H}'_e}{dt}. \qquad (4\text{–}20a)$$

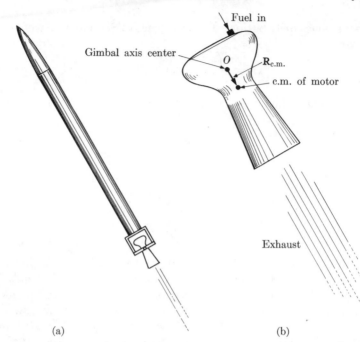

Fig. 4–14. Schematic representation of a gimballed liquid-fuel rocket motor.

If observer ③ sees steady internal flow and puts the origin at an unaccelerated point or at the center of mass of the control volume (solidified body), we have the simpler expression

$$\sum (\mathbf{R}' \times \mathbf{F}_e) = \frac{d\mathbf{H}_s}{dt} + \int_m \mathbf{R}' \times (2\mathbf{\Omega} \times \mathbf{v}') \, \delta m - \frac{d'\mathbf{H}'_i}{dt} + \frac{d'\mathbf{H}'_e}{dt}. \quad (4\text{–}20\text{b})$$

If the control volume is not rotating, we get a moment equation as a *companion to the force equation* (4–18) *for the nonrotating observer* ② as

$$\sum (\mathbf{R} \times \mathbf{F}_e) = m\mathbf{R}_{\text{c.m.}} \times \mathbf{a}_0 + \frac{d\mathbf{H}_{\text{c.v.}}}{dt} - \frac{d\mathbf{H}_i}{dt} + \frac{d\mathbf{H}_e}{dt}. \quad (4\text{–}20\text{c})$$

Unfortunately, in Eqs. (4–20a) and (4–20b) there is no convenient way of writing the "Coriolis moment" in integrated form.

EXAMPLE 4–9. Sometimes the liquid-fueled rocket motors are mounted in a vehicle with gimbals so that they may be rotated as directed by an automatic control or stabilization system. To design properly the actuating mechanisms and calculate vehicle stability, we must be able to predict the forces and moments which are needed to produce an arbitrary motion of the motor.

Let's assume that the rigid shell of the motor is pivoted by the gimbals about point O (Fig. 4–14). This point is usually accelerating since it is moving with the base of the rocket vehicle. We can instruct our rotating observer at O to ride with the motor shell so that he does not see it move but is in a good position to watch the internal flow. The angular motion of the motor shell is thus symbolized by $\mathbf{\Omega}$.

If the linear and angular accelerations of the rocket motor are not too large, it is a good (as well as useful) assumption that observer ③ sees essentially steady flow inside the motor. If we define the control surface to enclose the rocket motor as shown in Fig. 4–14(b), we see fuel come in near the top and exhaust gases leave the nozzle at the bottom. The appropriate force and moment equations [Eqs. (4–19) and (4–20)] are

$$\sum \mathbf{F}_e = m\left[\mathbf{a}_0 + \frac{d\mathbf{\Omega}}{dt} \times \mathbf{R}'_{\text{c.m.}} + \mathbf{\Omega} \times (\mathbf{\Omega} \times \mathbf{R}'_{\text{c.m.}})\right]$$
$$+ 2\mathbf{\Omega} \times \mathbf{P}'_{\text{c.v.}} - \frac{d'\mathbf{P}'_i}{dt} + \frac{d'\mathbf{P}'_e}{dt},$$

$$\sum (\mathbf{R}' \times \mathbf{F}_e) = m\mathbf{R}'_{\text{c.m.}} \times \mathbf{a}_0 + \frac{d\mathbf{H}_s}{dt} + \int_m \mathbf{R}' \times (2\mathbf{\Omega} \times \mathbf{v}')\, \delta m$$
$$- \frac{d'\mathbf{H}'_i}{dt} + \frac{d'\mathbf{H}'_e}{dt}.$$

Note that for this steady flow, the vector $\mathbf{R}'_{\text{c.m.}}$ from O to the center of mass is of constant length. Thus the bracketed quantity in the force equation is physically the absolute acceleration of the point in the control volume which is at any instant the center of mass. If the average inflow and out-flow velocities are $\mathbf{v}'_i$ and $\mathbf{v}'_e$, respectively, we have

$$- \frac{d'\mathbf{P}'_i}{dt} + \frac{d'\mathbf{P}'_e}{dt} = (\mathbf{v}'_e - \mathbf{v}'_i)\frac{dm_i}{dt},$$

where the mass inflow equals the mass outflow.

Actually, if we assume axial symmetry for the flow (especially through the nozzle where the momentum contributions are substantial), we can say the mass flow is the same at every station along the X-axis. This permits us to write the momentum as

$$\mathbf{P}'_{\text{c.v.}} = \int_m \mathbf{v}'\, \delta m = \int \mathbf{v}'\rho A\, dx = \frac{dm_i}{dt}\int_{\mathbf{x}_i}^{\mathbf{x}_e} d\mathbf{x} = (\mathbf{x}_e - \mathbf{x}_i)\frac{dm_i}{dt}.$$

Thus, the force equation becomes

$$\sum \mathbf{F}_e = m\mathbf{a}_{\text{c.m.}} + 2\mathbf{\Omega} \times (\mathbf{x}_e - \mathbf{x}_i)\frac{dm_i}{dt} + (\mathbf{v}'_e - \mathbf{v}'_i)\frac{dm_i}{dt}.$$

The external forces are made up of the direct forces from the gimbals and inlet hose connection, gravity forces, and the integral of the fluid pressure and shear around the surface of the control volume. This integral may be fairly difficult to evaluate unless quite a bit is known about the flow around the case and particularly across the exit of the nozzle. Note that for a nonrotating rocket motor, the "Coriolis term" is zero, and the expression reduces to that usually obtained for a rocket motor. Remember also that $\mathbf{v}_i'$ is much smaller than $\mathbf{v}_e'$.

Turning our attention to the moment equation, we can see that the moment of the surface pressures and the moment due to gravity are probably negligibly small (unless $\mathbf{R}_{\text{c.m.}}'$ is large). Thus the main external moment is applied by the gimbal system. With the assumption of axial symmetry of the flow about X, we get

$$\frac{d'\mathbf{H}_e'}{dt} = \frac{d'\mathbf{H}_i'}{dt} = 0.$$

This assumption of steady symmetrical flow which excludes the flexing inlet hose and its oscillating fluid stream from the control volume permits the integration of the "Coriolis moment" term as

$$\int_m \mathbf{R}' \times (2\mathbf{\Omega} \times \mathbf{v}') \, \delta m = \frac{dm_i}{dt} \int \mathbf{R}' \times (2\mathbf{\Omega} \times d\mathbf{x})$$

$$= 2\frac{dm_i}{dt} \mathbf{\Omega}_\perp \int_{x_i}^{x_e} x \, dx = \frac{dm_i}{dt} \mathbf{\Omega}_\perp (x_e^2 - x_i^2)$$

$$= \frac{dm_i}{dt} \mathbf{\Omega}_\perp (x_e + x_i)(x_e - x_i),$$

where $\mathbf{\Omega}_\perp$ is the component of $\mathbf{\Omega}$ perpendicular to the X-axis. Thus, we have

$$\sum (\mathbf{R}' \times \mathbf{F}_e) = m\mathbf{R}_{\text{c.m.}}' \times \mathbf{a}_0 + \frac{d\mathbf{H}_s}{dt} + \frac{dm_i}{dt} \mathbf{\Omega}_\perp (x_e + x_i)(x_e - x_i),$$

where $m\mathbf{R}_{\text{c.m.}}' \times \mathbf{a}_0$ is our usual correction term for an accelerated origin not at the center of mass, and $d\mathbf{H}_s/dt$ would reduce to $I(d\mathbf{\Omega}/dt)$ if the rotational motion were about a fixed axis. For the more general case, this rate of change of momentum for the solidified rocket motor can be handled like the rigid bodies of Chapters 5 and 6. ▲

EXAMPLE 4–10. As another example of the use of the general moment equation (4–20) for bodies of variable mass, we might look at the rotor blade of a helicopter which is driven by a tip jet. We may suppose that the type under study employs a large compressor in the fuselage which supplies

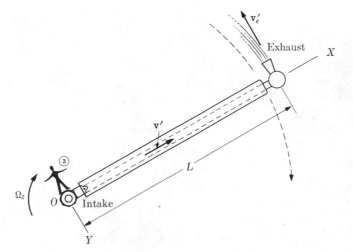

FIG. 4–15. A hollow helicopter blade with a tip jet.

air to the tip jets through passages in the rotor blades. As can be seen in Fig. 4–15, the device is quite similar to many types of lawn sprinklers.

If we assume that the blade is simply rotating about the vertical axis Z at the constant rate Ω while the tip jet spews air horizontally in the negative Y-direction, it is convenient to use O as our origin. The external torque applied to the blade about O will be the integrated effect of the pressure distribution all over the blade's surface; that is, the moment of the drag forces. If we say that our control volume includes not only the material within the external surfaces of the blade but also within the external surface of the tip nozzle, including an imaginary plane across the tip nozzle exit, the pressure integral must include contributions from these nozzle surfaces. If we further assume that the Z-axis is a principal axis (see Chapter 5) of the "solidified" blade and nozzle combination, we can write the rate of change of moment of momentum $\mathbf{H}_s$ of the solidified body as $I_{zs}\,(d\Omega/dt)$. This is zero for our assumed steady motion. Remember that to figure I_{zs}, we think of the moving air in our blade and nozzle as though it were instantaneously "solidified" with the same density distribution as when it is flowing.

Since the origin O is assumed to be unaccelerated, the correction term $m\mathbf{R}'_{\text{c.m.}} \times \mathbf{a}_0$ in the moment equation (4–20) is zero. If we assume that our observer ③ rotating with the blade sees steady internal flow, we are left with

$$\sum(\mathbf{R}' \times \mathbf{F}_e) = \int_m \mathbf{R}' \times (2\mathbf{\Omega} \times \mathbf{v}')\,\delta m - \frac{d'\mathbf{H}'_i}{dt} + \frac{d'\mathbf{H}'_e}{dt}.$$

In integrating the Coriolis term, if we observe that no appreciable contribu-

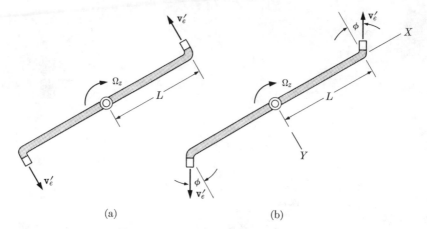

FIG. 4–16. A simple lawn sprinkler.

tion can come from the rearward nozzle flow because $\mathbf{\Omega} \times \mathbf{v}'_e$ is parallel to $\mathbf{R}'$, we have

$$\int_m \mathbf{R}' \times (2\mathbf{\Omega} \times \mathbf{v}')\, \delta m = 2\frac{dm_i}{dt}\mathbf{\Omega}_z \int_0^L x\, dx = \frac{dm_i}{dt}\mathbf{\Omega}_z L^2.$$

Since the moment arm of the inlet is zero,

$$\frac{d'\mathbf{H}'_i}{dt} = 0.$$

However, at the exhaust,

$$\frac{d'\mathbf{H}'_e}{dt} = \mathbf{L} \times \mathbf{v}'_e \frac{dm_e}{dt}.$$

Thus,

$$M_{z_e} = -L\frac{dm_i}{dt}(v'_e - \Omega_z L).$$

The blade will rotate at the constant Ω_z in the presence of a net retarding or drag moment for which $\Omega_z L$ is sufficiently smaller than v'_e. To put it differently, if the blade is to feel a net forward thrust in the Y-direction from the air flowing through it, the air leaving the blade at the nozzle must have a negative absolute momentum in the Y-direction since the entering air has no Y-momentum.

If we look at the analogous problem of the lawn sprinkler (Fig. 4–16a) where M_{z_e} is usually negligible, we see that the equilibrium spin-rate is

$$\Omega_z = \frac{v'_e}{L}.$$

However, this means the exit water velocity relative to the ground is zero, a somewhat undesirable value for a practical sprinkler. If the tip jet is turned an angle ϕ (Fig. 4–16b), you can show that now

$$\Omega_z = \frac{v_e' \cos \phi}{L},$$

and the velocity of the water over the ground is

$$v_x = v_e' \sin \phi, \qquad v_y = 0.$$

Of course, to get any range for the spray we must tilt the jet up as well. ▲

4–4 Reaction propulsion. The ideas of the variable-mass body which we have just developed are particularly valuable in studying the overall flow dynamics of various propulsion systems. Vehicles such as ships and aircraft are less fortunate than their automotive counterparts in the sense that they must develop propulsive forces or thrust from the surrounding fluid rather than by pushing against a solid surface. We know from experience that in order to propel a rowboat forward, we must force the oar blades to the rear through the water, giving some of the water an extra rearward momentum. If the boat is moving rapidly, we must also move the oars even more rapidly so that we actually increase the rearward speed of some of the passing water. Paddle wheels and ordinary ship's propellers function in just this way, as do aircraft propellers, turbojets, and ramjets.

If we obtain thrust by increasing the rearward momentum of some surrounding fluid, we pay the price by expending energy stored in us or in our vehicle's fuel tanks. The efficiency of producing useful thrust from stored energy is of paramount importance both economically and militarily. Since it is not always easy to separate thrust from drag, please be very careful in evaluating the claims of engine designers as compared with the counterclaims of the drag-conscious fluid dynamicist.

EXAMPLE 4–11. In order to illustrate these ideas let's look at the engine pod in Fig. 4–17(a). It may contain either a ramjet or turbojet power plant. We will just look at it from the outside and merely assume steady internal flow. If this pod is mounted on a vehicle moving at the constant velocity V in the negative X-direction, let's employ an inertial observer riding on the pod. Our control volume encloses the surface of the pod and cuts across the air and fuel intakes and the exhaust. Exactly where we cut these flows depends on how we find it convenient to evaluate both the pressure at the control surface and the momentum flow through it.

The horizontal external forces on this control surface are those F_s due to structural connections to the craft and the pressure and shear integral

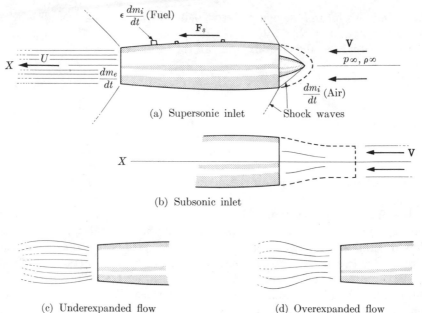

(a) Supersonic inlet

(b) Subsonic inlet

(c) Underexpanded flow   (d) Overexpanded flow

FIGURE 4–17

F_p. In the ideal supersonic flow shown (Fig. 4–17a), the dotted control surface around the intake makes it easy to evaluate the intake portion of the pressure integral because the air properties simply are those of the undisturbed stream. For a subsonic inlet (Fig. 4–17b) the flow is disturbed a considerable distance upstream. Similarly the exhaust pressure integral depends on knowledge of the matching of engine operation and configuration to external flow. The exhaust stream may be underexpanded in the nozzle and continue to expand beyond (Fig. 4–17c), or it may be overexpanded (Fig. 4–17d).

The continuity equation for the engine pod for steady flow says that what comes out in the exhaust as dm_e/dt went in as air, dm_i/dt, or fuel, $\epsilon \, (dm_i/dt)$, where ϵ is the fuel-air ratio.

$$\frac{dm_e}{dt} = (1 + \epsilon) \frac{dm_i}{dt}.$$

The force equation (4–19) for this case becomes simply, for the X-direction,

$$F_s + F_p = -\frac{dP_i}{dt} + \frac{dP_e}{dt} = -V\frac{dm_i}{dt} + U\frac{dm_e}{dt}$$

if we neglect the inflow X-momentum of the fuel. Thus the net force transmitted to the structure is of magnitude

$$F_s = [U(1 + \epsilon) - V]\frac{dm_i}{dt} - F_p,$$

where F_p is normally positive.

Observe that for a substantial propelling force, the discharge speed U must be substantially larger than the approach speed V of the air. This force is also directly related to the mass flow through the engine. Except for the effects of F_p, the propulsive force thus depends on giving the flow through the engine an increase in rearward momentum. If the flow has been given a net rearward momentum, the kinetic energy exhausted per unit time will be larger than the kinetic energy coming in the intake. This excess kinetic energy per unit time, for a given momentum increase, will be smaller, the larger the mass flow through the engine; that is, if a larger mass is given a smaller velocity increase to produce the same momentum change, the increase in kinetic energy will also be less. Since the rate of expenditure of fuel energy is closely related, for a given type of engine, to the change in kinetic energy (as complicated by the pressure levels at which the kinetic energy is measured), the efficient use of fuel calls for giving a large mass flow a small velocity increment.

Following this idea we can expect the bypass or fan engines to be more efficient because they handle more air than can be reasonably passed through the engine itself. Of course, engine weight and combustion problems will place limitations on handling increased mass flows.

A device for giving small velocity increments to very large mass flows at reasonably low forward speeds is the ordinary aircraft propeller. Here the air handled to produce thrust is often entirely separate from the combustion air of the engine. Consequently propeller sizes may be limited more by ground clearance problems than anything else. Ships' propellers, of course, operate on the same principle but are severely limited by cavitation and clearance problems. The helicopter rotor is an extreme example of a small amount of power being delivered to a large mass flow of air to produce a large thrust.

The rocket motor is somewhat different in that it does not attempt to obtain thrust by pushing on the surrounding fluid. Instead, it merely ejects exhaust gases to the rear from a completely self-contained fuel supply and may even work better in a vacuum than in a fluid medium. We have already shown in Example 4–7 that the net propulsive force of a rocket engine is of magnitude

$$F_s = c\frac{dm}{dt} + F_p,$$

where c is the exhaust speed, and F_p is positive toward the rear. Contrary to the air-breathing engine, the rocket gets thrust even from a small exhaust speed. ▲

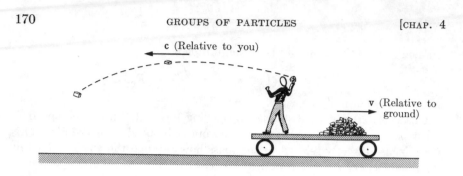

FIG. 4–18. The fundamental idea of rocket propulsion.

EXAMPLE 4–12. To get a good "feel" for how a rocket works, look at yourself on a cart piled high with bricks (Fig. 4–18). Presume the floor is level, the wheels frictionless and of negligible mass. Suppose you pick up a brick and throw it to the rear. You, the cart, and remaining bricks will have gained a small velocity forward. You can look at it as a conservation of horizontal momentum so that the center of mass of brick plus you, the cart, and the bricks does not move. Alternatively, you say that you push to the rear on the brick so that the reaction force is pushing forward on you, the cart, and the bricks.

In any event, we can forget about that first brick and throw a second, a third, and a fourth. If you throw each one in the same manner, you find that each successive one gives you, the cart, and the remaining bricks a slightly larger speed increment. In fact, throwing the last brick will give you and the cart the largest increment in speed. Can you see why? Where is the center of mass of you, the cart, and all the bricks, assuming the frictionless floor is of very large extent?

If we idealize the process into a steady stream of particles at the constant relative exhaust speed c and neglect F_p (or include its effect in an equivalent exhaust speed), we have, as in Example 4–7,

$$ma_0 = -c\,\frac{dm}{dt},$$

$$\int_0^v dv_0 = -c\int_{m_0}^m \frac{dm}{m}, \qquad v = c\ln\frac{m_0}{m}.$$

For a constant mass flow $\beta = dm_e/dt = -dm/dt$, we can write

$$v = c\ln\left(\frac{m_0}{m_0 - \beta t}\right).$$

If you throw away one-half of your initial mass, you will get a speed of about 70% of c; throw away three quarters and you will attain $1.4\,c$. Can the turbojet achieve $V > U$? ▲

Problems

4–1. Show that in the absence of any external forces, the total linear momentum of a group of particles remains unchanged regardless of any internal interactions between particles.

4–2. Relate the impulse of the external forces acting on a group of particles to the motion of the group's center of mass.

4–3. Suppose a 200-lb man stands up in a 50-lb canoe which is floating quietly on still water. If the man moves from one end of the canoe to the other (the length of the canoe is 8 ft), (a) how much does the canoe move if we assume there is only negligible water resistance due to friction? (b) What is the final velocity of the canoe and man? (c) Does your answer in (b) change if we admit there is appreciable water resistance? If it does, which way does it change?

4–4. Show that the total kinetic energy of a group of particles is equal to its kinetic energy, as seen by a nonrotating observer ② moving with the center of mass, plus the kinetic energy of the group's total mass as if moving with the velocity of the center of mass.

4–5. Show that the angular momentum $\mathbf{H}_A$ about a stationary origin A can be written in terms of $\mathbf{H}_B$ about a stationary origin B at a distance $\mathbf{R}_{B/A}$ as

$$\mathbf{H}_A = \mathbf{H}_B + \mathbf{R}_{B/A} \times (\textstyle\sum m)\mathbf{v}_{\text{c.m.}}.$$

4–6. If the origin B in the previous problem is moving with velocity $\mathbf{v}_{B/A}$, show that the angular momentum $\mathbf{H}_{B2}$ about B, as seen by an observer ② moving with B, is related to $\mathbf{H}_{A1}$ seen by ① at A as

$$\mathbf{H}_{A1} = \mathbf{H}_{B2} + \mathbf{R}_{B/A} \times (\textstyle\sum m)\mathbf{v}_{\text{c.m.}/A} + \mathbf{R}_{\text{c.m.}/B} \times (\textstyle\sum m)\mathbf{v}_{B/A}.$$

If B happens to be at the center of mass, show that

$$\mathbf{H}_{A1} = \mathbf{H}_{\text{c.m.}2} + \mathbf{R}_{\text{c.m.}/A} \times (\textstyle\sum m)\mathbf{v}_{\text{c.m.}/A}.$$

4–7. Show that, for a rigid body, the moment of inertia I_z about axis Z is related to $I_{z\text{c.m.}}$, the moment of inertia about a parallel axis through the center of mass, as

$$I_z = \int_m (x^2 + y^2)\, dm = I_{z\text{c.m.}} + (x_{\text{c.m.}}^2 + y_{\text{c.m.}}^2)\, m.$$

4–8. A slender rod of mass m and length a is pivoted about one end. If it falls from the horizontal position to the vertical, find its angular velocity just as it becomes vertical. Assume that there is a small constant frictional torque T in the pivot and that the rod's radius of gyration about the pivot

$$k_p = \sqrt{I_p/m} = \frac{a}{\sqrt{3}}.$$

4–9. The radius of gyration $k = \sqrt{I/m}$ of a 40-lb flywheel about its vertical shaft is 6 in., and the center of gravity of the wheel is 0.003 in. from the axis of the shaft. If a constant moment of 10 ft-lb is applied to the flywheel through its shaft, find the horizontal force **F** exerted on the bearing 5 sec after the wheel starts from rest. (Solve by using d'Alembert's principle.)

4–10. A uniform rod of length L and mass m is clamped rigidly at one end by a massive body which is accelerating at **a** in a direction perpendicular to the axis of the rod. Assuming that the clamped end is not permitted to rotate as it is accelerated, let's find the moment which is being exerted on the rod at the clamped end.

*4–11. Find the distribution of shear force and bending moment along the rod of the previous problem.

4–12. Show for a rigid body rotating about a fixed axis Z that $I_z\omega_z$ is in general only one component of the moment of momentum **H** and that the complete expression is

$$\mathbf{H} = (-\mathbf{i}J_{xz} - \mathbf{j}J_{yz} + \mathbf{k}I_z)\omega_z,$$

where

$$J_{xz} = \int_m xz\, dm, \quad \text{and} \quad J_{yz} = \int_m yz\, dm.$$

4–13. If the products of inertia J in the previous problem are not zero, will moments about X and Y be required to maintain even a constant angular velocity of the rigid body about the fixed axis Z? Explain carefully.

4–14. For a rigid body in planar motion, find an expression relating the angular impulse and the change in angular momentum about the body's center of mass.

4–15. Show for a rigid body in planar motion that its total kinetic energy can be considered as the sum of translational kinetic energy and rotational kinetic energy if the motion is viewed as translation of and rotation about the body's center of mass.

4–16. The captain of a 100-ton flying saucer (Fig. 4–19) which has just begun a trip through space decides to start the saucer rotating at 1 rad/sec by firing his tangential rockets. How much fuel will he need if each pound of fuel can provide an impulse of 200 lb-sec? The radius of gyration $k = \sqrt{I/m}$ of the saucer about its center is 10 ft.

4–17. A wheel of mass m and moment of inertia I about its axis has the force **F** suddenly applied to it (Fig. 4–20). Find the initial acceleration of point A (a) if the surface is frictionless; (b) if the surface friction is high enough to prevent slipping.

4–18. Suppose the wheel of Example 4–1 has its center of mass displaced slightly from its axis and is rolling at constant speed V. What is the maximum V at which it will roll without hopping periodically from the ground?

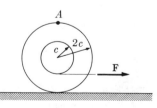

FIGURE 4–19   FIGURE 4–20

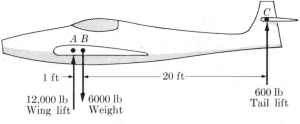

FIGURE 4–21

4–19. An airplane encountering a gust is subject to the forces shown in Fig. 4–21, where the moment of inertia I_B about the center of mass = 25,400 slug-ft^2. (a) Calculate the moments about points A, B, and C and decide whether the airplane is going to nose up or down. Give clear reasons for your answer. (b) What acceleration does a passenger, 3 ft behind the center of gravity, feel?

4–20. The circular cylinder of weight W and radius r (Fig. 4–22) is released from rest in the position shown and rolls without slipping on the circular surface. Determine the reaction N between the surface and the cylinder when the bottom position is reached.

4–21. A careless automobile driver starts off at an acceleration **A** when one of his doors is open 90°. Assume that the door has a frictionless hinge. What is the initial angular acceleration of the door as it begins to slam shut? You are given the door mass M, moment of inertia about the hinge I_h, and distance D from the hinge to the door's center of mass.

4–22. Suppose a bowler starts a ball sliding down the alley in pure translation ($\omega_0 = 0$) at 30 ft/sec. If the coefficient of friction is 0.2, find the time it takes for the ball to cease slipping. Solve this problem by using impulse-momentum ideas. (I of ball about its center is $2/5mr^2$.)

4–23. Suppose a circular cylinder of radius r, as in Problem 4–20, is rolling without slipping in a circular cylindrical horizontal trough of (larger) radius R. What is the period of the oscillations characteristic of this system for small angular motions near the lowest point? ($I_{c.m.} = \frac{1}{2}mr^2$.)

*4–24. A thin-walled cylinder of mass m and radius 3 ft rolls down an incline of angle θ without slipping. Inside the hollow cylinder, a solid cylinder of the same

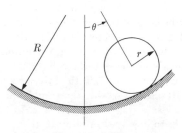

FIGURE 4–22

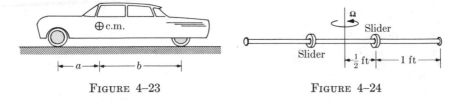

FIGURE 4–23   FIGURE 4–24

mass m and of radius 1 ft rolls without slipping. (a) The line joining the centers of the cylinders is observed to make a constant angle δ with the vertical. Find δ for any given θ. (b) If the hollow and solid cylinders were allowed to roll separately down the incline, which would accelerate more rapidly? Why?

4–25. An engineer helping to assemble a space station way out in space fires his personal rocket to move toward a drifting assembly. Assume the thrust is 10 lb for $\frac{1}{2}$ sec and that his weight (on earth) is 186 lb. Unfortunately, the line of action of the thrust is 6 in. above his center of mass. (a) What is his motion after the rocket ceases firing? (His radius of gyration about a transverse axis is $k = \sqrt{I_{\text{c.m.}}/m} = 2$ ft.) (b) What is his total change in kinetic energy as seen by a friend initially at rest with respect to the engineer?

4–26. Suppose that it is desired to build an automobile (Fig. 4–23) so that when the front wheels go over a bump, the vertical force transmitted by the front springs tends simply to rotate the car about the rear wheels without compressing the rear springs. Similarly, a bump at the rear wheels shall not tend to compress the front springs. If the car has a mass of 100 slugs and a moment of inertia of 2500 slug-ft² about its center of gravity, what is the necessary relation between a and b?

4–27. A flying saucer is at rest out in space (it is unaccelerated and nonrotating). The captain wants to rotate the saucer through 90° about its axis as quickly as possible by turning on a motor-driven flywheel whose axis is parallel to that of the saucer. (a) Which way should the flywheel be rotated? (b) If the moments of inertia of the flywheel and the saucer are 1 slug-ft² and 10^5 slug-ft², respectively, and the maximum flywheel speed is 3600 rev/min, how long will it take to turn the saucer the desired 90°? Make reasonable assumptions about the time required to accelerate the flywheel.

4–28. A rod is rotating freely at 10 rad/sec about a vertical axis when two sliders are released simultaneously (Fig. 4–24). If the rod is 3 ft long, has a central transverse radius of gyration $k = \sqrt{I/m} = 1$ ft, has a mass of 0.10 slug, and the sliders each weigh 1 lb, (a) find the angular velocity of the system after the two sliders come to rest at the ends of the rod, (b) find the loss of kinetic energy, and *(c) find the radial position of the sliders as a function of time after release.

4–29. Suppose two identical elastic rods on a frictionless surface are given an axial acceleration **A**, but in one case the rod is pushed from behind, and in the other it is pulled from in front. (a) Will the forces required be the same in both cases? (b) Will the internal stresses be the same? (c) Find the internal stress distributions for both rods.

4–30. A steel drum is rolling horizontally at the velocity **V** while a stone is sliding inside at the angle θ from the vertical because of the friction between the stone and the inside surface of the drum. (Assume that the friction coefficient is 0.3.) (a) For a constant $\mathbf{V}$ find the equilibrium value of θ. (b) If $\mathbf{V}$ is increasing at the rate A, will there be an equilibrium value of θ? If so, find an expression for it.

4–31. It has been noticed that when tall slender brick chimneys topple over, they break as shown in Fig. 4–25 while still falling. Assume that the chimney is approximately a uniform rod hinged at the base. (a) Find the angular velocity and acceleration as a function of time. (b) Sketch the forces acting on a short segment of the chimney considered as a free body. *(c) Using d'Alembert's principle, consider the chimney as a beam under transverse gravity and inertia loading and find the shear and bending moment distributions. *(d) Considering also the axial stresses, can you see why the chimneys fail as they do? Explain carefully.

FIGURE 4–25

4–32. Suppose an incompressible fluid is emanating from the origin of coordinates at a constant rate, and it is flowing radially outward in a spherically symmetrical manner.

(a) Use the concept of the continuity equation to find how the velocity (which is entirely radial) varies with distance R from the origin.

(b) Find the acceleration of a particle when it is at radius R.

(c) Consider only pressure forces (no gravity, shear, etc.). How must the pressure vary with R? (You may find it convenient to work along the X-axis which is a typical radial line in this spherically symmetrical flow.)

*4–33. By watching mass flow in and out of a fixed volume element in cylindrical coordinates (shaped like a truncated wedge), show that the mass accumulated inside in time interval dt equals the negative of the net outflow as

$$\frac{\partial}{\partial t} (\rho r \, dr \, d\theta \, dz) \, dt =$$
$$-\left[\frac{\partial}{\partial r} (\rho v_r r \, d\theta \, dz) \, dr + \frac{\partial}{\partial \theta} (\rho v_\theta \, dr \, dz) \, d\theta + \frac{\partial}{\partial z} (\rho v_z r \, d\theta \, dr) \, dz \right] dt,$$

and then show that the equation of continuity in cylindrical coordinates can be written as

$$r \frac{\partial \rho}{\partial t} + \frac{\partial}{\partial r} (\rho r v_r) + \frac{\partial}{\partial \theta} (\rho v_\theta) + r \frac{\partial}{\partial z} (\rho v_z) = 0.$$

4–34. Suppose we have a flow of an incompressible fluid in which

$$v_r = 0, \qquad v_\theta = \frac{1}{r}, \qquad v_z = 0.$$

(a) Does it satisfy the equation of continuity derived in the previous problem?

(b) Neglecting gravity, shear forces, etc., what is the pressure distribution in this flow? The appropriate equations of motion for a fluid particle can be shown to be in cylindrical coordinates

$$\frac{dv_r}{dt} - \frac{v_\theta^2}{r} = -\frac{1}{\rho}\frac{\partial p}{\partial r},$$

$$\frac{dv_\theta}{dt} + \frac{v_r v_\theta}{r} = -\frac{1}{\rho r}\frac{\partial p}{\partial \theta},$$

$$\frac{dv_z}{dt} = -\frac{1}{\rho}\frac{\partial p}{\partial z}.$$

4–35. Suppose a bucket of water is being rotated at constant Ω about its vertical axis of symmetry so that the water appears to be rotating as though it were a rigid body.

(a) Find the pressure distribution as a function of radial position and height. Assume that the atmospheric pressure is p_0 and that the water has the density ρ slugs/ft^3.

(b) What is the shape of the free surface of the water?

(c) If the flow of the previous problem (4–34) had a free surface, what would be its shape? Have you seen this shape in a whirlpool?

4–36. Find the pressure distribution in the planar source flow of Example 4–3. (See also Problem 4–34.)

*4–37. In terms of the substantial or total derivative [see Eq. (4–11)], show in polar coordinates that

$$a_r = \frac{dv_r}{dt} - \frac{v_\theta^2}{r} = \frac{\partial v_r}{\partial t} + v_r\frac{\partial v_r}{\partial r} + \frac{v_\theta}{r}\frac{\partial v_r}{\partial \theta} - \frac{v_\theta^2}{r},$$

$$a_\theta = \frac{dv_\theta}{dt} + \frac{v_r v_\theta}{r} = \frac{\partial v_\theta}{\partial t} + v_r\frac{\partial v_\theta}{\partial r} + \frac{v_\theta}{r}\frac{\partial v_\theta}{\partial \theta} + \frac{v_r v_\theta}{r}.$$

4–38. By analogy to the work-kinetic-energy expressions in particle dynamics, start with the dynamical equations for a fluid [Eq. (4–13)] and integrate along the displacement of a fluid particle to come up with, for steady flow, (a) Bernoulli's equation for an incompressible fluid in a gravity field parallel to Z

$$p + \tfrac{1}{2}\rho v^2 + \rho gz = \text{constant},$$

and *(b) Bernoulli's equation for adiabatic flow of a compressible fluid [$\rho = \rho_0(p/p_0)^{1/\gamma}$]

$$\frac{\gamma}{\gamma - 1}\frac{p_0^{1/\gamma}}{\rho_0}p^{(\gamma-1)/\gamma} + \frac{v^2}{2} + gz = \text{constant}.$$

4–39. To study the vibration characteristics of a thin cylindrical shell, let us assume that the frequency of vibration ω depends on the shell material properties of density ρ and Young's modulus E, as well as shell thickness t and radius R. Use dimensional analysis to find as much as you can about how ω depends on E, ρ, R, t.

4–40. The flutter speed V of a wing is thought to depend on its torsional natural frequency ω, its chord C, its mass per foot of span m, and its mass moment of inertia per foot of span I, as well as the air density ρ. Using the ideas of dimensional analysis, find the dimensionless parameters of importance in this problem.

4–41. When an atomic bomb explodes, a blast or shock wave travels away from the center of the explosion. Find a relation between the speed of the shock wave and the energy E released in the explosion, the distance R of the shock wave from the center, the pressure p and the speed of sound A of the undisturbed atmosphere.

4–42. The load P that a bearing can carry depends on the bearing area A, on the angular velocity ω of the shaft, and on the viscosity μ of the lubricant. Find the form of the expression for P.

4–43. Can you deduce from your answer to the previous problem the change in load P if, using the same lubricant, we test a bearing of twice the area A at $\frac{1}{3}$ the angular velocity?

4–44. The water resistance encountered by a ship arises partly from the creation of waves. Determine the dependence of this "wave-making resistance" R on the vessel's speed V and size (indicated by some typical length L), on the density ρ of the water, and on the gravitational acceleration g.

4–45. The flutter of panels on high-speed missiles depends on the stiffness of the panels and the properties of the air stream. Use dimensional analysis to find a relation between the dynamic pressure q of the flow ($q = \frac{1}{2}\rho V^2$) and the following parameters: K, the stiffness per foot of the panel ($K = Et^3/12$ where E is Young's modulus and t is the panel thickness); a, the speed of sound in air; R, the panel length; and of somewhat less importance m, the mass per unit area of the panel.

4–46. If the thrust P of a propeller depends on the propeller diameter D, on the forward velocity V, on the number of revolutions per second n, and on the density ρ and the viscosity μ of the air, what is the form of the expression for P (a) with ρ, V, and D as preferred variables, and (b) with ρ, n, and D as preferred variables?

4–47. A sounding rocket is fired vertically upward from an initial altitude of 50,000 ft. Neglecting air resistance and assuming g is constant at 32 ft/sec^2, what altitude will the rocket reach if its initial weight is 4 tons, its rate of burning fuel is 1 ton/sec, its total burning time is 3 sec, and the exhaust velocity is 6000 ft/sec?

4–48. A man is pushing a wheelbarrow full of sand at constant speed along a smooth horizontal surface. He is exerting whatever horizontal force is necessary to overcome wheel friction effects. Unfortunately, there is suddenly a large hole in the bottom of the wheelbarrow and sand is pouring out and falling to the ground. To maintain the constant forward speed, must the man exert a larger, smaller, or unchanged horizontal force on the wheelbarrow? Explain your reasoning carefully.

4–49. A cylindrical water bucket slides without friction on a horizontal plane. There is a hole in its side at the bottom through which water escapes in a horizontal jet of velocity $\sqrt{2gh}$ where h is the (varying) height of water in the bucket.

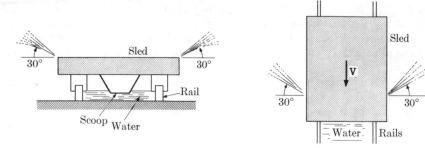

FIGURE 4–26

If the cross-sectional area of the bucket is A_1 and of the jet A_2, find the acceleration of the bucket as a function of time. Assume that the mass of the bucket is negligible and the water density is ρ.

4–50. The test sleds on the long desert test tracks are usually slowed down with a water brake which works as follows: a scoop mounted on the sled picks up water from between the tracks and sprays it up and to the sides, as shown in the front and top view in Fig. 4–26.

(a) For a sled weighing 3200 lb and traveling 2000 ft/sec, how much water per second must be handled by the scoop to produce a deceleration of 10 g's?

(b) If the deceleration of the sled is not constant, derive an expression for the sled's speed as a function of time, assuming it to be traveling at 2000 ft/sec when the brake first starts scooping water.

4–51. In principle, does a man pushing a lawn mower do extra work when the grass is caught in a tray attached to the mower? If so, how could you compute the extra power necessary?

4–52. A rocket-driven test sled is used on a long desert track to accelerate airplane components to speeds above the speed of sound. Suppose that 10 rockets can be fitted to the rear of the sled which itself weighs 3200 lb. Each of the rockets can develop a test-stand thrust of 4000 lb for 20 sec with an exhaust velocity of 8000 ft/sec.

(a) Ignore the weight of rocket casing and nozzle. How much does each rocket weigh?

(b) If all 10 rockets are fired simultaneously, what speed will the sled reach? (Ignore air resistance and rail friction.)

(c) If the rockets are fired consecutively, what speed will the sled reach? (Again ignore air resistance and rail friction.)

(d) How would the answers for (b) and (c) compare if air resistance and rail friction were included? Explain your conclusions.

4–53. A high-speed snowplow is being designed for runway snow clearance. For a blade angle of 30° as shown in Fig. 4–27 and a constant forward speed of 40 mi/hr, we can assume that the snow leaves the blade at a relative speed of 30 mi/hr (it compacts somewhat) tangent to the blade. We can also assume a snow depth of one foot, a plowing width of 10 ft, and a snow density of 0.20 slugs/ft^3.

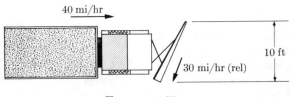

40 mi/hr

30 mi/hr (rel)

10 ft

FIGURE 4–27

(a) Find the engine power required for plowing the snow (beyond that required to propel the truck itself at 40 mi/hr).

(b) What horizontal side force must the wheels experience from the road in order to maintain a straight path?

4–54. A crack British steam locomotive was designed to replenish its water supply without stopping by lowering a scoop into a trough between the tracks. If the locomotive is traveling at a constant 60 mi/hr and scooping 30 ft^3/sec of water (water weighs about 64 lb/ft^3) into its tank, which is 10 ft above the trough, what additional horizontal driving force is required beyond that normally required to maintain a constant 60 mi/hr? (Explain the basis for each of your assumptions clearly and fully.)

4–55. Suppose a thrust reverser goes into operation on the jet engine of Fig. 4–17 and turns the relative flow U through an angle of 135° without appreciably reducing the relative speed of the flow. If the forward speed of the engine is V and the mass flow of air through it is β, find an expression for the change in thrust due to the reverser's action.

4–56. A vehicle of mass m is accelerated along a straight track by means of a strong jet of water from a fixed nozzle striking it from behind. The water hitting the vehicle is deflected 90° to all sides frictionlessly. The absolute velocity of the jet is V, its cross-sectional area is A, the density of the water is ρ, and at any instant the vehicle velocity is v. (a) Show that the mass of water hitting the vehicle per second is $\rho A(V - v)$. (b) How long will it take the vehicle to accelerate from rest to a velocity v_1?

4–57. Discuss the different mechanisms involved in supporting in a gravitational field (a) a ball on a vertical jet of water, and (b) a hovering rocket ship on its vertical exhaust.

*4–58. What must a fireman do to a nozzle on a fire hose to make it swing at a rate of 30°/sec while spewing out 2 ft^3/sec of water at 60 ft/sec? Assume $\rho_{water} = 2$ slugs/ft^3.

*4–59. Small solid-fuel artillery rockets are sometimes stabilized by spinning about the fore-and-aft axis of symmetry X. The buildup in angular velocity Ω is achieved by using a row of small canted nozzles at a radius L around the periphery of the base to obtain a torque as well as a forward thrust. If the thrust axis of each of the n nozzles is canted an angle ϕ with respect to X, write an equation of rotational motion about X. If we assume that the external moment about X, due to external fluid shears and pressures, is small and independent of forward speed and angular velocity, find Ω as a function of time. (You may have to make some reasonable assumptions as to the manner in which the solid fuel is consumed.)

*4–60. Evaluate the terms on the right-hand sides of Eqs. (4–19) and (4–20) for a solid-fuel rocket yawing at angular velocity Ω in a fixed plane (including the axis of the rocket). Assume that the solid fuel burns progressively from back to front and that the flow through the nozzle appears essentially steady to an observer ③ riding on the rocket. Some of the integrations may be easier to carry out if you apply the continuity equation, $\rho A v$ = constant, to the flow inside the chamber and nozzle. State your simplifying assumptions carefully.

CHAPTER 5

GENERAL MOTION OF RIGID BODIES

In Chapters 2 and 4, we have studied some of the fundamentals of rigid-body motion. The kinematics of planar motion (Section 2–3) were developed in some detail and the corresponding dynamical equations were derived (Section 4–1) with considerable generality by regarding the rigid body as a special case of a finite group of particles. We have experienced the usefulness of describing rigid-body motion by superimposing ideas of translation and rotation so that the motion of the many particles of a rigid body can be described by using only a few coordinates. We have shown that when the internal forces cancel, the net external force is directly related to the linear motion of the center of mass, whereas the angular motion is related to the net moment of the external forces. In this chapter we will look carefully at the general rotational motion of a rigid body, its mass properties, and its equations of motion from a number of viewpoints so that you may gain sufficient facility with the ideas and knowledge of the techniques to tackle difficult applications such as those in Chapter 6.

5–1 Angular displacements. One of the tremendous advantages inherent in the idealized concept of "the rigid body" is that only six independent coordinates are needed to specify its position. An arbitrary group of n particles requires in general $3n$ coordinates to completely specify the arrangement. On the other hand, a rigid body made up of n particles has many independent relationships which permit a reduction in independent coordinates and state, in essence, that the distance between particles is constant. Thus, if we know the distance of each particle P from three non-collinear particles ABC (Fig. 5–1), we need only know the nine coordinates of A, B, and C to fix the position of the body. These coordinates can be further reduced to six because of the known fixed separations between the three particles. From another point of view, A's position is determined by three coordinates; B requires only two coordinates to specify the line on which it is located because the distance to it from A is known; and the third point, C, requires only one additional coordinate, making six, to specify the orientation of the plane formed by it and the line joining the first two points.

Of these six independent coordinates, three are quite naturally chosen as the components of the position vector of a reference point in the rigid body. This implies that the remaining three can be used to describe the orientation of the body about this point. It would be very helpful if we

181

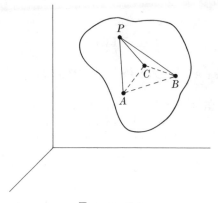

FIGURE 5–1

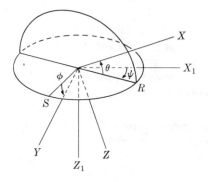

FIG. 5–2.   A set of Euler's angles for locating XYZ with respect to $X_1Y_1Z_1$.

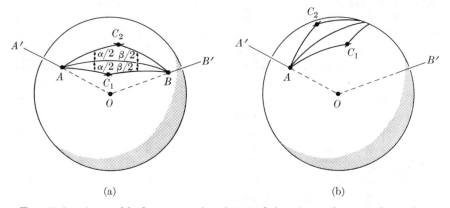

(a)   (b)

FIG. 5–3.   A graphical construction for studying successive rotations about fixed axes.

could define an angular position vector whose three components are just these coordinates. This cannot be done, however, because as we shall soon prove, angular displacements do not have all the properties required of vectors.

In order to help visualize the position of our rigid body, let's set up in the body a set of perpendicular axes XYZ with the origin at our reference point in the body. We can locate the X-axis with respect to a basic set $X_1Y_1Z_1$ (Fig. 5–2) by the same ideas used in spherical coordinates, defining first the azimuth ψ of the vertical plane XRZ_1 and then the elevation θ of X above the reference plane X_1Y_1. The position of Y can then be defined by the angle ϕ about X to Y from the intersection S of the YZ-plane and the reference plane X_1Y_1. If we know the positions of X and Y, we can easily construct Z, the third member of the triad (Fig. 5–2). These angles are one of a number of sets known as *Euler's angles* for expressing the orientation of a rigid body as conveniently as possible. We will come back to them later.

Another scheme for specifying the orientation of the X-axis involves the use of the three angles, or rather the cosines of the angles, between X and X_1, Y_1, and Z_1. Similarly Y and Z can be located by three *direction cosines* each, making a total of nine. These direction cosines are not entirely independent,* but they form a symmetrical and useful set, as we shall see.

Before we get involved in mathematics, perhaps we should try to develop a feeling for some of the properties of angular displacements. We said in Chapter 2 (see Fig. 2–26) that in rigid-body planar motion a general displacement could be visualized as a translation of the reference point plus a single rotation of the body about an axis through the reference point. How about a general "six-dimensional" displacement of the rigid body? Can this be separated into a single translation followed by a single rotation about one axis? Take a pair of pencils or books and try it. The translation is easy but can you always visualize a single rotation which takes the body from its initial orientation to the final one? Euler could, and now he has a theorem to his credit which states: *Any number of rotations about different axes through a point must in the end remain equivalent to a single rotation.* Rather than prove *Euler's theorem*, let's demonstrate several ways of finding the *single, equivalent rotation* for a pair of arbitrary rotations. If we can reduce a pair to one rotation, we can, in steps, reduce any number to one.

Look at the spherical shell centered at the fixed point O in Fig. 5–3(a) and pierced by two axis directions OA' and OB' around which we will rotate the sphere by amounts α and then β, respectively. Before rotating

---

* The relations among direction cosines are closely related to the properties of orthogonal transformations. See the problems at the end of the chapter.

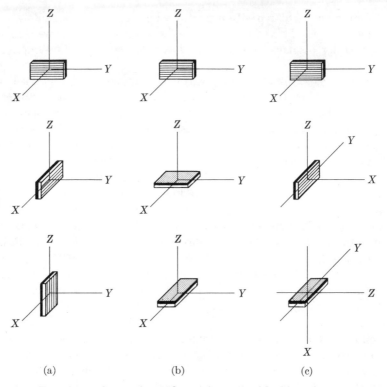

FIG. 5–4.   Successive 90° rotations of a blackboard eraser.

the sphere by α about OA', sketch, on the sphere, the arc of a great circle joining points A and B. Then lay off from A similar arcs $\alpha/2$ on both sides of AB, as shown. Corresponding arcs at $\beta/2$ from B intersect at C_1 and C_2. Note that spherical triangles ABC_1 and ABC_2 are similar; that is, corresponding sides and angles are equal.

Keeping OA' and OB' fixed in space, we rotate the sphere with its construction lines through an angle α about OA'. As shown in Fig. 5–3(b), A does not move, B swings up to the rear and, because of the construction, C_1 swings to where C_2 was. If we now rotate the sphere about OB' by an amount β, C_1 will return to its original position. Other points such as A, B, and C_2 will not. Of course, C_1 does not return by the same path on which it left, but because of the nature of the original construction in Fig. 5–3(a), we have been able to identify C_1 as the point which need not have moved at all. Thus a single rotation about OC_1 could produce the same final orientation of the sphere as α about OA' and β about OB'.

A moment's thought will tell you that if we had first rotated β about OB' and then α about OA', the axis for the single equivalent rotation would have been OC_2 instead of OC_1. Besides demonstrating Euler's theorem, we have thus shown that *angular displacements are not vectors* because the sum depends on the order of addition. We will show later, analytically, that the magnitude, if not the axis, of the single rotation equivalent to two successive rotations is independent of the order of addition, so that angular displacements are almost vectors.

EXAMPLE 5–1. To emphasize the effect of order of addition, look at the three blackboard erasers in Fig. 5–4. Let's rotate the first one (a) 90° around Z and then 90° around Y. With the second one (b) we reverse the order, first 90° about Y and then 90° about Z. Do they have the same final orientation?

You might want to try the same procedure but about axes fixed in the erasers. With the third eraser in (c), we show the same order of rotations as in (a) but for body axes, not space axes. Try the reverse order for body axes and see what happens. ▲

Returning to the concept of direction cosines, we will find that it is closely related to the coordinate transformation matrices that we studied in Section 2–2. There we related the components of a vector **A** in cartesian coordinates to those in cylindrical coordinates by the set of simultaneous equations written as

$$\begin{Bmatrix} A_r \\ A_\theta \\ A_z \end{Bmatrix} = \begin{bmatrix} \cos\theta & \sin\theta & 0 \\ -\sin\theta & \cos\theta & 0 \\ 0 & 0 & 1 \end{bmatrix} \begin{Bmatrix} A_x \\ A_y \\ A_z \end{Bmatrix}, \qquad (2\text{–}28)$$

or

$$\{A_{\text{cyl}}\} = [\theta_{\text{rot}}]\{A_{\text{cart}}\}. \qquad (2\text{–}29)$$

The inverse relationship took the form

$$\{A_{\text{cart}}\} = [\theta_{\text{rot}}]^{-1}\{A_{\text{cyl}}\},$$

where

$$[\theta_{\text{rot}}][\theta_{\text{rot}}]^{-1} = [1]. \qquad (2\text{–}30)$$

For simple rotation transformations the *inverse matrix* $[\theta_{\text{rot}}]^{-1}$ was found to be just the one obtained by transposing the terms of $[\theta_{\text{rot}}]$ across the main diagonal (see Appendix A). Thus, for these orthogonal transformations, the *transposed matrix* $[\theta]'$ and the *inverse matrix* $[\theta]^{-1}$ are the same.

$$[\theta]^{-1} = [\theta]' = \begin{bmatrix} \cos\theta & -\sin\theta & 0 \\ \sin\theta & \cos\theta & 0 \\ 0 & 0 & 1 \end{bmatrix}. \qquad (2\text{–}33)$$

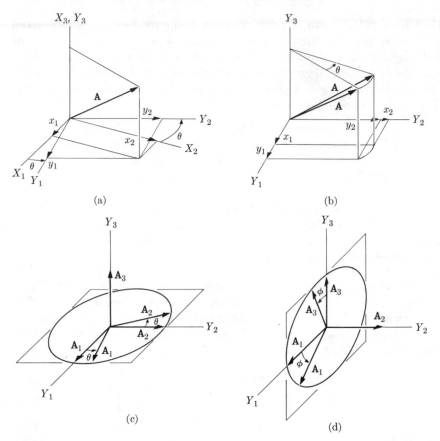

FIG. 5–5. Components in rotated axis systems compared with components of rotated vectors.

For convenience in notation, let's think of two sets of orthogonal axes $X_1X_2X_3$ and $Y_1Y_2Y_3$ as shown in Fig. 5–5(a) with the Y-triad rotated an angle θ about axes 3. The components $\{y\}$ of a vector $\mathbf{A}$ on the Y-triad can be converted to components $\{x\}$ on the X-triad, as we did above.

$$\{x\} = \begin{Bmatrix} x_1 \\ x_2 \\ x_3 \end{Bmatrix} = [\theta]'\{y\}. \tag{5–1}$$

This is the conversion of components from one triad to another triad rotated $-\theta$ about axes 3. This same relationship can be interpreted differently as shown in Fig. 5–5(b). Here we say that $\{x\}$ represents the new components along the original Y-triad of the vector $\mathbf{A}$ after the vector has been rotated an angle θ about axes 3. *Thus, with the same transforma-*

tion, we can think either of rotating the coordinate system $-\theta$ *for a fixed vector or of rotating the vector* $+\theta$ *for a fixed coordinate system.*

Suppose we think of $\mathbf{A}$ as a unit vector $\mathbf{A_1}$ attached to a rigid body so that it points initially in the Y_1 direction (Fig. 5–5c):

$$\{y\} = \{A_1\} = \begin{Bmatrix} 1 \\ 0 \\ 0 \end{Bmatrix}.$$

If the body is rotated θ about axis Y_3, $\mathbf{A_1}$ has the new components along $Y_1 Y_2 Y_3$, as given by Eq. (5–1), and we have

$$\begin{Bmatrix} x_1 \\ x_2 \\ x_3 \end{Bmatrix} = \begin{bmatrix} \cos\theta & -\sin\theta & 0 \\ \sin\theta & \cos\theta & 0 \\ 0 & 0 & 1 \end{bmatrix} \begin{Bmatrix} 1 \\ 0 \\ 0 \end{Bmatrix} = \begin{Bmatrix} \cos\theta \\ \sin\theta \\ 0 \end{Bmatrix}.$$

Note that these are just the direction cosines of the unit vector $\mathbf{A_1}$ on our Y-triad.

We can erect two other unit vectors, $\mathbf{A_2}$ and $\mathbf{A_3}$, in our rigid body so that, before the body is rotated, they are in the Y_2 and Y_3 directions.

$$\{A_2\} = \begin{Bmatrix} 0 \\ 1 \\ 0 \end{Bmatrix}, \qquad \{A_3\} = \begin{Bmatrix} 0 \\ 0 \\ 1 \end{Bmatrix}.$$

We can represent our three unit vectors simultaneously in a square matrix as

$$\begin{bmatrix} 1 & 0 & 0 \\ 0 & 1 & 0 \\ 0 & 0 & 1 \end{bmatrix} = [1].$$

Here they represent the direction cosines of the body triad before rotation. If we rotate the body by θ about Y_3, we can form at once all of the new direction cosines $[\alpha]$ for the rotated triad as

$$\begin{bmatrix} \alpha_{11} & \alpha_{12} & \alpha_{13} \\ \alpha_{21} & \alpha_{22} & \alpha_{23} \\ \alpha_{31} & \alpha_{32} & \alpha_{33} \end{bmatrix} = [\theta]' \begin{bmatrix} 1 & 0 & 0 \\ 0 & 1 & 0 \\ 0 & 0 & 1 \end{bmatrix} = \begin{bmatrix} \cos\theta & -\sin\theta & 0 \\ \sin\theta & \cos\theta & 0 \\ 0 & 0 & 1 \end{bmatrix},$$

or

$$[\alpha] = [\theta]', \tag{5–2a}$$

where the first column represents the direction cosines in our reference triad for A_1, the second for A_2, and the third for A_3.

Alternatively, positive rotation of the body by ϕ about axis Y_2† (Fig. 5–5d) gives the direction cosines for the A-triad

$$[\phi]' = [\phi]^{-1} = \begin{bmatrix} \cos\phi & 0 & \sin\phi \\ 0 & 1 & 0 \\ -\sin\phi & 0 & \cos\phi \end{bmatrix}. \qquad (2\text{–}41)†$$

Going one step further, if the body triad A is originally lined up with the reference triad Y, we can represent the sum of two rotations by first rotating θ about Y_3 to get the direction cosines $[\alpha]$ as

$$[\alpha] = [\theta]'[1]. \qquad (5\text{–}2b)$$

Then a subsequent rotation about Y_2 by ϕ gives the direction cosines $[\bar\alpha]$ as

$$[\bar\alpha] = [\phi]'[\alpha] = [\phi]'[\theta]'[1] = [\phi]'[\theta]'$$

$$= \begin{bmatrix} \cos\phi\cos\theta & -\cos\phi\sin\theta & \sin\phi \\ \sin\theta & \cos\theta & 0 \\ -\sin\phi\cos\theta & \sin\phi\sin\theta & \cos\phi \end{bmatrix}. \qquad (5\text{–}3)$$

Note that a rotation of the body first by ϕ about Y_2 and then θ about Y_3 would give the different set of direction cosines $[\bar{\bar\alpha}]$

$$[\bar{\bar\alpha}] = [\theta]'[\phi]' = \begin{bmatrix} \cos\phi\cos\theta & -\sin\theta & \sin\phi\cos\theta \\ \cos\phi\sin\theta & \cos\theta & \sin\phi\sin\theta \\ -\sin\phi & 0 & \cos\phi \end{bmatrix}. \qquad (5\text{–}4)$$

Again we see that rotations are not vector quantities because the order of addition affects the final orientation.

We are now in a position to find the axis for and the magnitude of the single rotation equivalent to the sum of θ and then ϕ. For this single rotation of the body to the position described by $[\bar\alpha]$ in Eq. (5–3), a vector $\mathbf{R}$ in the body coincident with the axis of this rotation would not be changed.

---

† As used here, ϕ is a positive (right-hand looking out) rotation about axis 2 and is thus opposite in sign to the elevation angle ϕ in the spherical coordinates of Chapter 2. Equation (2–41), as reproduced here, thus has the signs of the sine terms reversed.

Let's look for this vector by stating

$$[\phi]'[\theta]'\{R\} = \{R\}.$$

Since we can always write

$$\{R\} = [1]\{R\},$$

this becomes

$$[[\phi]'[\theta]' - [1]]\{R\} = 0,$$

or

$$\begin{bmatrix} \cos\phi\cos\theta - 1 & -\cos\phi\sin\theta & \sin\phi \\ \sin\theta & \cos\theta - 1 & 0 \\ -\sin\phi\cos\theta & \sin\phi\sin\theta & \cos\phi - 1 \end{bmatrix} \begin{Bmatrix} R_1 \\ R_2 \\ R_3 \end{Bmatrix} = 0. \quad (5\text{--}5a)$$

This is a set of homogeneous algebraic equations in the unknowns R_1, R_2, and R_3. We may remember that, in such a case, we can have nonzero solutions only if the determinant of the coefficients of the unknowns is zero.* If you actually evaluate the determinant formed from the array of terms making up the coefficient matrix, you will find that it is zero. Thus, we can proceed to find two of the unknowns in terms of the third. Let's impose the additional condition that **R** be of unit magnitude,

$$R_1^2 + R_2^2 + R_3^2 = 1, \quad (5\text{--}5b)$$

so that we can interpret $\{R\}$ as the direction cosines of the axis for the single, equivalent rotation. With this condition and the homogeneous equations (5–5a), we can find $\{R\}$ and thus the orientation of the axis for the single, equivalent rotation. Note that there is some ambiguity in this result because **R** can define the axis by pointing either way along it.

To find the magnitude of the single, equivalent rotation, observe that if this single rotation happens to be entirely about axis 3 of a fixed Z-triad, it would be represented by the matrix

$$[\Phi]' = \begin{bmatrix} \cos\Phi & -\sin\Phi & 0 \\ \sin\Phi & \cos\Phi & 0 \\ 0 & 0 & 1 \end{bmatrix},$$

where Φ is the magnitude which we are seeking. In Appendix A, we are

---

* See Sokolnikoff and Redheffer, Ref. 5, Appendix A–2, or Thomas, Ref. 3, Sections 8–6 and 8–7. Also, see in Appendix A, Cramer's rule, Eq. (A–1) and Eq. (A–6) for $\{y\} = \{0\}$.

able to show that two matrices representing, in different reference systems, the same rotation of a rigid body are related by a *similarity transformation** and have equal traces where *the trace of a matrix* is the sum of its diagonal terms. Thus, from the preceding discussion and Eq. (5–3), we can equate traces

$$1 + 2 \cos \Phi = \cos \phi \cos \theta + \cos \theta + \cos \phi,$$

or

$$\cos \Phi = \tfrac{1}{2}(\cos \phi \cos \theta + \cos \theta + \cos \phi - 1). \qquad (5\text{–}5c)$$

Equations (5–5a, b, c) thus define completely the single, equivalent rotation for θ and then ϕ. Note that the Φ for the reverse order of addition is of the same magnitude (but about a different axis) because the trace for Eq. (5–4) is the same as for Eq. (5–3).

EXAMPLE 5–2.   Let's tackle the blackboard eraser manipulation of Example 5–1 using the matrix techniques. Referring to Fig. 5–4, we can call θ the 90° rotation about Z and ϕ the 90° rotation around Y. Thus

$$[\theta]' = \begin{bmatrix} 0 & -1 & 0 \\ 1 & 0 & 0 \\ 0 & 0 & 1 \end{bmatrix}, \qquad [\phi]' = \begin{bmatrix} 0 & 0 & 1 \\ 0 & 1 & 0 \\ -1 & 0 & 0 \end{bmatrix}.$$

For case (a),

$$[\bar{\alpha}] = [\phi]'[\theta]' = \begin{bmatrix} 0 & 0 & 1 \\ 1 & 0 & 0 \\ 0 & 1 & 0 \end{bmatrix}.$$

For case (b),

$$[\bar{\bar{\alpha}}] = [\theta]'[\phi]' = \begin{bmatrix} 0 & -1 & 0 \\ 0 & 0 & 1 \\ -1 & 0 & 0 \end{bmatrix}.$$

For both cases,

$$\Phi = \cos^{-1}(-\tfrac{1}{2}) = 120°.$$

In (a), the axis for the single, equivalent rotation is centered in the first quadrant.

$$R_1 = R_2 = R_3 = \sqrt{\tfrac{1}{3}}.$$

---

* The similarity transformation will come up again when we study the inertia tensor later in this chapter. It has the characteristic form $\Phi = [\gamma][\bar{\alpha}][\gamma]^{-1}$, where $[\gamma]$ is the set of direction cosines for the Z-triad. The third row of $[\gamma]$ is $\{R\}$.

Where is the axis for (b)? (To handle rotations about the body axes of (c), see problems at the end of the chapter and Section 2 of Appendix A.) ▲

There is one more property of angular displacements which we should study before turning to kinematics. It is the change in nature of an angular displacement when it is infinitesimal in size. Let's look at a rotation θ about axis 3 [Eq. (5–2)] in the limit as θ becomes $d\theta$. Discarding terms smaller than first-order differentials, we get

$$\begin{bmatrix} \cos\theta & -\sin\theta & 0 \\ \sin\theta & \cos\theta & 0 \\ 0 & 0 & 1 \end{bmatrix} \rightarrow \begin{bmatrix} 1 & -d\theta & 0 \\ d\theta & 1 & 0 \\ 0 & 0 & 1 \end{bmatrix}.$$

Remembering that the unit matrix produces no rotation at all, we can rewrite this as

$$[1] + [\epsilon_1] = \begin{bmatrix} 1 & 0 & 0 \\ 0 & 1 & 0 \\ 0 & 0 & 1 \end{bmatrix} + \begin{bmatrix} 0 & -d\theta & 0 \\ d\theta & 0 & 0 \\ 0 & 0 & 0 \end{bmatrix}. \tag{5–6a}$$

Similarly, a rotation $d\phi$ about axis 2 is

$$[1] + [\epsilon_2] = \begin{bmatrix} 1 & 0 & 0 \\ 0 & 1 & 0 \\ 0 & 0 & 1 \end{bmatrix} + \begin{bmatrix} 0 & 0 & d\phi \\ 0 & 0 & 0 \\ -d\phi & 0 & 0 \end{bmatrix}. \tag{5–6b}$$

Note that the combination of these infinitesimal rotations is independent of the order of their addition. Thus, remembering that products such as $[\epsilon_1][\epsilon_2]$ are infinitesimal compared to $[\epsilon_1]$ and $[\epsilon_2]$,

$$[[1] + [\epsilon_1]][[1] + [\epsilon_2]] = [1] + [\epsilon_1] + [\epsilon_2]$$

$$= [[1] + [\epsilon_2]][[1] + [\epsilon_1]]$$

$$= \begin{bmatrix} 1 & -d\theta & d\phi \\ d\theta & 1 & 0 \\ -d\phi & 0 & 1 \end{bmatrix}. \tag{5–7}$$

This last form can be obtained in the limit directly from the matrices representing both $[\phi]'[\theta]'$ and $[\theta]'[\phi]'$ [Eqs. (5–3) and (5–4)].

Infinitesimal rotations are thus simpler to handle than finite angular displacements and actually have all the properties of vectors.* While this may seem of small importance, it leads directly to the idea that *angular velocities are vector quantities* since they are just infinitesimal rotations divided by the time interval dt. (When necessary we will designate with bars vectors, such as $\overline{d\theta}$. To avoid implying that θ is a vector, we will not use the customary boldface type.)

5–2 Kinematics. It is perhaps a relief to return to familiar ground with the conclusion that angular velocities are vector quantities. We now see why we must take special care with angular displacements, but our routine treatment of angular velocity as a vector in earlier chapters apparently was justified. This does not mean that angular velocities and their changes are easy to visualize. We are much more familiar with linear motion than angular motion. For example, in Fig. 5–6(a), I suspect that we can quickly say what linear velocity increment should be added to **V** of the ball to change its direction of motion to vertical without changing the magnitude of **V**. In Fig. 5–6(b) the ball is spinning about an axis with the angular velocity **ω**. What change in angular velocity is needed to make the ball spin about a vertical axis at the same rate? Both problems can be solved using the vector diagram in Fig. 5–6(c), but how good was your physical intuition in the angular motion case?

Much in the analysis of rotational motion is analogous to that of linear motion where we found it helpful to watch the movement of the head of the displacement vector **R** along the path and of the velocity vector **v** along the hodograph. In Fig. 2–3(a), we related the direction of the velocity to the tangent to the path and the magnitude to the distance traveled along the path in unit time. In Fig. 2–3(b), the motion of **v** along the hodograph similarly indicated the direction and magnitude of the

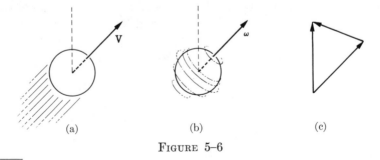

(a)   (b)   (c)

FIGURE 5–6

---

* Sometimes it is necessary to distinguish between vectors and pseudovectors or axial vectors such as infinitesimal angular displacements and even any cross product between two vectors. Their properties are almost identical—see Goldstein, Ref. 2, p. 130.

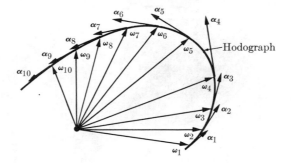

FIG. 5–7. The hodograph in general rotational motion.

linear acceleration **a**. Since angular displacements are not vectors, we have no direct analog of the path. We can construct the hodograph, however, and from it deduce the angular acceleration vector $\boldsymbol{\alpha}$.* Thus in Fig. 5–7, we see angular velocity vectors drawn from a common origin for equal increments of time. The magnitudes and directions of the corresponding angular accelerations are not hard to visualize. The rate of change of an angular velocity vector is, of course, partly stretching and partly swinging just like any other vector. The swinging part, particularly when the magnitude of $\boldsymbol{\omega}$ is constant, has become known as *precession*. The term is often applied to the swinging of other vectors as well.

EXAMPLE 5–3. A relatively simple angular motion is shown in Fig. 5–8(a). The rigid body is spinning about a horizontal shaft at the rate ω_r while the whole shaft system is rotating about the vertical axis at the rate Ω. We can say the body is precessing about the vertical axis. What is the resultant angular velocity $\boldsymbol{\omega}$ of the rigid body? Is it merely the vector sum of $\boldsymbol{\omega}_r$ and $\boldsymbol{\Omega}$? I think you will readily agree if we change the appearance of the problem without changing its character. Think of the precessing body as a cone rolling under an inverted stationary cone as in Fig. 5–8(b). Note that the axis of the angular velocity $\boldsymbol{\omega}$ is at any instant the line of contact of the cones. It is quite reasonable to think here of $\boldsymbol{\omega}$ as the resultant angular velocity with components $\boldsymbol{\Omega}$ and $\boldsymbol{\omega}_r$.

Another path to the same conclusion requires the employment of a rotating observer ③ who is willing to ride on the swinging shaft system. He sees only the spinning motion $\boldsymbol{\omega}_r$. A stationary observer on the ground would say that the observation of ③ is correct so far as it goes, but in order to get absolute angular velocity, we must add his own angular velocity to the rotating observer's observation. Thus, again we get

$$\boldsymbol{\omega} = \boldsymbol{\omega}_r + \boldsymbol{\Omega}.$$

---

* Can you see why angular acceleration is also a vector? Is the rate of change of a vector always a vector?

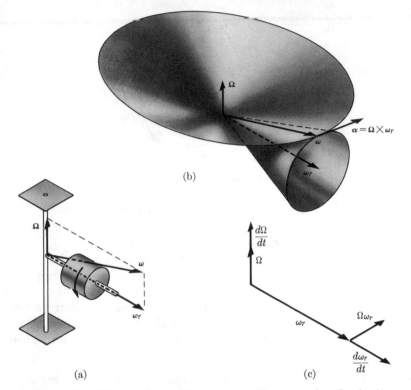

FIG. 5–8.   The angular motion of a steadily precessing flywheel.

If we assume that $\boldsymbol{\omega}_r$ and $\boldsymbol{\Omega}$ are constant in magnitude, what does the hodograph look like? The head of the resultant angular velocity vector $\boldsymbol{\omega}$ is steadily tracing out a circle of radius ω_r. Its rate of change (the velocity of its head along the hodograph) is simply $\Omega\omega_r$ tangent to the hodograph. For this simple motion, we can write

$$\boldsymbol{\alpha} = \frac{d\boldsymbol{\omega}}{dt} = \boldsymbol{\Omega} \times \boldsymbol{\omega}_r.$$

Suppose $\boldsymbol{\Omega}$ and $\boldsymbol{\omega}_r$ are both increasing with time. The hodograph now looks like an expanding rising spiral, and it is a little difficult to visualize quantitatively the magnitude and direction of the angular acceleration $\boldsymbol{\alpha}$. We can find its components easily, however, by watching the changes in $\boldsymbol{\Omega}$ and $\boldsymbol{\omega}_r$, the components of the resultant $\boldsymbol{\omega}$. As shown in Fig. 5–8(c), $\boldsymbol{\Omega}$ is merely stretching at the rate $d\Omega/dt$, but $\boldsymbol{\omega}_r$ is swinging at $\Omega\omega_r$ as well as stretching at $d\omega_r/dt$. ▲

In the last part of the above example you may have had the feeling that matters could be simplified by laying out an XYZ-axis system and talking

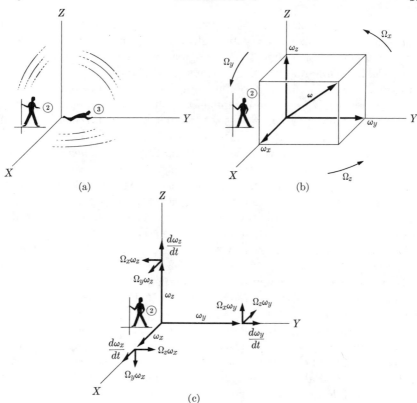

Fig. 5–9. Components of angular velocity and their rates of change along changing reference directions.

only in terms of components rather than resultants. Certainly in that example it is easier to visualize the changing components rather than the gyrating resultant angular velocity $\boldsymbol{\omega}$. We will often find it very useful to employ a set of orthogonal reference directions in analyzing rotational motion but not if their directions are fixed. Note that in the above example the naturally convenient component direction along the horizontal axis is not a fixed direction. It is swinging at the rate $\boldsymbol{\Omega}$. Visualize a fixed set of axes and the corresponding expressions for the $\boldsymbol{\alpha}$ components.

This sort of reasoning leads us to adopt rotating reference directions as a normal tool in studying angular motion despite the complications of keeping track of the axes as well as the rigid body. Of course rotating axes usually imply rotating observers who delight in riding on them. However, the observations of these fellows must always be corrected before being used in Newton's second law, and it is often best to use them only when their point of view is particularly illuminating. In Fig. 5–9(a), we have both a nonrotating observer ② and a rotating observer ③ at the origin of a rotating set of axes. They are sighting along the Y-axis to determine the Y-component of a rigid body's angular velocity (the body and axes in general have different angular motions as in Example 5–3). Observer ③ sees the component about Y of the rotation of the body relative to the axes.* Observer ② sees the component about Y of the absolute angular velocity of the body. He also sees the component about Y of the absolute angular velocity of the axes themselves.

We will normally deal with observer ② and thus *components of absolute angular motion*. Of course these components will be *taken along ever-changing axis directions;* but then, at any instant, we can take components of a vector along any directions that we find to be convenient.

Let's use $\boldsymbol{\omega}$ and $\boldsymbol{\alpha}$ for the absolute angular velocity and acceleration of the rigid body, $\boldsymbol{\omega}'$ and $\boldsymbol{\alpha}'$ where necessary for the observations of ③, and $\boldsymbol{\Omega}$ for the absolute angular velocity of the axes (and thus of ③ when we use him).

To get a general expression for $\boldsymbol{\alpha}$ in component form, we must look at the rates of change of the components of $\boldsymbol{\omega}$. In Fig. 5–9(b) the $\boldsymbol{\omega}$ components are shown along rotating axis directions. If $\boldsymbol{\omega}$ changes, the components will, of course, change. But observe that even if $\boldsymbol{\omega}$ is constant, the components will change with time because the axes directions along which the components are taken will change. Thus the components ω_x, ω_y, ω_z swing with the axes and also stretch in such a way that their resultant is always $\boldsymbol{\omega}$. The possible rates of change of each of the components are sketched in Fig. 5–9(c). The sum of the rates of change in the X-direction of the components must equal that of the resultant, and then we can say

$$\alpha_x = \frac{d\omega_x}{dt} - \Omega_z\omega_y + \Omega_y\omega_z. \tag{5–8}$$

Similarly, for Y and Z,

$$\alpha_y = \frac{d\omega_y}{dt} - \Omega_x\omega_z + \Omega_z\omega_x,$$

$$\alpha_z = \frac{d\omega_z}{dt} - \Omega_y\omega_x + \Omega_x\omega_y. \tag{5–8}$$

Observe that this result can also be obtained directly from the Coriolis theorem where we related the rate of change of a vector $\mathbf{A}$ seen by ② to that seen by ③ who had the angular velocity $\boldsymbol{\Omega}$ as

$$\frac{d\mathbf{A}}{dt} = \frac{d'\mathbf{A}}{dt} + \boldsymbol{\Omega} \times \mathbf{A}. \tag{2–55}$$

---

* See problems at the end of the chapter.

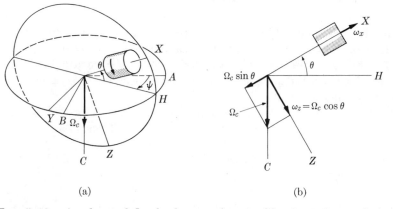

(a)   (b)

FIG. 5–10.   An elevated flywheel precessing steadily about the vertical.

If we replace **A** with the absolute angular velocity **ω** of the body, we get

$$\frac{d\boldsymbol{\omega}}{dt} = \frac{d'\boldsymbol{\omega}}{dt} + \boldsymbol{\Omega} \times \boldsymbol{\omega}.$$

The only rate of change that ③ would see for **ω** (that is for ω_x, ω_y, and ω_z, which he would only observe as a favor to us, because he doesn't identify **ω** as the body's angular velocity) is the stretching of the components, namely

$$\frac{d\omega_x}{dt}, \qquad \frac{d\omega_y}{dt}, \qquad \frac{d\omega_z}{dt}.$$

Note that the remaining terms of Eq. (5–8) come directly from the cross products $\boldsymbol{\Omega} \times \boldsymbol{\omega}$.

(Try applying the above ideas and Eq. (5–8) to the motion in Example 5–3 taking X along the horizontal shaft and Z vertical. When you are satisfied that you understand the ideas, go on to the following example.)

EXAMPLE 5–4. This steady precession is somewhat more complex than the one in the previous example. In this problem let's assume that our spinning flywheel is precessing about the vertical axis C in Fig. 5–10(a) but with the flywheel's axis of symmetry held at a constant angle θ above the horizontal AB-plane.

To help in the description of the flywheel's motion, we can use an axis system whose motion is somewhat less complicated than that of the flywheel so that it offers a convenient set of reference directions. Neither a stationary axis system ABC nor one rigidly connected to the body has the advantages of the following intermediate one. An obvious choice for one axis, say X, is the flywheel's axis of symmetry. We see that Y and Z can then be anywhere in the perpendicular plane. Let's try Y in the horizontal plane AB which puts Z in the vertical plane XC. We can keep track of the position of X by using two of the Euler angles mentioned earlier (Fig. 5–2), ψ for azimuth to the vertical plane XZC, and θ the elevation of X in this plane. The third Euler angle could be used to describe the angular position of the flywheel about X.

With θ held constant, the motion of the XYZ-axis system is simply a rotation about the vertical axis C at the rate Ω_c. Thus,

$$\Omega = \Omega_c,$$

$$\Omega_x = -\Omega_c \sin \theta,$$

$$\Omega_y = 0,$$

$$\Omega_z = \Omega_c \cos \theta.$$

The motion of the flywheel is more complicated. About X it has a given constant angular velocity so that ω_x is a constant. About the instantaneous position of Y, it has no angular velocity, as can be seen in Fig. 5–10(b) in a view along the Y-axis. Keeping θ constant means neither the axes nor the body rotate about Y. About the Z-axis, the body has the same angular velocity as X, which is its axis of symmetry. Thus we have, for the flywheel, the components of absolute angular velocity,

$$\omega_x = \text{constant},$$

$$\omega_y = 0 = \Omega_y,$$

$$\omega_z = \Omega_c \cos \theta = \Omega_z.$$

If we use Eq. (5–8), the components of absolute angular acceleration are

$$\alpha_x = 0,$$

$$\alpha_y = \Omega_c^2 \sin \theta \cos \theta + \omega_x \Omega_c \cos \theta,$$

$$\alpha_z = 0.$$

The convenience of our XYZ rotating axis system is demonstrated by the fact that the components of both angular velocity and acceleration have simple unchanging forms. Would this be so when components are taken along ABC? Note that the angular velocity is entirely in the XZ-plane while the angular acceleration is perpendicular to it along Y. Do you see the analogy between the steady swinging of this angular velocity vector and the steady swinging of the linear velocity of a particle moving steadily in a circular path? In both instances, the acceleration is perpendicular to the velocity.

We can check the results of using Eq. (5–8) by merely watching the swinging of ω_x and ω_z in Fig. 5–10(b). Note that the heads of both ω_x and ω_z are tracing circles around C. The swingings are both in the Y-direction (out of the page) so that they add as

$$\alpha_y = (\omega_x \cos \theta)\Omega_c + (\omega_z \sin \theta)\Omega_c,$$

which is the result we have above. ▲

It can be useful to classify, in our minds, two ways in which XYZ-axis motion can be fruitfully related to rigid-body motion. Of course in many problems, we may have no control over the reference axes we must use so that axis motion and body motion may be essentially unrelated. If we have a choice, however, it is often very convenient to put one axis, such as X, along a particular axis of the body. We did this in the last example and normally will for bodies with any axial symmetry. The consequences of *putting X along a body axis* are that the axis motion is related to the body motion as

$$\Omega_y = \omega_y,$$

$$\Omega_z = \omega_z. \tag{5–9}$$

But, generally,

$$\Omega_x \neq \omega_x.$$

This was true in Example 5–4 and is related to the fact that to keep X along a body axis, we must rotate the axis system about Y and Z at the same rates as the chosen body axis.

As a second relationship we may choose to line up two (and therefore all three) axes with particular body axes. As we will see later in this chapter, *attaching XYZ directly to the body* will often be desirable for bodies lacking much symmetry. In this case the axis motion and the body motion are identical:

$$\boldsymbol{\Omega} = \boldsymbol{\omega}$$

or,

$$\Omega_x = \omega_x,$$

$$\Omega_y = \omega_y, \tag{5–10}$$

$$\Omega_z = \omega_z.$$

Other relationships which we will find useful are those connecting the components of $\boldsymbol{\Omega}$ with the *rates of change of Euler's angles*. So far we have used the Euler angles ψ, θ, and ϕ (Fig. 5–2) to describe the position of our axis system and $\boldsymbol{\Omega}$ to describe its angular motion (Fig. 5–9). Looking at

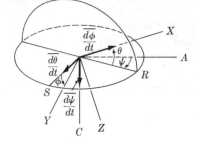

FIG.   5–11.   Rates of change of Euler's angles.

Fig. 5–11, we note that $\overline{d\phi}/dt$ is a vector along X, $\overline{d\theta}/dt$ along S, and $\overline{d\psi}/dt$ along C. But how do they combine to form the absolute angular velocity $\mathbf{\Omega}$ of XYZ?

To see this, I find it very useful to employ a succession of rotating observers. We can ask the first to stand on RS and tell us what he sees, knowing that we will have to add his angular velocity $\overline{d\psi}/dt$ about C to what he tells us. He in turn can ask a friend to keep his feet on S but hold on to X so that, to him, the friend has the angular velocity $\overline{d\theta}/dt$ about S. The friend looks at XYZ and merely sees YZ going around X at the rate $\overline{d\phi}/dt$. This observation must be corrected by our first observer whom we then correct to give

$$\mathbf{\Omega} = \frac{\overline{d\phi}}{dt} + \frac{\overline{d\theta}}{dt} + \frac{\overline{d\psi}}{dt}. \qquad (5\text{--}11a)$$

In terms of components along XYZ this relation becomes,

$$\Omega_x = \frac{d\phi}{dt} - \frac{d\psi}{dt}\sin\theta,$$

$$\Omega_y = \frac{d\theta}{dt}\cos\phi + \frac{d\psi}{dt}\cos\theta\sin\phi, \qquad (5\text{--}11b)$$

$$\Omega_z = -\frac{d\theta}{dt}\sin\phi + \frac{d\psi}{dt}\cos\theta\cos\phi.$$

We can also use our ideas of matrix transformations between coordinate systems to find Eq. (5–11b) and similar relations by noting that $\overline{d\phi}/dt$ is already in XYZ, $\overline{d\theta}/dt$ requires a transformation ϕ (about an axis 1) to XYZ, $\overline{d\psi}/dt$ requires an additional transformation θ (about an axis 2). Thus

$$\begin{Bmatrix} \Omega_x \\ \Omega_y \\ \Omega_z \end{Bmatrix} = \begin{Bmatrix} \dot{\phi} \\ 0 \\ 0 \end{Bmatrix} + [\phi]\begin{Bmatrix} 0 \\ \dot{\theta} \\ 0 \end{Bmatrix} + [\phi][\theta]\begin{Bmatrix} 0 \\ 0 \\ \dot{\psi} \end{Bmatrix}. \qquad (5\text{--}11c)$$

If we want components of $\boldsymbol{\Omega}$ along ABC rather than XYZ, we can get them by

$$\begin{Bmatrix} \Omega_A \\ \Omega_B \\ \Omega_C \end{Bmatrix} = [\psi]'[\theta]'[\phi]' \begin{Bmatrix} \Omega_x \\ \Omega_y \\ \Omega_z \end{Bmatrix}, \tag{5–12a}$$

or by

$$\begin{Bmatrix} \Omega_A \\ \Omega_B \\ \Omega_C \end{Bmatrix} = [\psi]' \begin{Bmatrix} 0 \\ 0 \\ \dot\psi \end{Bmatrix} + [\psi]'[\theta]' \begin{Bmatrix} 0 \\ \dot\theta \\ 0 \end{Bmatrix} + [\psi]'[\theta]'[\phi]' \begin{Bmatrix} \dot\phi \\ 0 \\ 0 \end{Bmatrix}. \tag{5–12b}$$

EXAMPLE 5–5. As an illustration of the use of rotating axes and Euler's angles, we might look at an aircraft in a steady climbing turn to the right. In attaching the XYZ-axis system to the aircraft at its center of mass, we notice a right-left plane of symmetry and decide to put Y perpendicular to it out the right wing. If the pilot is flying a properly coordinated turn, the aircraft velocity vector $\mathbf{v}$ will be in the XZ-plane of symmetry. Let's choose to put X in the direction of $\mathbf{v}$. Thus,

$$v_x = v, \qquad v_y = v_z = 0.$$

The absolute acceleration $\mathbf{a}$ of the center of mass can be expressed as the sum of the rates of change of the components for $\mathbf{v}$ along the moving axes just like $\mathbf{A}$ or $\boldsymbol{\omega}$ in Eq. (5–8). Thus,

$$a_x = \frac{dv_x}{dt} - \Omega_z v_y + \Omega_y v_z,$$

$$a_y = \frac{dv_y}{dt} - \Omega_x v_z + \Omega_z v_x,$$

$$a_z = \frac{dv_z}{dt} - \Omega_y v_x + \Omega_x v_y.$$

To find the components of $\boldsymbol{\Omega}$ along XYZ, note that of the three Euler angles of Fig. 5–11, θ and ϕ are constant in this example so that, from Eq. (5–11b), we get

$$\Omega_x = -\frac{d\psi}{dt} \sin\theta,$$

$$\Omega_y = \frac{d\psi}{dt} \cos\theta \sin\phi,$$

$$\Omega_z = \frac{d\psi}{dt} \cos\theta \cos\phi,$$

where $d\psi/dt$ is the rate of turn. The linear acceleration is then

$$a_x = 0,$$

$$a_y = \Omega_z v = v\frac{d\psi}{dt}\cos\theta\cos\phi,$$

$$a_z = -\Omega_y v = -v\frac{d\psi}{dt}\cos\theta\sin\phi.$$

If we think of the external forces as coming only from the surrounding fluid and gravity, we can write

$$\sum \mathbf{F}_e = \mathbf{F}_{\text{aero}} + \mathbf{F}_{\text{grav}} = m\mathbf{a},$$

where

$$F_{\text{aero}_x} = T - D,$$

$$F_{\text{aero}_y} = 0,$$

$$F_{\text{aero}_z} = -L$$

in terms of thrust T, lift L, and drag D. The gravitational force is in the C-direction like $d\psi/dt$ and gives components in XYZ as

$$\{F_{\text{grav}}\}_{xyz} = [\phi][\theta]\begin{Bmatrix} 0 \\ 0 \\ mg \end{Bmatrix} = mg\begin{Bmatrix} -\sin\theta \\ \cos\theta\sin\phi \\ \cos\theta\cos\phi \end{Bmatrix}.$$

From the resulting Y-equation, we can get, for a coordinated climbing turn,

$$\frac{d\psi}{dt} = \frac{g}{v}\tan\phi.$$

From the Z-equation, we get

$$L = mg\,\frac{\cos\theta}{\cos\phi}.$$

The resultant acceleration is horizontal and comes out to be

$$a = \frac{L}{m}\sin\phi.$$

Do these results agree with your ideas of flying steady climbing turns? To what extent would they apply to the lighthouse keeper of Examples 2–2 and 3–4? ▲

5–3 Inertial properties. When we considered a body to be a single particle, we found we could relate its linear motion to the applied forces through the scalar quantity *mass*. For finite groups of particles in Chapter 4, we conveniently described the general translational motion of the group as related to only the external forces by watching that "average" point we called the *center of mass*. This convenience was largely the result of the assumption that the forces internal to the group summed to zero. For rotational motion of the group (even considered about the center of mass), the relationship between external moments and rate of change of moment of momentum was not very easy to handle, largely because of the difficulty of expressing conveniently the group's average rotational motion.

For that special idealized group called the rigid body, we have been able to discuss in a straightforward way general rotational motion in terms of angular displacements, velocities, and accelerations. These angular quantities along with the many expressions defining the fixed relative separations of the particles in the rigid body suggest the definition of another inertial property often called the *inertia tensor*. Note that we have progressed from the scalar mass, to the vector locating the center of mass, to the tensor representing, as we will see, a second-order mass distribution. From another point of view, we have first simply summed the masses, then taken first moments, and now we will look carefully at second moments.

Although we are already familiar with a second moment in rigid-body planar motion, the moment of inertia about the axis of rotation, let's look quantitatively at the general rotational motion of a rigid body. The required inertial properties must be contained in the expression, derived in Chapter 4, for moment of momentum $\mathbf{H}$ as seen by an observer ② moving with point O of the rigid body,

$$\mathbf{H} = \int_m \mathbf{R} \times (\boldsymbol{\omega} \times \mathbf{R}) \, dm \qquad (4\text{–}7)$$

because this form of $\mathbf{H}$ appeared in the general rotational-motion equation,

$$\sum (\mathbf{R} \times \mathbf{F}_e) = \frac{d\mathbf{H}}{dt} + m(\mathbf{R}_{\text{c.m.}} \times \mathbf{a}_0). \qquad (4\text{–}8)$$

Although Eq. (4–7) has a nice concise vector form, we can gain a better understanding of it if we expand in terms of components along XYZ-axes centered at point O of the rigid body. We can do this by writing $\mathbf{H}$, $\mathbf{R}$, and $\boldsymbol{\omega}$ in terms of the unit vectors $\mathbf{i}$, $\mathbf{j}$, $\mathbf{k}$, and by carrying out the cross products, or we can remember the identity

$$\mathbf{A} \times (\mathbf{B} \times \mathbf{C}) = \mathbf{B}(\mathbf{A} \cdot \mathbf{C}) - \mathbf{C}(\mathbf{A} \cdot \mathbf{B})$$

and write

$$\mathbf{H} = \int_m [\boldsymbol{\omega} R^2 - \mathbf{R}(\mathbf{R} \cdot \boldsymbol{\omega})] \, dm \qquad (5\text{–}13)$$

which quickly becomes, in the X-direction,

$$H_x = \int_m [\omega_x(R^2 - x^2) - xy\omega_y - xz\omega_z]\, dm$$

or,

$$H_x = \omega_x \int (y^2 + z^2)\, dm - \omega_y \int xy\, dm - \omega_z \int xz\, dm,$$

and, similarly,

$$H_y = -\omega_x \int xy\, dm + \omega_y \int (z^2 + x^2)\, dm - \omega_z \int yz\, dm,$$

$$H_z = -\omega_x \int xz\, dm - \omega_y \int yz\, dm + \omega_z \int (x^2 + y^2)\, dm.$$

Note that the integrals have the form of second moments of mass and that for an axis system directly attached to the rigid body, they have unchanging values.

These integrals are usually called *moments and products of inertia* and are given the symbols I and J, respectively. Thus,

$$I_x = \int (y^2 + z^2)\, dm, \qquad\qquad J_{xy} = J_{yx} = \int xy\, dm,$$

$$I_y = \int (z^2 + x^2)\, dm, \qquad\qquad J_{yz} = J_{zy} = \int yz\, dm, \quad (5\text{–}14)$$

$$I_z = \int (x^2 + y^2)\, dm, \qquad\qquad J_{xz} = J_{zx} = \int xz\, dm.$$

In these terms, we can easily see that the components of moment of momentum about a point in the rigid body,

$$H_x = I_x\omega_x - J_{xy}\omega_y - J_{xz}\omega_z,$$

$$H_y = -J_{yx}\omega_x + I_y\omega_y - J_{yz}\omega_z, \qquad\qquad (5\text{–}15\mathrm{a})$$

$$H_z = -J_{zx}\omega_x - J_{zy}\omega_y + I_z\omega_z$$

are linearly related through the moments and products of inertia to the components of angular velocity. In matrix form (ideal for such equations), they become*

$$\begin{Bmatrix} H_x \\ H_y \\ H_z \end{Bmatrix} = \begin{bmatrix} I_x & -J_{xy} & -J_{xz} \\ -J_{yx} & I_y & -J_{yz} \\ -J_{zx} & -J_{zy} & I_z \end{bmatrix} \begin{Bmatrix} \omega_x \\ \omega_y \\ \omega_z \end{Bmatrix}, \qquad (5\text{–}15\mathrm{b})$$

or simply

$$\{H\} = [I]\{\omega\}. \qquad\qquad (5\text{–}15\mathrm{c})$$

---

* Many people define the J's to include the minus sign so that Eq. (5–15a) may appear in simple positive fashion. When using other people's work, be sure to check their definitions.

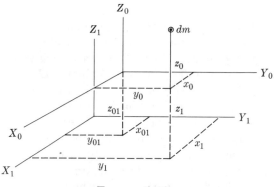

FIGURE 5–12

Note that of the nine elements of the inertia matrix $[I]$ only six are independent because there really are only three products of inertia, not six [Eq. (5–14)].

In more physical terms, we see that the moment of inertia about an axis represents, for each particle in the body, the square of its distance from the axis times its mass. The product of inertia, however, cannot be related to a single axis but rather to a pair of axes or the pair of planes perpendicular to these axes. Although moments of inertia are always positive, products of inertia may have either sign.

If we presume that we are given the inertia properties for axes $X_0 Y_0 Z_0$ with the origin at the center of mass, we can easily find the *inertia properties for a parallel but displaced set of axes* $X_1 Y_1 Z_1$. As shown in Fig. 5–12, we have, for each particle dm in the body, the coordinate transformation

$$x_1 = x_0 + x_{01}, \qquad y_1 = y_0 + y_{01}, \qquad z_1 = z_0 + z_{01}$$

so that, for example,

$$I_{x_1} = \int (y_1^2 + z_1^2)\, dm$$

$$= \int (y_0^2 + z_0^2)\, dm + 2y_{01}\int y_0\, dm + 2z_{01}\int z_0\, dm + \int (y_{01}^2 + z_{01}^2)\, dm,$$

$$J_{y_1 z_1} = \int y_1 z_1\, dm$$

$$= \int y_0 z_0\, dm + y_{01}\int z_0\, dm + z_{01}\int y_0\, dm + \int y_{01} z_{01}\, dm.$$

Using the definition of the center of mass to eliminate some terms, we get, typically,

$$I_{x_1} = I_{x_0} + (y_{01}^2 + z_{01}^2)m, \tag{5–16}$$

$$J_{y_1 z_1} = J_{y_0 z_0} + (y_{01} z_{01})m.$$

In words, the inertia matrix for a set of axes in a rigid body of mass m is that for the parallel set at the center of mass plus the inertia matrix about the origin of a mass m concentrated at the center of mass.*

Before investigating the transformation to a nonparallel axis system, we should look more closely at Eq. (5–15). Although $[I]$ represents a linear transformation, it differs substantially from the rotation matrices (orthogonal transformations) with which we have worked. Whereas they could be interpreted either as rotating a vector in a fixed axis system or rotating the reference system for a fixed vector, only one interpretation is possible here. The inertia matrix represents an operator which transforms one vector $\boldsymbol{\omega}$ into another vector $\mathbf{H}$ of different dimensions and physical significance. Thus $[I]$ has dimensions, does not have a determinant equal to unity, and is not restricted by orthogonality conditions. Nevertheless, it is symmetrical about the main diagonal and must be transformable to any new rotated orthogonal reference system.

Actually, the inertia matrix has those properties peculiar to quantities given the name of *tensor of the second rank*, and such a tensor may be defined according to its properties in an orthogonal transformation. Thus a second-rank tensor T in three-dimensional space transforms term by term from one reference system A to a rotated reference system B as

$$T_{ij}^{B} = \sum_{l,m} \gamma_{il}\gamma_{jm}T_{lm}^{A}, \qquad i, j, l, m = 1, 2, 3, \qquad (5\text{–}17a)$$

where the coefficients γ are just the elements of the rotation matrices that we have been using. In fact, we have been transforming the somewhat simpler quantities, vectors, in much this manner from one coordinate system to another [see Eq. (2–29)]. Observe that the analogous form for vector transformation in this summation notation is simply

$$T_{i}^{B} = \sum_{l} \gamma_{il}T_{l}^{A}, \qquad i, l = 1, 2, 3. \qquad (5\text{–}17b)$$

From this point of view a vector can be called a tensor of the first rank, and going one step further, a scalar is a tensor of zero rank. Tensors of higher rank can easily be defined and when extended to noncartesian coordinates have both covariant and contravariant forms.†

---

* Corollaries and extensions are among the problems at the end of the chapter.

† We will stick to cartesian tensors. Equations (5–17) are usually written without the summation sign with the convention that summations are to be carried out over any repeated indices such as l and m. This notation makes the manipulation of high-rank tensors and of many simultaneous linear equations quite manageable. See various references, such as Goldstein, Ref. 2, pp. 146, 196, and Sokolnikoff and Redheffer, Ref. 5, p. 324.

To investigate the transformation properties of $[I]$, let's look at first the vector $\mathbf{H}$. When written in our usual matrix form rather than in summation form, the vector $\mathbf{H}$ with components $\{H_A\}$ in axis system A is transformed into the components $\{H_B\}$ in rotated system B as

$$\{H_B\} = [\gamma]\{H_A\},$$

where the $[\gamma]$ set of direction cosines is like our special $[\theta]$ and $[\phi]$ sets and our general $[\alpha]'$ set, the transpose of Eq. (5–2). To illustrate the character of $[I]$, let's transform Eq. (5–15c) from components in axis system A to components in axis system B. We start with

$$\{H_A\} = [I_A]\{\omega_A\}.$$

If we premultiply both sides by the rotation matrix $[\gamma]$ between axis sets A and B, we have

$$[\gamma]\{H_A\} = [\gamma][I_A]\{\omega_A\}.$$

But we know that

$$[\gamma]^{-1}[\gamma] = [1]$$

and that multiplication by $[1]$ produces no changes, so we can write

$$[\gamma]\{H_A\} = [\gamma][I_A][\gamma]^{-1}[\gamma]\{\omega_A\}.$$

In general we can write in system B

$$\{H_B\} = [I_B]\{\omega_B\},$$

which by comparison gives the expected result that the transformation of the inertia tensor is more complicated than that of a vector, and it is just

$$[I_B] = [\gamma][I_A][\gamma]^{-1}. \tag{5–18a}$$

This transformation which is characteristic of a tensor quantity is called a *similarity transformation*.* Remembering that for these orthogonal transformations

$$[\gamma]^{-1} = [\gamma]',$$

that is, the inverse is merely the transpose, we see that the similarity transformation takes the form

$$[I_B] = [\gamma][I_A][\gamma]'. \tag{5–18b}$$

---

* See Appendix A.

This is identical with the summation form Eq. (5–17a) for the general tensor of second rank T_{ij}.

We can use this similarity transformation to find directly the I's and J's in terms of a tilted axis system B from known values in system A because $[\gamma]$ is just the transpose of the direction cosine matrix $[\alpha]$ we have been using regularly [see Eq. (A–17) in Appendix A].

$$[\gamma] = \begin{bmatrix} \gamma_{11} & \gamma_{12} & \gamma_{13} \\ \gamma_{21} & \gamma_{22} & \gamma_{23} \\ \gamma_{31} & \gamma_{32} & \gamma_{33} \end{bmatrix} = [\alpha]' = \begin{bmatrix} \alpha_{11} & \alpha_{21} & \alpha_{31} \\ \alpha_{12} & \alpha_{22} & \alpha_{32} \\ \alpha_{13} & \alpha_{23} & \alpha_{33} \end{bmatrix}. \quad (5\text{–}19)$$

Note that the direction cosines of the tilted axis 1 are γ_{11}, γ_{12}, γ_{13} or, as defined earlier [after Eq. (5–2b)], α_{11}, α_{21}, α_{31}. To expand the similarity transformation [Eq. (5–18b)] for the first term of $[I_B]$, we need only evaluate the rows and columns which contribute to it. Thus,

$$I_{x_B} = \lfloor \gamma_{11} \quad \gamma_{12} \quad \gamma_{13} \rfloor \begin{bmatrix} I_x & -J_{xy} & -J_{xz} \\ -J_{yx} & I_y & -J_{yz} \\ -J_{zx} & -J_{zy} & I_z \end{bmatrix} \begin{Bmatrix} \gamma_{11} \\ \gamma_{12} \\ \gamma_{13} \end{Bmatrix}$$

$$= \left\lfloor \begin{pmatrix} \gamma_{11}I_x - \gamma_{12}J_{yx} \\ -\gamma_{13}J_{zx} \end{pmatrix} \begin{pmatrix} -\gamma_{11}J_{xy} + \gamma_{12}I_y \\ -\gamma_{13}J_{zy} \end{pmatrix} \begin{pmatrix} -\gamma_{11}J_{xz} - \gamma_{12}J_{yz} \\ +\gamma_{13}I_z \end{pmatrix} \right\rfloor$$

$$\times \begin{Bmatrix} \gamma_{11} \\ \gamma_{12} \\ \gamma_{13} \end{Bmatrix},$$

where the subscript A is not indicated in each term of $[I_A]$. Finishing the expansion and collecting terms, we get

$$I_{x_B} = \gamma_{11}^2 I_x + \gamma_{12}^2 I_y + \gamma_{13}^2 I_z - 2\gamma_{11}\gamma_{12}J_{xy}$$

$$- 2\gamma_{12}\gamma_{13}J_{yz} - 2\gamma_{13}\gamma_{11}J_{zx}. \quad (5\text{–}18c)$$

Here I_{x_B} is expressed in terms of the direction cosines in system A of the tilted axis X_B and the given inertia properties expressed in system A. Similar expressions can be evaluated for the other moments and products of inertia.

EXAMPLE 5–6. To relate some of these ideas to a familiar situation, we can return to the precessing flywheel of Fig. 5–8 in Example 5–3. Shown

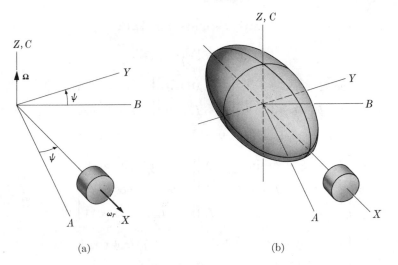

FIG. 5-13.   The precessing flywheel and its ellipsoid of inertia.

again in Fig. 5-13(a) with a fixed set of axes ABC and an azimuth angle ψ, we will presume to know the flywheel's inertia tensor in XYZ and try to find its form in ABC. Actually the I's and J's in XYZ can be calculated without too much trouble for a homogeneous flywheel of known dimensions directly from the definitions [Eq. (5-14)]. Try calculating the J's, for instance, and show to yourself that they are zero.

We can write the given inertia matrix for any instant as

$$[I]_{xyz} = \begin{bmatrix} I_x & 0 & 0 \\ 0 & I_y & 0 \\ 0 & 0 & I_z \end{bmatrix}.$$

The direction cosines of the fixed axes ABC correspond to a negative rotation* about axis 3 of amount ψ. Then $[\gamma]$ is [Eqs. (5-2) and (5-19)]

$$[\gamma] = \begin{bmatrix} \cos\psi & \cos(90+\psi) & 0 \\ \cos(90-\psi) & \cos\psi & 0 \\ 0 & 0 & 1 \end{bmatrix} = \begin{bmatrix} \cos\psi & -\sin\psi & 0 \\ \sin\psi & \cos\psi & 0 \\ 0 & 0 & 1 \end{bmatrix}.$$

Remember that the first row across represents the direction cosines of A, the second B, and the third C. When we use the similarity transformation

* See $[\theta]'$ in Eq. (5-1) and its first interpretation in Fig. 5-5(a).

Eq. (5–18b), the inertia matrix becomes, for ABC,

$$[I]_{ABC} = [\gamma][I]_{xyz}[\gamma]',$$

$$[I]_{ABC} = \begin{bmatrix} \cos\psi & -\sin\psi & 0 \\ \sin\psi & \cos\psi & 0 \\ 0 & 0 & 1 \end{bmatrix} \begin{bmatrix} I_x & 0 & 0 \\ 0 & I_y & 0 \\ 0 & 0 & I_z \end{bmatrix} \begin{bmatrix} \cos\psi & \sin\psi & 0 \\ -\sin\psi & \cos\psi & 0 \\ 0 & 0 & 1 \end{bmatrix}$$

$$= \begin{bmatrix} I_x\cos\psi & -I_y\sin\psi & 0 \\ I_x\sin\psi & I_y\cos\psi & 0 \\ 0 & 0 & I_z \end{bmatrix} \begin{bmatrix} \cos\psi & \sin\psi & 0 \\ -\sin\psi & \cos\psi & 0 \\ 0 & 0 & 1 \end{bmatrix}$$

$$= \begin{bmatrix} I_x\cos^2\psi + I_y\sin^2\psi & (I_x - I_y)\sin\psi\cos\psi & 0 \\ (I_x - I_y)\sin\psi\cos\psi & I_x\sin^2\psi + I_y\cos^2\psi & 0 \\ 0 & 0 & I_z \end{bmatrix}$$

$$= \begin{bmatrix} \dfrac{I_x + I_y}{2} + \dfrac{I_x - I_y}{2}\cos 2\psi & (I_x - I_y)\dfrac{\sin 2\psi}{2} & 0 \\ (I_x - I_y)\dfrac{\sin 2\psi}{2} & \dfrac{I_x + I_y}{2} - \dfrac{I_x - I_y}{2}\cos 2\psi & 0 \\ 0 & 0 & I_z \end{bmatrix}$$

$$= \begin{bmatrix} I_A & -J_{AB} & -J_{AC} \\ -J_{BA} & I_B & -J_{BC} \\ -J_{CA} & -J_{CB} & I_C \end{bmatrix}.$$

Of course I_z is unchanged by the transformation and becomes I_C. Note that J_{AB} becomes zero every 90° and that both I_A and I_B have a periodicity of 180° in ψ. Note also that I_x, I_y, and I_z are independent of time if the flywheel is fully symmetrical about X. If you are familiar with the graphical Mohr's circle technique for plane stresses, you will notice that it could be applied here in the XY-AB-plane for this simple tensor transformation. ▲

The transformation of tensor quantities is not as easy to visualize as that of vector quantities which can be represented by sized and directed lines in space. The second-rank tensor has nine elements compared with three for the first-rank tensor, or vector. Of course the scalar has only one element and can be represented simply by a number. If we are to find a geometric representation for a second-rank tensor, it must be a considerable generalization of the directed line. Perhaps it is a three-dimensional surface with more than one characteristic direction.

In order to investigate further, let's search our memories for our knowledge of the analytic geometry of three-dimensional surfaces. We can also look at the expression for the moment of inertia I about a single axis tilted with respect to XYZ and with direction cosines γ_1, γ_2, γ_3 as a slightly simplified form of Eq. (5–18c),

$$I = \gamma_1^2 I_x + \gamma_2^2 I_y + \gamma_3^2 I_z - 2\gamma_1\gamma_2 J_{xy} - 2\gamma_2\gamma_3 J_{yz} - 2\gamma_3\gamma_1 J_{zx}.$$

Here I is seen to be related to the tilt of the axis through the given elements of $[I]_{xyz}$. If this represents a surface, it is hard to see because we are not used to describing surfaces in terms of direction cosines. Dividing by I and rearranging, we get

$$1 = I_x\left(\frac{\gamma_1}{\sqrt{I}}\right)^2 + I_y\left(\frac{\gamma_2}{\sqrt{I}}\right)^2 + I_z\left(\frac{\gamma_3}{\sqrt{I}}\right)^2$$

$$- 2J_{xy}\frac{\gamma_1}{\sqrt{I}}\frac{\gamma_2}{\sqrt{I}} - 2J_{yz}\frac{\gamma_2}{\sqrt{I}}\frac{\gamma_3}{\sqrt{I}} - 2J_{zx}\frac{\gamma_3}{\sqrt{I}}\frac{\gamma_1}{\sqrt{I}}.$$

If we now think of $1/\sqrt{I}$ as a length plotted along the tilted axis,

$$\frac{\gamma_1}{\sqrt{I}}, \qquad \frac{\gamma_2}{\sqrt{I}}, \qquad \frac{\gamma_3}{\sqrt{I}}$$

are the components of this length along X, Y, Z. If we give them the more familiar symbols x_I, y_I, z_I, the equation becomes

$$1 = I_x x_I^2 + I_y y_I^2 + I_z z_I^2 - 2J_{xy}x_I y_I - 2J_{yz}y_I z_I - 2J_{zx}z_I x_I,$$

which is the equation of an ellipsoidal surface. You may recall the equation in the form

$$\frac{x^2}{a^2} + \frac{y^2}{b^2} + \frac{z^2}{c^2} = 1,$$

but there you were using the very special axis system which coincided with the principal axes of the ellipsoid. The fact that the cross product terms appear in tilted axis systems is the subject of some problems at the end of the chapter.

Now let's draw some very useful conclusions. If for any point of a rigid body we plot along each axis through that point the reciprocal of the square root of the body's moment of inertia about that axis, we will always generate an ellipsoid called the *ellipsoid of inertia*. Since we know that for at least one set of reference axes through this point the equation for the ellipsoidal surface contains no cross product terms, and since x_I, y_I, z_I are never zero, the coefficients J_{xy}, J_{yz}, J_{zx} must disappear for these axes. This set of axes for which the products of inertia are zero are called the *principal axes* and are the main axes of the ellipsoid. The moments of inertia about the principal axes for a given origin represent the extreme values (or stationary values) for axes through that point. Note that there is an ellipsoid of inertia and a set of principal axes for every point in or associated with a rigid body. The set for the center of mass is called central.

In terms of the set of principal axes, the inertia matrix for the given point in the rigid body takes on a simple diagonal form,

$$[I]_{\text{principal}} = \begin{bmatrix} I_x & 0 & 0 \\ 0 & I_y & 0 \\ 0 & 0 & I_z \end{bmatrix}, \tag{5-20}$$

and moment of momentum is very simply related to angular velocity,

$$\{H\} = [I]_{\text{principal}} \{\omega\} = \begin{Bmatrix} I_x\omega_x \\ I_y\omega_y \\ I_z\omega_z \end{Bmatrix}. \tag{5-21}$$

The use of principal axes of inertia can thus greatly simplify the handling of rotational motion of rigid bodies. Also the representation of the moment of inertia variation for different axes through a point in terms of an ellipsoidal surface will help us to visualize the locations of the principal axes, particularly when the mass symmetries of the body follow from its geometric symmetries.

EXAMPLE 5-7. Let's find for the flywheel of the previous example the ellipsoid of inertia associated with the origin of XYZ. Note that the inertia matrix is already diagonal so that XYZ must be a set of principal axes. Note also (Fig. 5-13a) that from symmetry I_y and I_z are equal and are much larger than I_x. Therefore the X-axis of the ellipsoid is much larger than the Y- and Z-axes (as shown in Fig. 5-13b), and it is a surface of revolution about X. Note also that A and B are nonprincipal axes and that $J_{AB} = J_{BA} \neq 0$. How about C? Is it principal?

We should recognize that many other physical quantities have the qualifications to be called second-rank tensors, among them stress and strain in elasticity. They too can be represented by ellipsoidal surfaces and have principal axes or directions for which the nondiagonal terms (such as shear stress) are zero. The fact that the trace of the matrix (sum of diagonal terms) for such a tensor is invariant under orthogonal transformations* is related to such useful physical concepts as bulk stress in elasticity and pressure in fluids. It also helps us to set up a general analytical procedure for *finding the principal directions and moments of inertia.*

The procedure is much the same as the one in Section 5–1 for finding the single, equivalent rotation except that the rotation matrix has only one real eigenvalue or characteristic value, and it is of unit size. By comparison, we expect the inertia matrix to have three real eigenvalues corresponding to the three principal moments of inertia. In matrix terms, we are looking for the orthogonal transformation $[\gamma]$ which diagonalizes the inertia matrix,

$$[\gamma][I][\gamma]' = [\,\diagdown I\diagdown]. \qquad (5\text{--}22)$$

If we premultiply by $[\gamma]'$ so that

$$[I][\gamma]' = [\gamma]'[\,\diagdown I\diagdown],$$

and then expand, with ABC the principal axes, we have

$$[I]\begin{bmatrix} \gamma_{11} & \gamma_{21} & \gamma_{31} \\ \gamma_{12} & \gamma_{22} & \gamma_{32} \\ \gamma_{13} & \gamma_{23} & \gamma_{33} \end{bmatrix} = \begin{bmatrix} \gamma_{11} & \gamma_{21} & \gamma_{31} \\ \gamma_{12} & \gamma_{22} & \gamma_{32} \\ \gamma_{13} & \gamma_{23} & \gamma_{33} \end{bmatrix}\begin{bmatrix} I_A & 0 & 0 \\ 0 & I_B & 0 \\ 0 & 0 & I_C \end{bmatrix}$$

$$\doteq \begin{bmatrix} I_A\gamma_{11} & I_B\gamma_{21} & I_C\gamma_{31} \\ I_A\gamma_{12} & I_B\gamma_{22} & I_C\gamma_{32} \\ I_A\gamma_{13} & I_B\gamma_{23} & I_C\gamma_{33} \end{bmatrix}.$$

Equating corresponding first columns gives

$$[I]\begin{Bmatrix} \gamma_{11} \\ \gamma_{12} \\ \gamma_{13} \end{Bmatrix} = I_A\begin{Bmatrix} \gamma_{11} \\ \gamma_{12} \\ \gamma_{13} \end{Bmatrix} = \begin{bmatrix} I_A & 0 & 0 \\ 0 & I_A & 0 \\ 0 & 0 & I_A \end{bmatrix}\begin{Bmatrix} \gamma_{11} \\ \gamma_{12} \\ \gamma_{13} \end{Bmatrix}.$$

Collecting terms on one side, we obtain

$$\begin{bmatrix} I_x - I_A & -J_{xy} & -J_{xz} \\ -J_{yx} & I_y - I_A & -J_{yz} \\ -J_{zx} & -J_{zy} & I_z - I_A \end{bmatrix}\begin{Bmatrix} \gamma_{11} \\ \gamma_{12} \\ \gamma_{13} \end{Bmatrix} = 0. \qquad (5\text{--}23)$$

---

* See general proof in Appendix A. The special case of the inertia tensor is a problem at the end of the chapter.

Thus, we have a set of homogeneous linear algebraic equations in the direction cosines of principal axis A. For a nonzero solution for the direction cosines, the determinant of their coefficients must vanish [see Eq. (5–5a)]. Thus,

$$\begin{vmatrix} I_x - I_A & -J_{xy} & -J_{xz} \\ -J_{yx} & I_y - I_A & -J_{yz} \\ -J_{zx} & -J_{zy} & I_z - I_A \end{vmatrix} = 0, \qquad (5\text{–}24)$$

which gives us a cubic polynomial in I_A. Realize that if we had proceeded instead with I_B or I_C, we would have obtained the same polynomial. The three solutions of this equation are then the magnitudes I_A, I_B, and I_C of the principal moments of inertia. The directions of the principal axes can be determined from Eq. (5–23) once I_A, I_B, and I_C are known if we use the usual additional relation among the direction cosines of any axis:

$$\sum \gamma_i^2 = 1, \qquad i = 1, 2, 3.$$

Very often one principal axis of a body, particularly for its center of mass, can be located by observing the inherent symmetries of the body. If one principal axis is found in this manner, the remaining problem is a two-dimensional one, as illustrated in the next example. ▲

EXAMPLE 5–8. It is a characteristic of most vehicles that they have a vertical plane of symmetry cutting fore-and-aft through the center of mass. Except for minor details, the left-hand side is a mirror image of the right in automobiles, ships, submarines, and aircraft. If we place the Y-axis perpendicular to this plane of symmetry through the center of mass with

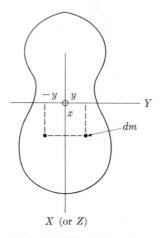

FIG. 5–14. A rigid body with XZ a plane of symmetry.

the origin in the plane of symmetry, we can quickly show that J_{xy} and J_{xz} are both zero and that therefore Y is the principal axis B.

Look at the body in Fig. 5–14 which has an XZ-plane of symmetry. The contribution of each particle dm to the product of inertia

$$J_{xy} = \int_m xy \; dm$$

is exactly cancelled by the corresponding particle on the other side of the plane of symmetry. Thus J_{xy} and similarly J_{yz} sum to zero, and Y is a principal axis.

To find the other two principal axes, we can use Eqs. (5–23) and (5–24) in reduced form. Solving now for I_A, we get

$$\begin{vmatrix} I_x - I_A & 0 & -J_{xz} \\ 0 & I_y - I_A & 0 \\ -J_{zx} & 0 & I_z - I_A \end{vmatrix} = 0,$$

or

$$(I_y - I_A)[(I_x - I_A)(I_z - I_A) - J_{zx}^2] = 0.$$

From the second bracket, we see that

$$I_A^2 - (I_x + I_z)I_A + I_x I_z - J_{zx}^2 = 0,$$

$$I_A = \frac{I_x + I_z}{2} \pm \sqrt{\left(\frac{I_x + I_z}{2}\right)^2 - (I_x I_z - J_{zx}^2)}$$

$$= \frac{I_x + I_z}{2} \pm \sqrt{\left(\frac{I_x - I_z}{2}\right)^2 + J_{zx}^2}.$$

If the plus sign is chosen for I_A, the minus is for I_C, and Eq. (5–23) becomes for I_A, where θ is the angle from X to A in the XZ-plane,

$$\begin{bmatrix} I_x - I_A & 0 & -J_{zx} \\ 0 & I_y - I_A & 0 \\ -J_{zx} & 0 & I_z - I_A \end{bmatrix} \begin{Bmatrix} \cos\theta \\ 0 \\ -\sin\theta \end{Bmatrix} = 0,$$

or

$$(I_x - I_A)\cos\theta = -J_{zx}\sin\theta,$$
$$-(I_z - I_A)\sin\theta = J_{zx}\cos\theta.$$

Either equation can be used to find θ.

An alternative form for I_A, I_B, and θ, where we first solve for θ and then I_A and I_C, can be derived by eliminating I_A from the pair of equations to give

$$\tan 2\theta = \frac{2J_{zx}}{I_x - I_z}.$$

Knowing θ, we can solve for I_A as

$$I_A = \frac{I_x + I_z}{2} + \frac{I_x - I_z}{2} \cos 2\theta + J_{zx} \sin 2\theta.$$

Similarly,

$$I_C = \frac{I_x + I_z}{2} - \frac{I_x - I_z}{2} \cos 2\theta - J_{zx} \sin 2\theta.$$

These last three forms are easily interpreted as a graphical solution usually called Mohr's circle. ▲

An ellipsoid is a rather symmetrical shape having at least three planes of symmetry passing through its center even if its principal axes are of different lengths. When two of its principal axes are equal, the ellipsoid is a surface of revolution about the third axis, and any perpendicular pair of axes in this plane perpendicular to the axis of revolution can be used as principal axes. If all three of the ellipsoid's axes are equal in length, the surface reduces to a sphere for which any set of orthogonal axes through the ellipsoid's center can be employed as a principal set.

We have already seen that the ellipsoid of inertia associated with the origin of the precessing flywheel was axially symmetric (Fig. 5–13b) so that Y and Z are principal regardless of the orientation of the flywheel about X. For many other *rigid bodies with mass symmetry deriving from geometric symmetry*, determining the location of principal axes is equally simple and straightforward. Note that in Example 5–8 we have already proved that an *axis perpendicular to a plane of symmetry* is a principal axis for the point of intersection of the plane and the axis. As a further step, observe that for the flywheel in Fig. 5–13(b) all planes containing the X-axis are planes of symmetry and therefore *any axis perpendicular to an axis of symmetry* can be considered principal for the point of intersection. This also implies that the axis of symmetry itself is a principal one.

These ideas can be extended to bodies with partial rotational symmetry in the sense of the three-bladed propeller. It can be rotated 120° either way about its shaft axis and will appear to be in its original position. This property is sometimes called trigonal symmetry. We can show that if a body has trigonal or higher symmetry, its ellipsoid of inertia for a point on its axis is a surface of revolution about the axis of symmetry. To illus-

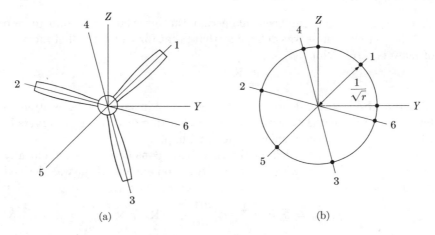

FIG. 5–15. A three-bladed propeller and the intersection with the YZ-plane of its inertial ellipsoid.

trate look at the three-bladed propeller in Fig. 5–15(a). Despite the twist and camber of the blades, we can say that the moment of inertia must be the same about equally spaced axes 1, 2, and 3. We can then plot three points on the intersection of the ellipsoid of inertia with the YZ-plane by marking equidistant points along 1, 2, and 3 (Fig. 5–15b). We can also plot points at the same radius on axes 4, 5, and 6 because they are really the same as 1, 2, and 3. The only ellipse centered at the origin which will go through all six equally spaced points is a circle. Thus the ellipsoid of inertia is axially symmetric about X, so that X is a principal axis and so are any two perpendicular axes YZ. The same reasoning holds for N-bladed propellers including turbines and compressors if N is 3 or larger. How about the two-bladed propeller? What does its ellipsoid of inertia look like?

5–4 Dynamical equations. We have now become familiar with the techniques of describing both the motion and the inertia properties of rigid bodies and are ready to apply them to writing equations of motion in the most useful forms. Thinking of the rigid body as a special case of the finite group of particles with only six independent coordinates or degrees of freedom, we need two vector or six scalar equations of motion to completely describe its behavior.

The *translational motion* of the body is, of course, best handled in terms of the *absolute acceleration of the center of mass*. As derived in Chapter 4, we can write

$$\sum \mathbf{F}_e = m\mathbf{a}_{\text{c.m.}} \qquad (5\text{–}25)$$

in terms of external forces and the total mass m of the body. Remember that the assumption has been made that the internal forces sum to zero and the center of mass was defined as that point for which the first moment of mass is zero. Thus

$$\int_m \mathbf{R} \, dm = 0.$$

Also the absolute acceleration of the center of mass may be written in terms of the corrected observations of accelerating or rotating observers in whatever manner is convenient (refer to Chapter 2).

With the *rotational motion* of the rigid body considered to be about any point moving directly with the body, the moment equation was derived in Chapter 4 as

$$\sum \mathbf{M}_e = \sum \mathbf{R} \times \mathbf{F}_e = \frac{d\mathbf{H}}{dt} + m\mathbf{R}_{\text{c.m.}} \times \mathbf{a}_0, \qquad (4\text{-}8)$$

where again we assumed that the internal forces cancelled. Here $\mathbf{a}_0$ is the acceleration of the chosen reference point of the body with $\mathbf{R}$ and $\mathbf{H}$ as seen by a nonrotating observer ② moving with this point. In the previous section, $\mathbf{H}$ was written as

$$\mathbf{H} = \int_m \mathbf{R} \times (\boldsymbol{\omega} \times \mathbf{R}) \, dm, \qquad (4\text{-}7)$$

or

$$\{H\} = [I]\{\omega\} = \begin{Bmatrix} I_x\omega_x - J_{xy}\omega_y - J_{xz}\omega_z \\ I_y\omega_y - J_{yz}\omega_z - J_{yx}\omega_x \\ I_z\omega_z - J_{zx}\omega_x - J_{zy}\omega_y \end{Bmatrix}, \qquad (5\text{-}15)$$

where $\boldsymbol{\omega}$ is the absolute angular velocity of the rigid body.

In most applications of the moment equation, the correction term $m\mathbf{R}_{\text{c.m.}} \times \mathbf{a}_0$ *can be made zero* because of the appropriate choice of origin in the body. In general, we can do this three ways:

(a) by putting the origin at the center of mass of the body so that $\mathbf{R}_{\text{c.m.}} = 0$;

(b) by putting the origin at an unaccelerated (or fixed) point of the body so that $\mathbf{a}_0 = 0$; or, less often,

(c) by using as origin a point in the body whose acceleration has no moment about the center of mass.

Nevertheless, in some applications it may be more useful to put the origin at a point whose acceleration is known but not directed through the center of mass in order to eliminate the moments of unknown external forces applied at the accelerating origin. In the writing of alternative forms of the moment equation on the next few pages, we will assume that an acceptable origin has been chosen; that is, that $\mathbf{R}_{\text{c.m.}} \times \mathbf{a}_0$ vanishes. You can put it in again if you need it.

For certain applications such as *gyros*, it is often convenient to leave the moment equation in vector form, particularly when **H** is essentially constant in magnitude but is precessing at the rate **Ω**. In this case, we can say that the applied moment is related just to the swinging of **H** as

$$\sum \mathbf{M}_e = \mathbf{\Omega} \times \mathbf{H}, \tag{5–26a}$$

and we will use this form in the next chapter.

For most other applications, the equation is best written in component form. These components can be taken *along fixed axis directions* to give

$$\sum M_{x_e} = \frac{dH_x}{dt} = \frac{d}{dt}(I_x \omega_x - J_{xy} \omega_y - J_{xz} \omega_z),$$

$$\sum M_{y_e} = \frac{dH_y}{dt} = \frac{d}{dt}(I_y \omega_y - J_{yz} \omega_z - J_{yx} \omega_x), \tag{5–26b}$$

$$\sum M_{z_e} = \frac{dH_z}{dt} = \frac{d}{dt}(I_z \omega_z - J_{zx} \omega_x - J_{zy} \omega_y).$$

In this form, we need look only at the stretching of the H-components, but this is a deceiving simplicity. With the body moving relative to the axes, the I's and J's become functions of time and the evaluation of the equations can be tedious, to say the least.

If we take components *along rotating axis directions*, we may, if we use our intelligence, obtain a more useful set of equations. Assuming at first an arbitrary angular velocity **Ω** for our axis system, we will then specialize to various simpler forms. Since the components of **H** must swing with the axes as well as stretch (see similar treatment of the vectors **ω** and **v** in Section 5–2), we get

$$\sum M_{x_e} = \frac{dH_x}{dt} - \Omega_z H_y + \Omega_y H_z,$$

$$\sum M_{y_e} = \frac{dH_y}{dt} - \Omega_x H_z + \Omega_z H_x, \tag{5–26c}$$

$$\sum M_{z_e} = \frac{dH_z}{dt} - \Omega_y H_x + \Omega_x H_y,$$

where the expanded form of the first component looks like

$$\sum M_{x_e} = \frac{d}{dt}(I_x \omega_x - J_{xy} \omega_y - J_{xz} \omega_z)$$
$$- \Omega_z(I_y \omega_y - J_{yz} \omega_z - J_{yx} \omega_x)$$
$$+ \Omega_y(I_z \omega_z - J_{zx} \omega_x - J_{zy} \omega_y).$$

Clearly, if we are foolish in our choice of angular motion **Ω** of the axes, we have a mess on our hands. However, we also have the opportunity to insist that the axes always coincide with principal axis directions. By this process we can eliminate all the J-terms. *Using principal axes* will put more or less of a restriction on possible motions of the axis system, depending on the degree of mass symmetry of the rigid body for the chosen origin. *If the ellipsoid of inertia has no axial symmetry* at all, there are only three principal axes through the origin. If we put XYZ along them and want to keep them coincident, we must make the axes rotate with the body,

$$\Omega = \omega,$$

so that

$$M_{x_e} = I_x \frac{d\omega_x}{dt} - (I_y - I_z)\omega_y\omega_z,$$

$$M_{y_e} = I_y \frac{d\omega_y}{dt} - (I_z - I_x)\omega_z\omega_x, \qquad (5\text{--}26\text{d})$$

$$M_{z_e} = I_z \frac{d\omega_z}{dt} - (I_x - I_y)\omega_x\omega_y.$$

These equations were quite important historically and are often called *Euler's dynamical equations.*

If our rigid body has enough symmetry so that, for the chosen origin, the *ellipsoid of inertia has an axis of symmetry*, we can be less restrictive about the motion of the axis system and yet have the axes always in principal directions. Remember that for an inertial ellipsoid of revolution, any perpendicular pair of axes which are both also perpendicular to the ellipsoid's axis of symmetry can be considered principal. Thus, we need only specify that one axis, say X, be made to follow the body's axis of mass symmetry and the other pair will always be principal too, regardless of the body's orientation around X. We looked at this situation in Section 5–2 and found that the necessary relationship between Ω and ω is for X to continually coincide with the body axis,

$$\Omega_y = \omega_y, \qquad \Omega_z = \omega_z, \qquad \Omega_x \neq \omega_x. \qquad (5\text{--}9)$$

The appropriate form of the moment equation is then, remembering that $I_y = I_z$,

$$M_x = I_x \frac{d\omega_x}{dt},$$

$$M_y = I_y \frac{d\Omega_y}{dt} - \Omega_x I_z \Omega_z + \Omega_z I_x \omega_x, \qquad (5\text{--}26\text{e})$$

$$M_z = I_z \frac{d\Omega_z}{dt} - \Omega_y I_x \omega_x + \Omega_x I_y \Omega_y.$$

Similar forms can be derived if Y or Z is chosen for the axis of mass symmetry.

Of course, if our rigid body has a *spherical ellipsoid of inertia* for the point at the origin, the equations become very simple because

$$I_x = I_y = I_z = I, \qquad J_{xy} = J_{yz} = J_{zz} = 0,$$

and

$$M_{x_e} = I\left(\frac{d\omega_x}{dt} - \Omega_z\omega_y + \Omega_y\omega_z\right) = I\alpha_x,$$

$$M_{y_e} = I\alpha_y, \qquad\qquad\qquad (5\text{–}26\text{f})$$

$$M_{z_e} = I\alpha_z,$$

or

$$\mathbf{M}_e = I\boldsymbol{\alpha}. \qquad\qquad (5\text{–}26\text{f})$$

In many practical situations, we will give up some of the possible simplicity of the right-hand side of the equations in order to simplify the writing of complicated external moments. In the case of the aircraft, for example, the X- and Z-directions are often better related to the lift and drag directions than the principal axis directions. Since Y is perpendicular to the plane of symmetry, it is nevertheless principal so that

$$J_{xy} = J_{yz} = 0, \quad \text{although } J_{zx} \neq 0.$$

Here the moments of inertia are all different, so we set

$$\boldsymbol{\Omega} = \boldsymbol{\omega}$$

and obtain, usually for origin at the center of mass,

$$\sum M_{x_e} = I_x\frac{d\omega_x}{dt} - (I_y - I_z)\omega_y\omega_z - J_{zx}\left(\frac{d\omega_z}{dt} + \omega_x\omega_y\right),$$

$$\sum M_{y_e} = I_y\frac{d\omega_y}{dt} - (I_z - I_x)\omega_z\omega_x - J_{zx}(\omega_z^2 - \omega_x^2), \qquad (5\text{–}26\text{g})$$

$$\sum M_{z_e} = I_z\frac{d\omega_z}{dt} - (I_x - I_y)\omega_x\omega_y - J_{zx}\left(\frac{d\omega_x}{dt} - \omega_y\omega_z\right).$$

Other special cases can be derived from the general form Eq. (5–26c). Don't forget that all the forms of Eq. (5–26) are written under the assumption that the correction term $m\mathbf{R}_{\text{c.m.}} \times \mathbf{a}_0$ is zero. If you do not use an acceptable origin, you must reintroduce this term in appropriate form.

EXAMPLE 5–9. Let's look again at our familiar flywheel in Fig. 5–13(a) precessing steadily about the vertical Z-axis while spinning about X. In Example 5-3, we studied its rotational motion and found

$$\Omega_x = 0, \qquad \omega_x = \omega_r, \qquad \alpha_x = 0,$$
$$\Omega_y = 0, \qquad \omega_y = 0, \qquad \alpha_y = \Omega\omega_r,$$
$$\Omega_z = \Omega, \qquad \omega_z = \Omega, \qquad \alpha_z = 0.$$

In Examples 5–6 and 5–7, we studied its inertial properties and wrote

$$[I]_{xyz} = \begin{bmatrix} I_x & 0 & 0 \\ 0 & I_y & 0 \\ 0 & 0 & I_z \end{bmatrix},$$

$$[I]_{ABC} = \begin{bmatrix} I_A & -J_{AB} & 0 \\ -J_{BA} & I_B & 0 \\ 0 & 0 & I_C \end{bmatrix}$$

$$= \begin{bmatrix} \dfrac{I_x + I_y}{2} + \dfrac{I_x - I_y}{2}\cos 2\psi & \dfrac{I_x - I_y}{2}\sin 2\psi & 0 \\[2ex] \dfrac{I_x - I_y}{2}\sin 2\psi & \dfrac{I_x + I_y}{2} - \dfrac{I_x - I_y}{2}\cos 2\psi & 0 \\[2ex] 0 & 0 & I_z \end{bmatrix}.$$

Now let's find the applied external moments required to produce the motion we have specified. The origin of both XYZ and ABC in Fig. 5–13(a) can be considered an unaccelerated point of the flywheel. (Even though the flywheel does not extend physically to the origin, just imagine a massless extension which does.) Thus the correction term is zero. It would also be zero for any point on the X-axis including the center of mass. Can you see why?

If we use rotating XYZ-axes, we note that they are principal and that $\omega_x \neq \Omega_x$, but $\omega_y = \Omega_y$, $\omega_z = \Omega_z$ as required for the axial symmetry case of Eq. (5–26e). With Ω and ω_r constant in magnitude,

$$M_x = M_z = 0,$$
$$M_y = \Omega I_x \omega_r.$$

Here we see the usefulness of properly chosen axis motion to simplify the statement of not only the kinematics but the dynamics as well.

For comparison, we might use Eq. (5–26b) for the fixed axes ABC. The angular velocity components are

$$\omega_A = \omega_r \cos \psi,$$
$$\omega_B = \omega_r \sin \psi,$$
$$\omega_C = \Omega.$$

The equations of motion become

$$M_A = \frac{d}{dt} (I_A \omega_r \cos \psi - J_{AB} \omega_r \sin \psi),$$

$$M_B = \frac{d}{dt} (I_B \omega_r \sin \psi - J_{AB} \omega_r \cos \psi),$$

$$M_C = \frac{d}{dt} (I_C \Omega) = 0,$$

where I_A, I_B, and J_{AB} are functions of ψ and therefore, time. If we substitute for them in terms of I_x, I_y and ψ, we can eventually obtain

$$M_A = -\Omega I_x \omega_r \sin \psi,$$
$$M_B = \Omega I_x \omega_r \cos \psi,$$
$$M_C = 0,$$

which can be seen to be equivalent to our answer for XYZ.

We could also have used axes XY^*Z^* fixed in the body with the additional coordinate ϕ measuring the position of Y^* from Y, clockwise around X. Here we would use Euler's dynamical equations (5–26d) with

$$\omega_x = \omega_r,$$
$$\omega_y^* = \Omega \sin \phi,$$
$$\omega_z^* = \Omega \cos \phi$$

to obtain, with $I_y^* = I_z^*$,

$$M_x = 0,$$

$$M_y^* = I_y^* \frac{d}{dt} (\Omega \sin \phi) - (I_z^* - I_x)\Omega \omega_r \cos \phi = \Omega I_x \omega_r \cos \phi,$$

$$M_z^* = I_z^* \frac{d}{dt} (\Omega \cos \phi) - (I_x - I_y^*)\omega_r \Omega \sin \phi = -\Omega I_x \omega_r \sin \phi.$$

This is again the same moment as before but referred to the different component directions XY^*Z^*.

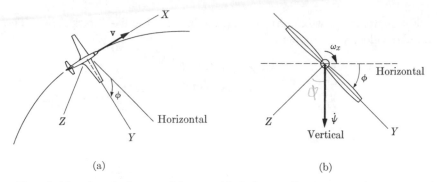

(a)   (b)

FIG. 5–16. An airplane and its two-bladed propeller in a steady horizontal turn.

The required external moment $\Omega I_x \omega_r$ about Y may be supplied by various means. The weight of the flywheel would certainly contribute, and the loads in the shaft system would supply the remainder. Note that the net external force on the flywheel required for this motion is

$$F_{x_e} = -m\Omega^2 x_{\text{c.m.}}, \qquad F_{y_e} = F_{z_e} = 0.$$

Thus in the Z-direction the weight of the flywheel must be balanced by the shear force in the horizontal shaft so that no net external F_z is applied to the flywheel. Some tension in the shaft would also be required by F_{x_e}.

If we had used an XYZ-system centered at the center of mass of the flywheel, the required moments about this center would have been exactly the same. This is compatible with the requirement of only an X-external force at the center of mass which gives no moment about our original stationary origin. Can you draw load, shear, and bending-moment diagrams for the horizontal shaft? How about the vertical shaft?

EXAMPLE 5–10. As another illustration of rigid-body rotational motion, we might look at a vehicle such as a light airplane making a turn. Of course moments must be applied to produce the required attitude for maintaining the turn, but let's overlook this transient maneuver and concentrate on the steady horizontal turn as shown in Fig. 5–16(a). In the steady turn, the wings are banked a constant angle ϕ from the horizontal (see Example 5–5 for the kinematics of a climbing turn) and the aircraft has an angular velocity about a vertical axis.

In order to make the correction term $\mathbf{R}_{\text{c.m.}} \times \mathbf{a}_0$ zero, let's put our origin at the center of mass. Since this is a point in the plane of symmetry of the aircraft, Y will be a principal axis if we stick it out the right wing perpendicular to this plane. Although we know that the X-principal axis is in the plane of symmetry and pointing more or less forward, it will not be exactly horizontal in the direction of flight. However, for the usual light aircraft at cruising speed, it will be pretty close to horizontal so let's assume it is. Thus the Y- and Z-principal axes form a vertical plane.

Since the aircraft has no axis of mass symmetry and thus has only three principal axes through the center of mass, we can use conveniently Euler's Eq. (5–26d) with $\mathbf{\Omega} = \boldsymbol{\omega}$. With the resultant angular velocity $\mathbf{\Omega}$ vertically downward, we have the components along the principal axis directions as

$$\omega_x = \Omega_x = 0,$$
$$\omega_y = \Omega_y = \Omega \sin \phi,$$
$$\omega_z = \Omega_z = \Omega \cos \phi,$$

and the required external moment components are

$$M_{x_e} = I_x \frac{d\omega_x}{dt} - (I_y - I_z)\omega_y\omega_z = (I_z - I_y)\Omega^2 \sin \phi \cos \phi,$$

$$M_{y_e} = I_y \frac{d\omega_y}{dt} - (I_z - I_x)\omega_z\omega_x = 0,$$

$$M_{z_e} = I_z \frac{d\omega_z}{dt} - (I_x - I_y)\omega_x\omega_y = 0.$$

Thus a moment about X is needed to maintain the steady turn, although most pilots don't know it because it is so small. For a turn at $\frac{1}{4}$ rad/sec at 45° bank with $(I_z - I_y)$ of the order of 300 slugs/ft^2, M_x is only about 10 ft-lb.

The higher angular velocities which require substantial applied moments may occur during an inadvertent spin. If we assume the spin is steady about a vertical axis, the nose will normally be substantially below the horizontal and the wings may or may not be horizontal. If we use the Euler angles of Fig. 5–11, knowing that θ will be negative, we can use the transformation equations (5–11b) to find the components of $\mathbf{\Omega}$ along XYZ. With θ and ϕ constant, and $\dot{\psi}$ the resultant spin rate Ω, we have

$$\Omega_x = \Omega \sin \theta,$$
$$\Omega_y = \Omega \cos \theta \sin \phi,$$
$$\Omega_z = \Omega \cos \theta \cos \phi.$$

Euler's dynamical equations (5–26d) now become

$$M_{x_e} = -(I_y - I_z)\Omega^2 \cos^2 \theta \sin \phi \cos \phi,$$
$$M_{y_e} = -(I_z - I_x)\Omega^2 \sin \theta \cos \theta \cos \phi,$$
$$M_{z_e} = -(I_x - I_y)\Omega^2 \sin \theta \cos \theta \sin \phi.$$

If the wings are level, the only moment is about Y and may be of the order of 1500 ft-lb for a spin rate near 1 rev/sec. Observe that the expression for the horizontal steady turn drops out of these equations for $\theta = 0$.

Of course our airplane is not really a rigid body. Quite obviously it has a large spinning propeller on its nose whose motion is far more complicated than that of the aircraft. If we return to our less violent steady horizontal turn and assume that the propeller shaft is essentially horizontal, let's find the moments required to precess or swing the propeller around the turn.

Putting an origin at the propeller's center of mass which is on the axis of the propeller shaft, we look for its principal axes. If we have a three-bladed propeller as in Fig. 5–15, the propeller shaft is an axis of mass symmetry. Thus the precession of the three-bladed propeller in the steady turn is directly analogous to the flywheel precession in the previous example. If we put X along the propeller shaft, Y horizontal, and Z vertical, we get

$$\Omega_x = 0, \qquad \qquad \omega_x = \text{propeller spin rate,}$$
$$\Omega_y = \omega_y = 0,$$
$$\Omega_z = \omega_z = \Omega,$$

and the required moments about the center of mass are, from Eq. (5–26e),

$$M_x = 0,$$
$$M_y = \Omega I_x \omega_x,$$
$$M_z = 0.$$

On a light airplane, however, we are liable to have a two-bladed propeller for which the propeller shaft is not an axis of mass symmetry. It is nevertheless a principal axis along with Y and Z, as illustrated in Fig. 5–16(b) from the pilot's point of view. Still assuming X to be essentially horizontal, we can find the components of absolute angular velocity for the propeller from the Euler angle transformation equations (5–11b) (or by inspection) as

$$\Omega_x = \omega_x = \dot{\phi} - \dot{\psi} \sin \theta = \dot{\phi},$$
$$\Omega_y = \omega_y = \dot{\theta} \cos \phi + \dot{\psi} \cos \theta \sin \phi = \dot{\psi} \sin \phi,$$
$$\Omega_z = \omega_z = -\dot{\theta} \sin \phi + \dot{\psi} \cos \theta \cos \phi = \dot{\psi} \cos \phi.$$

Using Euler's dynamical equations (5–26d) because $\boldsymbol{\Omega} = \boldsymbol{\omega}$, we get, assuming $\dot{\phi}$ is constant,

$$M_{x_e} = I_x \frac{d\omega_x}{dt} - (I_y - I_z)\omega_y \omega_z = -(I_y - I_z)\dot{\psi}^2 \sin \phi \cos \phi,$$
$$M_{y_e} = I_y \dot{\psi}\dot{\phi} \cos \phi - (I_z - I_x)\dot{\psi}\dot{\phi} \cos \phi,$$
$$M_{z_e} = -I_z \dot{\psi}\dot{\phi} \sin \phi - (I_x - I_y)\dot{\psi}\dot{\phi} \sin \phi.$$

These messy expressions look better if we resolve $\mathbf{M}_e$ along XHV (which involves a rotation $-\phi$ about an axis 1) to obtain

$$M_X = -\tfrac{1}{2}(I_y - I_z)\dot{\psi}^2 \sin 2\phi,$$

$$M_H = I_x\dot{\phi}\dot{\psi} + (I_y - I_z)\dot{\phi}\dot{\psi} \cos 2\phi,$$

$$M_V = (I_y - I_z)\dot{\phi}\dot{\psi} \sin 2\phi.$$

Note that M_H contains the same steady term $I_x\dot{\phi}\dot{\psi}$ required for the three-bladed propeller. In addition, we get sizeable terms varying sinusoidally with 2ϕ or twice the propeller spin rate. Light-plane pilots and manufacturers have been bothered by these for years and will quickly verify that a two-bladed propeller will often "feel rough" in a turn. Actually each blade in a three-bladed propeller requires oscillatory moments to precess it in a turn, but this merely produces stresses in the hub. When the requirements of all three blades are summed, only the steady moment $I_x\dot{\phi}\dot{\psi}$ remains to be supplied by the propeller shaft.

5–5 Integrated forms. As in the particle dynamics of Section 3–3, many problems involving rigid-body motion are most easily formulated mathematically directly in terms of impulse, momentum, work, and kinetic energy. Rather than first writing Newton's second law for linear or angular motion and then integrating, it may be conceptually better to think directly in the integrated forms. This procedure often leads to concepts such as conservation of linear or angular momentum or, with conservative systems, the conservation of mechanical energy.

In order to see what these integrated forms may be like, let's start with the force and moment expressions that we derived in Chapter 4 for a finite group of particles and then specialize to the rigid body:

$$\sum \mathbf{F}_e = (\sum m)\mathbf{a}_{\text{c.m.}}, \tag{4–4}$$

$$\sum (\mathbf{R} \times \mathbf{F}_e) = \frac{d}{dt} \sum (\mathbf{R} \times m\dot{\mathbf{R}}) + (\sum m)\mathbf{R}_{\text{c.m.}} \times \mathbf{a}_0. \tag{4–5b}$$

If we multiply both sides by dt and integrate over time, we have, for the first equation,

$$\int_{t_1}^{t_2} \sum \mathbf{F}_e \, dt = (\sum m)\mathbf{v}_{\text{c.m.}} \Big|_1^2, \tag{5–27a}$$

which relates linear impulse of the external forces to change in momentum, as if the entire mass moved with the center of mass as a single particle. This should not be surprising because we define the center of mass in such a way that an observer ② riding with it would see no net linear momentum for the particles. Remember that the use of Eq. (5–27a) involves the services of an unaccelerated, nonrotating Galilean observer ①.

If we operate in a similar fashion on Eq. (4–5b) from an origin such that $\mathbf{R}_{\text{c.m.}} \times \mathbf{a}_0$ is zero, we get

$$\int_{t_1}^{t_2} \sum (\mathbf{R} \times \mathbf{F}_e)\, dt = \int_{t_1}^{t_2} \sum \mathbf{M}_e\, dt = \sum (\mathbf{R} \times m\mathbf{v})\Big|_1^2. \qquad (5\text{–}28a)$$

Thus the angular impulse is related to the change in angular momentum, where both are seen by a nonrotating observer at an origin for which $\mathbf{R}_{\text{c.m.}} \times \mathbf{a}_0$ is zero. This observer is usually either unaccelerated ($\mathbf{a}_0 = 0$) or moving with the center of mass ($\mathbf{R}_{\text{c.m.}} = 0$).

Note that the angular momentum or moment of momentum seen by an unaccelerated observer ① can be written in two parts. Thus,

$$\begin{aligned}
\sum (\mathbf{R}_1 \times m\mathbf{v}_1) &= \sum [(\mathbf{R}_{\text{c.m.}} + \mathbf{R}) \times m(\mathbf{v}_{\text{c.m.}} + \mathbf{v})] \\
&= \sum (\mathbf{R} \times m\mathbf{v}) + \mathbf{R}_{\text{c.m.}} \times (\sum m)\mathbf{v}_{\text{c.m.}} \qquad (5\text{–}29a) \\
&\quad + \mathbf{R}_{\text{c.m.}} \times \sum (m\mathbf{v}) + \sum (m\mathbf{R}) \times \mathbf{v}_{\text{c.m.}}.
\end{aligned}$$

From the definition of center of mass, $\sum (m\mathbf{v})$ and $\sum (m\mathbf{R})$ are zero, so that, about an unaccelerated origin,

$$\begin{aligned}
\int_{t_1}^{t_2} \sum \mathbf{M}_e\, dt &= \int_{t_1}^{t_2} \sum (\mathbf{R} \times \mathbf{F}_e)\, dt + \int_{t_1}^{t_2} \mathbf{R}_{\text{c.m.}} \times \sum \mathbf{F}_e\, dt \\
&= \sum (\mathbf{R} \times m\mathbf{v})\big|_1^2 + \mathbf{R}_{\text{c.m.}} \times (\sum m)\mathbf{v}_{\text{c.m.}}\big|_1^2, \qquad (5\text{–}30a)
\end{aligned}$$

where the moment of momentum is the sum of that seen by observer ② at the center of mass and that seen by observer ① as if all the mass were

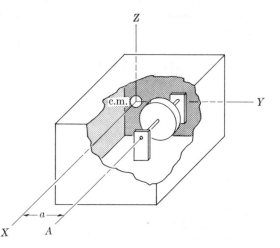

Fig. 5–17. Rotational control of a space probe by an internal flywheel.

moving with the center of mass. Subtracting Eq. (5–28a) figured for an observer ② at the center of mass, we get the relation

$$\int_{t_1}^{t_2} \mathbf{R}_{\text{c.m.}} \times \sum \mathbf{F}_e \, dt = \mathbf{R}_{\text{c.m.}} \times (\sum m)\mathbf{v}_{\text{c.m.}} \Big|_1^2. \qquad (5\text{–}31)$$

If the external linear or angular impulse is zero in any one of these forms, the corresponding momentum is conserved. Since these are all vector relationships, the same can be said of components.

Specializing to a rigid body, we can immediately write the analogous equations

$$\int_{t_1}^{t_2} \sum \mathbf{F}_e \, dt = m\mathbf{v}_{\text{c.m.}} \Big|_1^2, \qquad (5\text{–}27\text{b})$$

$$\int_{t_1}^{t_2} \sum \mathbf{M}_e \, dt = \mathbf{H} \Big|_1^2, \qquad (5\text{–}28\text{b})$$

$$\int_m \mathbf{R}_1 \times \mathbf{v}_1 \, dm = \mathbf{H} + \mathbf{R}_{\text{c.m.}} \times m\mathbf{v}_{\text{c.m.}}, \qquad (5\text{–}29\text{b})$$

$$\int_{t_1}^{t_2} \sum \mathbf{M}_e \, dt = \mathbf{H} \Big|_1^2 + \mathbf{R}_{\text{c.m.}} \times m\mathbf{v}_{\text{c.m.}} \Big|_1^2, \qquad (5\text{–}30\text{b})$$

where each involves definite assumptions about origins and observers. Thus Eq. (5–27b) is for an observer ①; Eq. (5–28b) is for an observer moving with a point in the body for which $\mathbf{R}_{\text{c.m.}} \times \mathbf{a}_0 = 0$; Eq. (5–29b) relates angular momentum seen by ① to that about the center of mass plus that of the center of mass; and Eq. (5–30b) relates the total angular momentum of Eq. (5–29b) to the angular impulse seen by any observer ①.

EXAMPLE 5–11. It has been suggested that space probes can change their orientation while drifting through space by the spinning of small internal flywheels. A single flywheel for rotating the probe about the X-axis is shown in Fig. 5–17. The axis A of the flywheel is parallel to X but displaced by the distance a. If the probe and flywheel have, respectively, the angular velocities ω_x and ω_A and moments of inertia I_{xP} and I_{AF}, the total moment of momentum about X through the center of mass of the probe including the flywheel is, if X is a principal axis of the probe,

$$\begin{aligned} \text{Total angular momentum} &= I_x\omega_x + I_{AF}\omega_A + a(m_F\omega_x a) \\ &= (I_x + m_F a^2)\omega_x + I_{AF}\omega_A \\ &= (I_x + m_F a^2 + I_{AF})\omega_x + I_{AF}(\omega_A - \omega_x) \\ &= I_{x_{\text{total}}}\omega_x + I_{AF}\omega_A'. \end{aligned}$$

If no external moments are applied, this total momentum will remain constant. Assuming that ω_x and ω_A' are initially zero (we have also tacitly assumed that ω_y and ω_z are zero in writing the above expressions), we can write

$$\omega_x = \frac{I_{AF}}{I_{x_{\text{total}}}} \omega_A',$$

where ω_A' is the flywheel's angular velocity as seen on the probe. Thus, if the flywheel spins relative to the probe, a certain number of revolutions can rotate the probe about X a proportional number of degrees. Note that to produce a steady change in the probe's angular velocity instead of its position, the flywheel must maintain a correspondingly high ω_A'. This sort of device thus seems limited to use in a probe initially very nearly nonrotating.

By assuming zero initial angular momentum and operating only about one axis X, we have perhaps oversimplified the basic problem in which we will normally have some initial angular momentum about each principal axis. This resultant initial angular momentum will remain constant as the probe and, thus, the principal axes are rotated. If we write

$$\mathbf{H}_{P_{\text{total}}} = I_{x_{\text{total}}}\boldsymbol{\omega}_x + I_{y_{\text{total}}}\boldsymbol{\omega}_y + I_{z_{\text{total}}}\boldsymbol{\omega}_z$$

and, for the three similar flywheels,

$$\mathbf{H}_F = I_A\boldsymbol{\omega}_A' + I_B\boldsymbol{\omega}_B' + I_C\boldsymbol{\omega}_C' = I_A\boldsymbol{\omega}',$$

we can spin the flywheels so that the probe is not rotating and all the initial angular momentum is in the flywheels as

$$\mathbf{H}_{\text{initial}} = I_A\boldsymbol{\omega}_{\text{initial}}'.$$

If we now wish to rotate the probe about the X-axis, we must first introduce a change $\Delta\omega_A'$ and then, as the probe rotates about X, continuously change $\boldsymbol{\omega}_B'$ and $\boldsymbol{\omega}_C'$ so that

$$I_A(\boldsymbol{\omega}' - \Delta\omega_A') = \mathbf{H}_{\text{initial}}. \quad \blacktriangle$$

Turning now to integration over space rather than time, we should not attempt to immediately separate linear and rotational motion because they both contribute to kinetic energy. By comparison, angular and linear momentum are vector quantities of different basic dimensions. Starting with the equation for a single particle, let's multiply both sides by the displacement of the particle and sum the equations for the entire group.

$$\sum(\mathbf{F} \cdot d\mathbf{R}) = \sum \left(m \frac{d\mathbf{v}}{dt} \cdot d\mathbf{R} \right)$$

$$= \sum(m\mathbf{v} \cdot d\mathbf{v})$$

$$= \sum d \left(m \frac{\mathbf{v} \cdot \mathbf{v}}{2} \right)$$

$$= d \left(\sum \frac{mv^2}{2} \right).$$

Integrating over the displacement of each particle, we get

$$\int_1^2 \sum(\mathbf{F} \cdot d\mathbf{R}) = \sum \left(\frac{mv^2}{2} \right) \Big|_1^2. \tag{5–31}$$

If each $\mathbf{F}$ actually has the displacement $d\mathbf{R}$ of the particle that it acts on, the left-hand side is the total work done by all forces, and it equals the total change in kinetic energy for the group.

If we try to break the integral into two parts by separating internal and external forces as

$$\int_1^2 \sum(\mathbf{F} \cdot d\mathbf{R}) = \int_1^2 \sum(\mathbf{F}_e \cdot d\mathbf{R}) + \int_1^2 \sum(\mathbf{F}_{\text{int}} \cdot d\mathbf{R}),$$

we normally cannot expect the work done by the internal forces to sum to zero. Even though the forces may be equal and opposite, they may act on particles whose displacements in the line of the forces may be different. If we are dealing with an ideal rigid body, however, the separation between particles is constant and the work done by internal forces sums to zero.

The kinetic energy of Eq. (5–31) is that seen by an observer ①. If we replace his observation $\mathbf{v}_1$ by that $\mathbf{v}$ of an observer moving with point O, we have

$$\mathbf{v}_1 = \mathbf{v}_0 + \mathbf{v},$$

$$\sum \frac{mv_1^2}{2} = \sum \frac{m}{2} (\mathbf{v}_0 + \mathbf{v}) \cdot (\mathbf{v}_0 + \mathbf{v})$$

$$= (\sum m) \frac{v_0^2}{2} + \sum \frac{mv^2}{2} + (\sum m\mathbf{v}) \cdot \mathbf{v}_0.$$

Thus the total kinetic energy seen by ① is that seen by ② plus that of the total mass as if moving with ② plus the dot product of the total momentum seen by ② with his velocity. If ② moves with the center of mass, he sees no net linear momentum and

$$\sum(\tfrac{1}{2}mv_1^2) = \sum(\tfrac{1}{2}mv^2) + (\sum m) \frac{v_{\text{c.m.}}^2}{2}. \tag{5–32}$$

The total kinetic energy is that of the group at the center of mass plus the kinetic energy as seen from the center of mass.

If the force equation (4–4) is multiplied by $d\mathbf{R}_{c.m.}$ and integrated, we get

$$\int_1^2 \Sigma \mathbf{F} \cdot d\mathbf{R}_{c.m.} = \left(\Sigma m\right) \frac{v_{c.m.}^2}{2}\Big|_1^2. \tag{5-33}$$

Subtracting this from Eq. (5–31) which is from the point of view of ①, we have left just a relation between quantities seen by observer ② at the center of mass as

$$\int_1^2 \Sigma(\mathbf{F} \cdot d\mathbf{R}) = \Sigma \left(\frac{mv^2}{2}\right)\Big|_1^2. \tag{5-34}$$

Thus the work by all forces as seen from the center of mass equals the change in kinetic energy.

Specializing now for a rigid body, we see that for an observer moving with a point O of the body, the kinetic energy T is*

$$T = \int_m \frac{v^2}{2} \, dm = \tfrac{1}{2}\int_m \mathbf{v} \cdot (\boldsymbol{\omega} \times \mathbf{R}) \, dm$$

$$= \tfrac{1}{2}\boldsymbol{\omega} \cdot \int_m (\mathbf{R} \times \mathbf{v}) \, dm$$

$$= \tfrac{1}{2}\boldsymbol{\omega} \cdot \mathbf{H}. \tag{5-35a}$$

In matrix form, this can be written as

$$T = \tfrac{1}{2}\lfloor \omega \rfloor \{H\} = \tfrac{1}{2}\lfloor \omega \rfloor [I]\{\omega\}. \tag{5-35b}$$

In principal axes XYZ the inertia matrix is diagonal and

$$T = \tfrac{1}{2}\lfloor \omega \rfloor [\diagdown I \diagdown]\{\omega\} = \tfrac{1}{2}I_x\omega_x^2 + \tfrac{1}{2}I_y\omega_y^2 + \tfrac{1}{2}I_z\omega_z^2. \tag{5-35c}$$

In terms of axes one of which is the axis A of the angular velocity $\boldsymbol{\omega}$

$$T = \tfrac{1}{2}\lfloor \omega, 0, 0\rfloor \begin{bmatrix} I_A & -- \\ --- \\ --- \end{bmatrix} \begin{Bmatrix} \omega \\ 0 \\ 0 \end{Bmatrix} = \tfrac{1}{2}I_A\omega^2. \tag{5-35d}$$

Remembering from above that work done by internal forces in a rigid body sums to zero, we see that the work-energy relation Eq. (5–31) combines with Eqs. (5–32) and (5–35) to give

$$\int_1^2 \Sigma(\mathbf{F}_e \cdot d\mathbf{R}) = \tfrac{1}{2}\boldsymbol{\omega} \cdot \mathbf{H}\Big|_1^2 + \frac{mv_{c.m.}^2}{2}\Big|_1^2. \tag{5-36}$$

---

* Here we use the identity $\mathbf{A} \cdot (\mathbf{B} \times \mathbf{C}) = \mathbf{B} \cdot (\mathbf{C} \times \mathbf{A})$.

Here the work of the external forces seen by ① equals the change in kinetic energy about the center of mass plus kinetic energy of the center of mass. Subtracting Eq. (5–33) gives the relation seen by ② at the center of mass:

$$\int_1^2 \sum (\mathbf{F}_e \cdot d\mathbf{R}) = \tfrac{1}{2}\boldsymbol{\omega} \cdot \mathbf{H} \Big|_1^2 = \tfrac{1}{2} I_A \omega^2 \Big|_1^2. \tag{5–37}$$

You can also show quite simply that Eq. (5–37) applies to an observer ① sitting at an unaccelerated point of the body. Note that for observer ② at the center of mass

$$d\mathbf{R} = \mathbf{R} \times \overline{d\theta},$$

$$\mathbf{F}_e \cdot d\mathbf{R} = \mathbf{F}_e \cdot (\mathbf{R} \times \overline{d\theta})$$

$$= (\mathbf{R} \times \mathbf{F}_e) \cdot \overline{d\theta}$$

$$= \mathbf{M}_e \cdot \overline{d\theta},$$

where $\overline{d\theta}$ is the infinitesimal angular displacement of the rigid body. Thus

$$\int_1^2 \sum (\mathbf{F}_e \cdot d\mathbf{R}) = \int_1^2 \sum (\mathbf{M}_e \cdot d\boldsymbol{\theta}). \tag{5–38}$$

These ideas are important for conservative systems in which the external forces can be represented in potential form (see Section 3–4). We can immediately write Eq. (5–36) or (5–37) as a first integral expressed as a conservation of mechanical energy like Eq. (3–21):

$$T + V = \text{constant.} \tag{5–39}$$

The choice of basic observer ① or ② and thus Eq. (5–36) or (5–37) depends on which fellow can better write the potential function V.

EXAMPLE 5–12. As a simple example of planar motion, let's look at the rocking chair of Fig. 5–18. If the rockers are circular arcs centered at O, then O moves only horizontally and the potential energy of the rocker in the gravitational field is

$$V = mga(1 - \cos \theta).$$

The kinetic energy, figured about P by the same observer ①, is

$$T = \tfrac{1}{2} I_P \dot{\theta}^2$$

where, by the law of cosines,

$$I_P = I_{\text{c.m.}} + ml^2$$

$$= I_{\text{c.m.}} + m(a^2 + h^2 - 2ah \cos \theta).$$

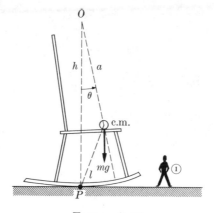

FIGURE 5–18

The conservation of energy is expressed as

$$T + V = \tfrac{1}{2}(I_{\text{c.m.}} + m[a^2 + h^2 - 2ah \cos \theta])\dot{\theta}^2 + mga(1 - \cos \theta)$$
$$= \text{constant.}$$

For small θ, this reduces to the more familiar form

$$\tfrac{1}{2}I_P\dot{\theta}^2 + mga\,\frac{\theta^2}{2} = \text{constant}$$

which, when integrated, again gives a sinusoidal oscillation for θ of the form

$$\theta = A \sin\left(\sqrt{mga/I_P}\,t + B\right). \;\blacktriangle$$

Another major use of kinetic and potential energy ideas in systems with a number of degrees of freedom (independent coordinates) is to find the equations of motion through Lagrange's equations (3–25). The advantage here is that it is often easier to formulate T and V than to write forces, moments, and the corresponding rates of change of momentum in complicated situations.

In Chapter 3, we derived Lagrange's equations initially for a single particle. Here we want to start with N particles which form a rigid body which has at most six independent coordinates. Paralleling the derivation of Chapter 3, we can write for the N particles

$$T = \sum_{j=1}^{N} \tfrac{1}{2}m_j(\dot{x}_j^2 + \dot{y}_j^2 + \dot{z}_j^2).$$

To transform to the M independent coordinates q_i, we can use the geometric

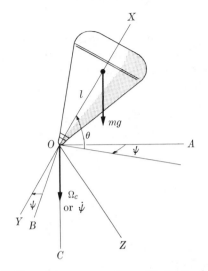

Fig. 5–19. A top precessing with its tip fixed.

relationships between the N particles making up the rigid body to obtain the $3N$ relations

$$x_1 = \phi_1(q_1, q_2, \ldots, q_M),$$
$$x_2 = \phi_2(q_1, q_2, \ldots, q_M),$$
$$\vdots$$
$$y_1 = \phi_{N+1}(q_1, q_2, \ldots, q_M).$$
$$\vdots$$

If these are substituted in T and if we write Newton's second law for each particle as $dW = -dV = dT$, we can, with much manipulation as in Chapter 3, get the analogous Lagrange equations

$$L(q_1, q_2, \ldots, q_M) = T(q_1, q_2, \ldots, q_M) - V(q_1, q_2, \ldots, q_M),$$
$$\frac{d}{dt}\left(\frac{\partial L}{\partial \dot{q}_i}\right) - \frac{\partial L}{\partial q_i} = 0, \qquad i = 1, 2, \ldots, M.$$
(5–40)

For rigid-body motion, M is a maximum of six and may be less, such as in planar motion. For basic limitations and extensions of the Lagrange procedure, see Chapter 11, particularly Section 11–7.

EXAMPLE 5–13. To show that Eqs. (5–40) are equivalent to the more familiar forms of Newton's second law for conservative systems, we can derive by the Lagrange procedure the same equations of motion that we will later derive directly. In Example 6–5, we will look at the precessing top reproduced in Fig. 5–19. Since X is an axis of symmetry and we will assume the tip to be a fixed point, we choose the tip as an origin, and X is a principal axis. As the other principal axes, we can use any pair through O perpendicular to X. Let's choose Y in the horizontal plane and Z in the vertical plane with X as shown. The motion of the rotating body can be described by three coordinates, which we can choose as the usual Euler angles. Thus ψ is from fixed axis A to the vertical XZ-plane, θ is the elevation of X above the horizontal AB-plane, and ϕ is the rotation of the body about X. The kinetic energy can be written as

$$T = \tfrac{1}{2}I_x\omega_x^2 + \tfrac{1}{2}I_y\omega_y^2 + \tfrac{1}{2}I_z\omega_z^2,$$

where in this special example in which the XYZ-axes are not rotating about X with the body,

$$\omega_x = \dot{\phi} - \dot{\psi}\sin\theta,$$
$$\omega_y = \dot{\theta},$$
$$\omega_z = \dot{\psi}\cos\theta.$$

The potential energy in the gravitational field is simply

$$V = mgl\sin\theta,$$

and the Lagrangian is

$$L = T - V = \tfrac{1}{2}I_x(\dot{\phi} - \dot{\psi}\sin\theta)^2 + \tfrac{1}{2}I_y\dot{\theta}^2$$
$$+ \tfrac{1}{2}I_z\dot{\psi}^2\cos^2\theta - mgl\sin\theta.$$

The equation of motion associated with ϕ is

$$\frac{d}{dt}\left(\frac{\partial L}{\partial\dot{\phi}}\right) - \frac{\partial L}{\partial\phi} = \frac{d}{dt}[I_x(\dot{\phi} - \dot{\psi}\sin\theta)] = 0$$

or, integrating immediately,

$$\dot{\phi} - \dot{\psi}\sin\theta = \omega_x = \text{constant.}$$

The equation associated with ψ will also be directly integrable because ψ does not appear in L. Thus,

$$\frac{\partial L}{\partial\dot{\psi}} = -I_x(\dot{\phi} - \dot{\psi}\sin\theta)\sin\theta + I_z\dot{\psi}\cos^2\theta = \text{constant.}$$

The third equation is

$$\frac{d}{dt}\left(\frac{\partial L}{\partial\dot{\theta}}\right) - \frac{\partial L}{\partial\theta} = I_y\ddot{\theta} + I_x(\dot{\phi} - \dot{\psi}\sin\theta)\dot{\psi}\cos\theta + I_z\dot{\psi}^2\cos\theta\sin\theta$$
$$+ mgl\cos\theta = 0.$$

Instead of this third equation, we can use the idea of conservation of mechanical energy to obtain a third integrated equation as

$$T + V = \tfrac{1}{2}I_x(\dot{\phi} - \dot{\psi}\sin\theta)^2 + \tfrac{1}{2}I_y\dot{\theta}^2$$
$$+ \tfrac{1}{2}I_z\dot{\psi}^2\cos^2\theta + mgl\sin\theta = \text{constant.}$$

All of these equations are derived and examined at considerable length in Example 6–5. Note how straightforward the Lagrange procedure is for obtaining them, and compare it with that of Example 6–5.

Problems

5–1. Use the matrix approach for axes X_1, X_2, and X_3 fixed in space to find the final position of a rigid body rotated first by 90° about the vertical axis X_3 and then swung up (increase in elevation) 90° about axis X_2. Compare this final position with that obtained by applying the rotations in reverse order.

5–2. For the second case in Problem 5–1, find the axis for a single rotation equivalent to the two 90° rotations. Find the magnitude of the single equivalent rotation and check your answer experimentally.

5–3. To show that the 9 direction cosines relating orthogonal axis directions XYZ and the rotated set $\overline{X}\,\overline{Y}\,\overline{Z}$ contain only three independent pieces of information, we can employ known properties of the respective triads of unit vectors. Thus $\bar{\imath}$ expressed as a vector sum of its components along $\mathbf{i}$, $\mathbf{j}$, and $\mathbf{k}$ is

$$\bar{\imath} = A_1\mathbf{i} + B_1\mathbf{j} + C_1\mathbf{k}.$$

Also

$$\bar{\jmath} = A_2\mathbf{i} + B_2\mathbf{j} + C_2\mathbf{k},$$
$$\bar{k} = A_3\mathbf{i} + B_3\mathbf{j} + C_3\mathbf{k},$$

where the A, B, and C quantities are the 9 direction cosines. Use the 6 relations

$$\bar{\imath}\cdot\bar{\imath} = \bar{\jmath}\cdot\bar{\jmath} = \bar{k}\cdot\bar{k} = 1,$$
$$\bar{\imath}\cdot\bar{\jmath} = \bar{\jmath}\cdot\bar{k} = \bar{k}\cdot\bar{\imath} = 0,$$

to obtain the 6 (orthogonality) relations between the direction cosines

$$A_lA_m + B_lB_m + C_lC_m = 0, \quad \text{for } l \neq m$$
$$A_l^2 + B_l^2 + C_l^2 = 1, \quad \text{for } l = m$$
$$\Bigg\} \; l, m = 1, 2, 3.$$

5–4. Show that the matrix equation below actually expresses the six orthogonality relations found in Problem 5–3; that is,

$$[\alpha][\alpha]' = [1] \quad \text{where } [\alpha] = \begin{bmatrix} A_1 & B_1 & C_1 \\ A_2 & B_2 & C_2 \\ A_3 & B_3 & C_3 \end{bmatrix}.$$

5–5. Find the magnitude and axis orientation for the single rotation which would rotate the rigid body from the first final position to the second final position described in Problems 5–1 and 5–2.

5–6. A triad of unit vectors representing the orientation of a rigid body is originally lined up with fixed axes X, Y, and Z. After two rotations it is observed to end up just 45° around the Z-axis. If the first rotation of the triad was 90° around the X-axis, (a) what must have been the size of the second rotation? (b) What was the axis for the second rotation?

5–7. Suppose an XYZ-axis system is rotated 45° about Z and then 45° about the new Y-direction. What are the direction cosines of the final X-axis direction as measured from the original XYZ-axis directions?

5–8. Using our usual Euler's angles to specify the orientation of a body relative to the fixed axes ABC (A north, B east, C vertically down), let's suppose they have the values $\psi = 90°$, $\theta = 45°$, $\phi = 90°$.

(a) If we imbed in our body a triad of unit vectors which are lined up with ABC when Euler's angles are all zero, find the direction cosines with respect to ABC of the triad for the body orientation defined by the given ψ, θ, and ϕ.

(b) Find the direction of the axis and the magnitude of the single equivalent rotation, which would *return* the body to its initial position ($\psi = \theta = \phi = 0$).

5 9. (a) Suppose that you are holding an airplane model horizontally pointing north and are visualizing its X-axis forward, its Y-axis out the right wing, and the Z-axis vertically downward. Considering the axes to move with the airplane, rotate the airplane 30° about X and then 15° about Y. Is its final orientation different from what it would be if the rotation about Y were made first and were followed by the one about X? If so, by how much, and why?

(b) Consider the axes in (a) to be fixed in space rather than to the airplane and carry out the same procedure. Are your answers modified? If so, how?

(c) Suppose your airplane is maneuvering and the flight test instruments indicate an angular velocity of 0.2 rad/sec about X, 0.1 about Z, and none about Y. Can these be vectorially combined into a resultant angular velocity? Is your answer under (c) consistent with (a) and (b)?

5–10. We have shown geometrically that $\{y\} = [\theta_3]\{x\}$ transforms the components $\{x\}$ of vector **A** into its components $\{y\}$ for a $Y_1Y_2Y_3$-axis system which is rotated on angle θ around X_3 where

$$[\theta_3] = \begin{bmatrix} \cos\theta & \sin\theta & 0 \\ -\sin\theta & \cos\theta & 0 \\ 0 & 0 & 1 \end{bmatrix}.$$

Show that, if the $Y_1Y_2Y_3$-axis system is instead rotated a positive angle θ about X_2 or X_1, the corresponding transformations are

$$[\theta_2] = \begin{bmatrix} \cos\theta & 0 & -\sin\theta \\ 0 & 1 & 0 \\ \sin\theta & 0 & \cos\theta \end{bmatrix}, \qquad [\theta_1] = \begin{bmatrix} 1 & 0 & 0 \\ 0 & \cos\theta & \sin\theta \\ 0 & -\sin\theta & \cos\theta \end{bmatrix}.$$

(Note again that $[\theta_2]$ is the same as $[\phi]$ in Eqs. (5–3) and (5–4) and corresponds to $[\phi]$ of Chapter 2 if we replace θ with $-\phi$. Remember that increase in elevation in spherical coordinates represents a negative rotation about the second axis of the $r\theta Z$ cylindrical system.)

5–11. What are the relative advantages of defining the orientation of a rigid body by a matrix of direction cosines or by a set of Euler's angles? Explain fully with illustrations.

5–12. Show that the magnitude of the single rotation $d\Phi$ equivalent to the successive infinitesimal rotations $d\theta$ and $d\phi$ is simply

$$d\Phi = \sqrt{d\theta^2 + d\phi^2}.$$

5–13. (a) With our usual set of Euler's angles, show that, to obtain the components of $\mathbf{A}$ in XYZ-axes from its components in ABC-axes, the proper transformation is

$$\begin{Bmatrix} A_x \\ A_y \\ A_z \end{Bmatrix} = [\phi][\theta][\psi] \begin{Bmatrix} A_A \\ A_B \\ A_C \end{Bmatrix}.$$

(b) Referring to Problem 5–10, let's find the correct forms for the elements of each of the three Euler angle matrices.

(c) Which *one* of the following transformations in the opposite direction is incorrect?

$$\begin{Bmatrix} A_A \\ A_B \\ A_C \end{Bmatrix} = [\psi]'[\theta]'[\phi]' \begin{Bmatrix} A_x \\ A_y \\ A_z \end{Bmatrix}, \qquad \begin{Bmatrix} A_A \\ A_B \\ A_C \end{Bmatrix} = [\phi]'[\theta]'[\psi]' \begin{Bmatrix} A_x \\ A_y \\ A_z \end{Bmatrix},$$

$$\begin{Bmatrix} A_A \\ A_B \\ A_C \end{Bmatrix} = [[\phi][\theta][\psi]]' \begin{Bmatrix} A_x \\ A_y \\ A_z \end{Bmatrix}.$$

5–14. Noting that $\overline{d\psi}/dt$ is easily expressed in component form in the RSC-system, $\overline{d\theta}/dt$ in XST, and $\overline{d\phi}/dt$ in XYZ as defined in Fig. 5–11, show that

$$\begin{Bmatrix} \Omega_x \\ \Omega_y \\ \Omega_z \end{Bmatrix} = [\phi][\theta]\{\dot{\psi}\} + [\phi]\{\dot{\theta}\} + \{\dot{\phi}\},$$

and that this is equivalent to the expressions for Ω_x, Ω_y, and Ω_z derived in Eq. (5–11b).

5–15. A coin of radius r rolls at a constant speed in a circle of radius R while tilted inward at the constant angle θ from the vertical. (a) Find the point in the coin (or its extension) which remains stationary throughout the motion. (b) Find the axis through this point about which the coin is instantaneously rotating. (c) Sketch the hodograph for this motion.

5–16. A gun on a rolling ship fires a projectile while the barrel is swinging up at a constant absolute angular velocity Ω. Due to the rifling in the barrel, the projectile acquires a spin ω_r about its axis of symmetry which is proportional to its instantaneous velocity as it accelerates up the barrel. Considering the motion as being made up of translation of the projectile's center of mass and rotation about the center of mass, find the angular acceleration of the projectile about its center of mass by (a) using Eq. (5–8), and (b) watching the stretching and swinging of the angular velocity vector ω.

5–17. An observer riding on a rotating axis system sees a rigid body rotating about the origin at the rates $\omega'_x = 0$, $\omega'_y = 0$, $\omega'_z = 1.73$ rad/sec. A stationary observer, looking at the same rotating body, says its resultant angular velocity is about a vertical axis and has components along the directions defined by the axis system of $\omega_x = 1$ rad/sec, $\omega_y = 0$, $\omega_z = 1.73$ rad/sec. What is the orientation of the axis system and what is its angular velocity?

5–18. (a) Derive the following expression for absolute angular acceleration α in terms of the observations α' and ω' of an observer ③ rotating at Ω.

$$\alpha = \alpha' + \Omega \times \omega' + \frac{d\Omega}{dt}.$$

(b) Must the observers ② and ③ have the same linear motion to use the transformation relation in (a)?

5–19. Check the results of Example 5–3 by using Eq. (5–8).

5–20. An airplane is banked at an angle of 45° while executing a constant-speed, constant-altitude turn. The airplane's forward speed is V, and it is moving on a circular path of radius R. The pilot, looking forward, sees the propeller of radius r rotating about a horizontal axis at the rate ω_x.

(a) Does the pilot see the absolute angular velocity of the propeller? If not, what is it?

(b) What is the angular acceleration of the propeller?

(c) Find an expression for the linear velocity of a propeller tip, and

(d) also find an expression for the absolute linear acceleration of the same tip.

5–21. A helicopter blade is observed to flap sinusoidally as it swings around. In Eulerian terms (with X along the blade) $\dot{\psi} = $ constant, $\theta = \theta_0 \sin at$, $\phi = \dot{\phi} = 0$.

(a) What is the angular acceleration of the blade at any instant?

(b) Assuming the rotor hub to be stationary, find the linear acceleration of a point on the center line of the blade a distance L from the root.

5–22. An airplane which has just reached the bottom of a rolling pullout so that its velocity is horizontal (in the X-direction) has the following Euler angle description for its angular motion at this instant: $\psi = 0$, $\theta = 0$, $\phi = 0$, $\dot{\psi} = 0$, $\dot{\theta} = 0.1$ rad/sec, $\dot{\phi} = 1.0$ rad/sec. (Assume $\dot{\theta}$ and $\dot{\phi}$ constant for a short period.)

(a) To a *nonrotating* observer moving with the linear motion of the airplane's center of mass, what is the resultant axis about which the airplane appears to be rotating at this instant?

(b) What velocity and acceleration would a point on the wing tip ($x = 0$, $y = 20$ ft, $z = 0$) appear to have to a stationary ground observer if he says the vertical acceleration of the airplane's center of mass is 4 g's and its forward speed is 300 ft/sec?

5–23. Suppose a jet transport which had been traveling due west at high altitude is suddenly observed to have the angular velocity components $\omega_x = -.905°/\text{sec}$, $\omega_y = 1.24°/\text{sec}$, $\omega_z = -2.16°/\text{sec}$, for Euler's angles of $\psi = -90°$, $\theta = -20°$, $\phi = -30°$.

(a) What maneuver is the airplane performing? Can you guess why? (Look at the rate of change of Euler's angles.)

(b) If the pilot is thoroughly experienced and thus flies coordinated turns only, can you estimate the airspeed of the transport?

(c) What does the rate-of-climb indicator probably read? [*Hint:* See Example 5–5.]

5–24. Consider a fighter aircraft heading north in steady level flight. If the axes XYZ are attached to the airplane in the usual manner, Euler's angles have the values $\psi = 0$, $\theta = 0$, $\phi = 0$. To reverse his flight direction and simultaneously gain some altitude, the pilot pulls up into a half-loop, and when he reaches the top he rolls the airplane right-side-up and proceeds south.

(a) What are the final values of Euler's angles at the end of the maneuver?

(b) Sketch the approximate variations of ψ, θ, and ϕ versus time during the maneuver.

5–25. A rapidly spinning gyrowheel, which is supported so that no external moments can be applied to it, will not change its "absolute" orientation in space. Suppose we align such a gyro with its spin axis (axis of symmetry) vertical. As observers rotating with the earth, we will see a motion of the spin axis. In terms of our latitude and the absolute angular velocities of the gyro ω_{abs} and of the earth $\mathbf{\Omega}_e$, what do we see

(a) for the angular velocity of the gyrowheel, and

(b) for the angular acceleration of the gyrowheel?

(c) Define a convenient set of Euler's angles for describing the motion that we see and write expressions for their rates of change, if any.

5–26. A very slender uniform rod of length L and mass per unit length m is rotating in the XY-plane about one end. Find I_x, I_y, I_z and J_{xy}, J_{yz}, J_{zx} [$I_x = \int (y^2 + z^2)\, dm$, $J_{xy} = \int xy\, dm$, etc.] in terms of the angle θ. Show that the J's are zero for $\theta = 0, 90, 180, \ldots$.

5–27. Use the general relationship $[I]_B = [\gamma][I]_A[\gamma]'$ to find an expression for J_{xy} in the set of tilted axes B in terms of the mass properties in axes A and the direction cosines $[\gamma]$ representing the tilt of axes B.

5–28. Presuming that we know the inertia properties of a rigid body with respect to axes $X_1Y_1Z_1$ not through its center of mass, find an expression for J_{yz}, the product of inertia with respect to Y and Z of a set of axes XYZ parallel to $X_1Y_1Z_1$.

5–29. Prove that the trace of the inertia matrix is invariant with respect to rotations of the coordinate axes XYZ about a given origin by first showing

$$\text{Trace} = 2 \int_m R^2\, dm.$$

5–30. Consider an arbitrarily shaped body with a set of principal axes $X_0 Y_0 Z_0$ through its center of mass. Show that the set of principal axes for a point on the X_0-axis which is not at the center of mass is made up of X_0, an axis parallel to Y_0, and an axis parallel to Z_0.

5–31. Suppose a body has, for a set of axes through its center of mass, $I_x = I_y = I_z = 10$ slugs-ft^2, $J_{xz} = J_{yz} = 0$, $J_{xy} = 3$ slugs-ft^2.

(a) Is X, Y, or Z a principal axis?

(b) Where is the principal set through the center of mass of this body?

5–32. An irregularly shaped body which weighs 96 lb has moments of inertia about perpendicular axes through its center of mass of $I_x = 4$ slugs-ft^2, $I_y = 4$ slugs-ft^2, $I_z = 12$ slugs-ft^2. The products of inertia are $J_{xy} = 4$ slugs-ft^2, $J_{yz} = 0$, $J_{zx} = 0$. Are there any points in the body for which the ellipsoid of inertia is axially symmetrical? In either case, state carefully the reasons for your conclusions.

*5–33. Prove that the propeller-shaft axis is a principal axis for a two-bladed propeller.

5–34. (a) Find the directions of a set of principal axes associated with the point at a corner of a homogeneous cube.

(b) Draw the ellipsoid of inertia associated with that point.

5–35. A cube is made up of two homogeneous halves glued together. Assume that the density of the lower half is three times that of the upper half.

(a) Sketch the ellipsoid of inertia associated with the geometric center of the cube. (Explain the reasoning involved.)

(b) Where is the center of mass of the cube?

(c) For whatever point seems convenient for you somewhere *on the surface* of the cube, locate the principal axes and calculate the principal moments of inertia [in terms of those in (a)].

5–36. A laminated wooden sphere which is resting on a table is made up of woods of different kinds so that its density decreases in each layer from the point of contact to the top. Thus its center of mass is only $\frac{1}{3}$ of a diameter up from the point of contact. (a) Find one or more sets of principal axes with origin at the center of mass. (b) Is there a set of principal axes with origin at the sphere's surface at the same height as the center of mass? If so, find it.

5–37. If we consider the mass properties of an ordinary blackboard eraser, (a) choose a point of the eraser for which you can readily specify the principal axis directions. Specify them. (b) Find a point for which the eraser's ellipsoid of inertia has an axis of symmetry. (c) Can you find a point for which it is spherical?

5–38. For that famous gyroscopic device, the Australian boomerang sketched in Fig. 5–20, (a) find the principal axes through its center of mass, explain your reasoning, and (b) sketch the corresponding ellipsoid of inertia. Assume that the boomerang is quite thin, untwisted, and looks the same whether viewed from top or bottom.

5–39. Sketch (in three views if you prefer) the ellipsoid of inertia associated with the point at one end of a football. Be careful to indicate the relative dimensions of the axes of the ellipsoid.

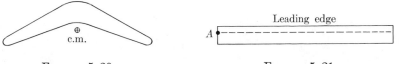

FIGURE 5–20   FIGURE 5–21

5–40. Figure 5–21 illustrates the top view of a helicopter blade hinged at A so that it can flap up and down. Assume that the blade has uniform properties along its span and that the airfoil section at each station is a symmetrical one. Assume, also, that the dotted line connects the centers of mass of each local section.

(a) Find the principal axis directions for point A and state the reasoning by which you obtained them.

(b) Sketch the ellipsoid of inertia associated with A.

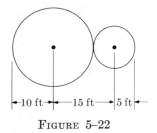

FIGURE 5–22

5–41. A new satellite is made up of two spheres as shown in Fig. 5–22. The larger sphere of radius 10 ft has a mass of 50 slugs and a moment of inertia about any central axis of the sphere of 4000 slugs-ft². The smaller sphere, of radius 5 ft, has a mass of 10 slugs and a moment of inertia about any one of its central axes of 40 slugs-ft².

(a) Find the center of mass of the satellite.

(b) Choose a convenient set of axes through the center of mass of the satellite and calculate its inertia tensor for those axes.

(c) Sketch the ellipsoid of inertia associated with the satellite's center of mass.

5–42. Start with the equation for an ellipse in the XY-plane $x^2/a^2 + y^2/b^2 = 1$, and write it in terms of a pair of axes $X_1 Y_1$ rotated about Z by an angle θ. Note that the cross-product terms go to zero when $\theta = n(\pi/2)$ for integral values of n.

5–43. Note that the matrix equation $\{H\} = [I]\{\omega\}$ can be written in an extended vector notation in which the inertia tensor is put in the dyadic form,

$$\mathbf{I} = I_x\mathbf{ii} + J_{xy}\mathbf{ij} + J_{xz}\mathbf{ik} + I_y\mathbf{jj} + J_{yz}\mathbf{jk} + J_{yx}\mathbf{ji} + I_z\mathbf{kk} + J_{zx}\mathbf{ki} + J_{zy}\mathbf{kj}.$$

With the definitions

$$\mathbf{ii} \cdot \mathbf{i} = \mathbf{i}, \qquad \mathbf{ii} \cdot \mathbf{j} = 0, \qquad \mathbf{ii} \cdot \mathbf{k} = 0,$$
$$\mathbf{ij} \cdot \mathbf{i} = 0, \qquad \mathbf{ij} \cdot \mathbf{j} = \mathbf{i}, \qquad \mathbf{ij} \cdot \mathbf{k} = 0, \text{ etc.,}$$

show that $\mathbf{H} = \mathbf{I} \cdot \boldsymbol{\omega}$. Also show that $T = \frac{1}{2}\boldsymbol{\omega} \cdot \mathbf{I} \cdot \boldsymbol{\omega}$.

FIGURE 5–23

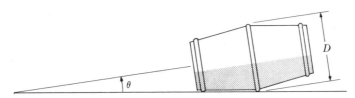

FIGURE 5–24

*5–44. Looking at the steadily precessing flywheel of Fig. 5–8(a) and Example 5–9, can you find the forces and moments transmitted by the flywheel to its horizontal shaft? Can you further find the load, shear, and bending-moment distributions of both the horizontal and vertical shafts?

5–45. Suppose our simple precessing flywheel model of Fig. 5–8(a) is sitting completely still. In order to start it up we apply simultaneously a constant torque A to the flywheel about the X-axis and a constant torque B to the vertical supporting axis Z. Assume that the axes supporting the flywheel are very stiff and very light. The mass properties of the flywheel (m, I_x, I_y, I_z, $r_{c.m.}$) are given known quantities.

(a) Describe the subsequent motion of the flywheel as a function of time.

(b) Find the size of the moment about Y which the supporting system must be applying *to the flywheel* at any later instant.

5–46. Ski jumpers have often been observed, when in flight, to rotate their arms rapidly in the vertical plane as shown (Fig. 5–23). Suppose a jumper suddenly rotates his arms in unison through 10 rev. Describe in detail the effect of this on his motion. (Assume that, except for his arms, his body and skis form a rigid unit.)

5–47. Another sport, not yet a part of the Olympic games, involves rolling an empty aluminum beer keg in a circular path on a smooth horizontal floor as illustrated in Fig. 5–24 so that two of the three rings remain in contact with the floor. In terms of θ, D, and whatever mass parameters you need, find the shortest time for the keg to complete a full circle on the ground without having the small ring lift from the floor (assume that there is no slipping).

5–48. A rigid body is rotating about an axis fixed in space. There are no external moments acting on the body. Show, using suitable equations, that the body is rotating about a principal axis.

5–49. Along the edges adjacent to one corner of a suitcase, we have painted a coordinate system $OXYZ$. The suitcase contains a flywheel running on bearings

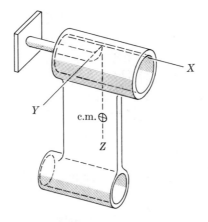

FIGURE 5–25

fixed in the suitcase. When moments M_x, M_y, and M_z are applied, one at a time, the suitcase tends to rotate at the first instant according to the following table:

$$M_x \text{ gives } \omega_y > 0, \quad \omega_z < 0, \quad \omega_x = 0,$$
$$M_y \text{ gives } \omega_x < 0, \quad \omega_y = \omega_z = 0,$$
$$M_z \text{ gives } \omega_x > 0, \quad \omega_y = \omega_z = 0.$$

Sketch the direction of the angular velocity of the flywheel with respect to the suitcase.

5–50. Suppose you were asked to swing a piece of an actuating linkage system as a physical pendulum, as shown in Fig. 5–25, to find its moment of inertia about X. It is supported at only a single point directly above the center of gravity in order to minimize friction. However, you soon find that no matter how carefully you start the piece swinging about X, it soon is doing some swinging about Z as well, which almost seems to be a higher frequency. Can you explain this somewhat unexpected behavior?

5–51. Suppose that in mounting a flywheel on a horizontal shaft, as shown in Fig. 5–8(a), the hole is drilled through the flywheel center of mass slightly askew. Thus the flywheel's axis of symmetry makes a small angle α with the shaft (the X-axis), and the flywheel appears to wobble as it is forced to spin at constant ω_x and precess at constant Ω about Z.

(a) What axes and set of equations will you use to find the moments required to produce this flywheel motion?

(b) Find the required moments, specifying the flywheel characteristics which you need.

5–52. A cylindrical homogeneous body is mounted on a shaft with its center of mass on the shaft center-line, but its axis of symmetry is fixed at a small angle θ with the shaft.

(a) If the shaft rotates in fixed bearings at constant ω, find the moment exerted by the body on the shaft.

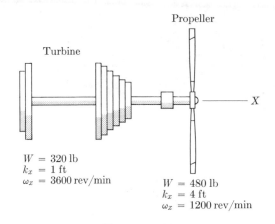

$W = 320$ lb
$k_x = 1$ ft
$\omega_x = 3600$ rev/min

$W = 480$ lb
$k_x = 4$ ft
$\omega_x = 1200$ rev/min

FIGURE 5–26

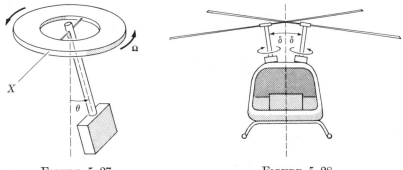

FIGURE 5–27   FIGURE 5–28

(b) Show that the body has a tendency to try to increase or decrease θ depending on its length-to-diameter ratio, L/D.

(c) Determine the range of L/D to which each of these tendencies corresponds and evaluate the ellipsoid of inertia for the critical L/D. $I_{\text{axial}} = \frac{1}{8}mD^2$, $I_{\text{c.m. transverse}} = \frac{1}{16}mD^2 + \frac{1}{12}mL^2$.

5–53. A turboprop single-engined airplane (Fig. 5–26) is making a steady horizontal left turn of 6°/sec. Ignore the rotating machinery in the speed reduction gear box and find the moment exerted *on the airplane* by the propeller-turbine assembly with the given weights, radii of gyration, and rotational speeds.

5–54. If the supporting ring (Fig. 5–27) is rotating about the vertical at the constant rate $\boldsymbol{\Omega}$, what steady angle θ about X may the suspended object assume? Consider that the necessary mass and inertia information is given and that X is a principal axis of the suspended object.

5–55. After hitting a gust, a jet airplane is pitching about its horizontal Y-axis at the angular velocity $\Omega_y = e^{-t/2} \sin 3t$. The jet turbine is simultaneously rotating about an axis parallel to the airplane's X-axis at an angular velocity of 10,000 rev/min. (a) What is the angular acceleration of the turbine? (b) What

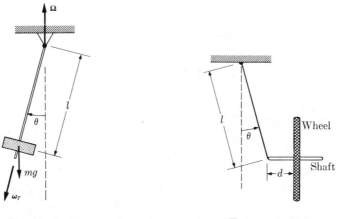

FIGURE 5–29   FIGURE 5–30

moments must be exerted on it by the airplane in this motion if $I_x = 40$, $I_y = 400$ slugs-ft^2?

5–56. A commercial helicopter employs two intermeshing rotors (Fig. 5–28) whose axes are tilted on either side of the vertical as shown. Considering each rotor as a flywheel, is any net precessional moment on the rotors required if the craft (a) executes a horizontal, unbanked turn, (b) attempts a loop? Explain briefly with the aid of diagrams.

*5–57. (a) Write down an expression for the work required to bring the pendulous gyro shown in Fig. 5–29 from a rest position hanging vertically without spinning to the steady state indicated. Note that ω_r represents the angular velocity about the flywheel axis seen by a nonrotating observer. (b) By using Lagrange's equations, find the differential equations of unsteady motion of the gyro.

5–58. As illustrated in Fig. 5–30, a bicycle wheel is mounted on a short hub, the end of which is supported by a string from a fixed point. It is observed that the wheel is perfectly happy to precess about the vertical dotted line while spinning with its axle horizontal. During this steady precession, the string is observed to make a constant angle θ with the vertical.

(a) Write down *all* of the necessary equations of motion for the steadily precessing wheel.

(b) Rederive them using Lagrange's equations.

CHAPTER 6

RIGID-BODY DYNAMICS

In this chapter, we will look at a variety of problem areas in which we can both illustrate different applications of the equations of rigid-body motion and indicate the body of knowledge which has developed historically. We will emphasize the rotational motion of the rigid body because the translational motion, as exemplified by the motion of the center of mass, is normally handled just like the particle motion of Chapters 2 and 3. Basic to our entire Newtonian approach, however, is the concept of the unaccelerated nonrotating Galilean observer who can see absolute linear acceleration and absolute angular velocity. Just as in particle dynamics we insisted on an "unaccelerated enough" reference system in each problem, we must be sure here that our observers are "nonrotating enough," even if they accelerate with the center of mass of the rigid body.

Thinking then primarily of the rotational motion and from a mathematical point of view, we have two broad classes of problems. In the first, we presume that we are given the motion of the rigid body and are seeking the forces and moments which produce it. Here the equations of motion (5–25) and (5–26) become merely algebraic equations in the unknown forces and moments, and the mathematics is quite trivial. In the second class, the forces and moments are given directly or are known in terms of the coordinates, and we seek the motion of the body. We now find that the equations of motion form a set of simultaneous differential equations which are ordinarily far from linear because in almost every form of the rotational equations (5–26) that we derived in Section 5–4, the components of the angular velocities appear as products. In many situations, we find it feasible and enlightening to linearize the equations about some equilibrium point or steady motion; that is, we look only at small changes in suitably defined perturbation variables so that squares and products of these quantities can be neglected. Nevertheless, this second class is far more difficult mathematically, and we soon develop a tendency to set up problems wherever possible in terms of the first class. In fact, the skill with which we state to ourselves the simplified problems from which we hope to gain insight into the actual problems before us can be far more important in obtaining useful information than knowledge of sophisticated and advanced analytical techniques

From another more physical point of view, we may remember that in particle dynamics we very often found ourselves using the concepts of steady circular motion or its close relative, simple harmonic motion. In rotational motion of rigid bodies, we will find, in a similar fashion, great use for the simple ideas of steady swinging or precession of vectors such as $\mathbf{H}$ and $\boldsymbol{\omega}$ and will also find that often our differential equations have sinusoidal solutions. Consequently, we will emphasize these ideas in our illustrations.

We will also find that many of our rigid bodies will have an axis of mass symmetry and will be much more amenable to analysis than those bodies lacking such an axis. Of course most objects which are designed primarily to rotate, such as rotors and flywheels, are naturally given some axial symmetry. Many other bodies, such as aircraft and ships for which rotation is only incidental to their main function, may well have only three principal axes through the appropriate reference points. In only a very few cases will our rigid bodies exhibit spherical mass symmetry.

6–1 Constraints and degrees of freedom. According to our ideas in Chapters 4 and 5, a major advantage of the rigid-body concept is that no more than six independent coordinates are required to completely specify the body's motion. We were further able to show that, insofar as the right-hand sides of the equations of motion were concerned, the translation and rotation could be handled independently; that is, the three translational coordinates need not appear in the rotational equations and vice versa. However, in many problems, this basic uncoupling of rotation and translation cannot be exploited because of the existence of specific kinematic constraints relating various coordinates or degrees of freedom. Thus, for a body rolling without slipping, the angular velocity of the body and the linear velocity of its center of mass are directly related and serve to couple the equations of motion.*

There is another situation in which we do not have the luxury of working with uncoupled equations. Quite often, we find that the moments exerted on our rigid body depend partly on its translation and that some external forces depend on its rotational motion. This is particularly true of bodies moving through liquids and gases. In this case it may still be possible, for small perturbations from equilibrium, to group the coordinates into two uncoupled sets of three. This is illustrated in Example 6–11 where the dynamic stability of an aircraft permits the three coordinates of motion in the vertical plane to be separated from those of the "lateral" motion.

EXAMPLE 6–1. In order to illustrate that the external moment may be dependent on the linear motion of a rigid body, let's look at a billiard ball

---

* If we expect to do much work involving constraints, we should be familiar with the classifications holonomic, nonholonomic, scleronomic, and rheonomic, which are often used in the literature. See various references, for example, Goldstein, Ref. 2, p. 11.

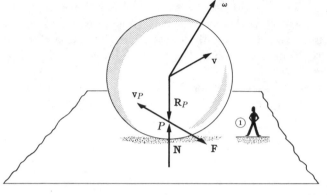

(a)

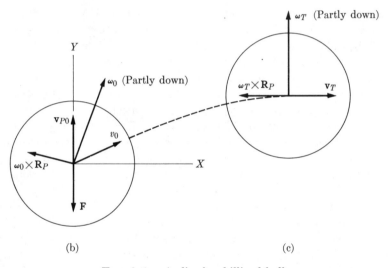

(b)   (c)

Fig. 6–1. A slipping billiard ball.

just after it has been struck off-center by a cue. We will assume that its center has a linear velocity $\mathbf{v}$ and that its angular velocity $\boldsymbol{\omega}$ is such that there is slipping at the point of contact with the flat table. In fact, the velocity of the point of contact P is just (see Fig. 6–1a)

$$\mathbf{v}_P = \mathbf{v} + \boldsymbol{\omega} \times \mathbf{R}_P,$$

where $\mathbf{R}_P$ is the vertical radius from the ball's center of mass. With a coefficient of friction μ, the ball will experience a friction force F of magnitude

$$F = \mu N = \mu m g$$

opposite in direction to $\mathbf{v}_P$. Note that since the ball has no vertical motion, the weight is exactly balanced by the normal reaction force $\mathbf{N}$.

The equations of motion are

$$\sum \mathbf{F}_e = \mathbf{F} = m\mathbf{a} = m\dot{\mathbf{v}}$$

for the horizontal motion of the center of mass and, since we have spherical mass symmetry about the center of mass [see Eq. (5–26f)],

$$\sum \mathbf{M}_e = \mathbf{R}_P \times \mathbf{F} = I\boldsymbol{\alpha} = I\dot{\boldsymbol{\omega}},$$

where I is the moment of inertia about the center of mass. These two vector equations represent five scalar equations in seven unknowns which are two components of $\mathbf{v}$, three of $\boldsymbol{\omega}$, and two of $\mathbf{F}$. The additional two scalar equations which we need are represented by the kinematic relation between $\mathbf{v}$, $\mathbf{v}_P$, and $\boldsymbol{\omega}$. We can see that the equations of motion are not uncoupled because the direction of $\mathbf{F}$, which determines the moment axis, is directly related to $\mathbf{v}_P$ and thus to the linear velocity $\mathbf{v}$ of the rigid body.

To solve for the motion during the slipping, let's look more closely at the direction of $\mathbf{v}_P$ and thus $\mathbf{F}$. Note that the change in velocity of successive points of contact is caused only by changes in $\mathbf{v}$ and $\boldsymbol{\omega}$ since, for each, $\mathbf{R}_P$ is a vertical vector.* This change in $\mathbf{v}_P$ is

$$\dot{\mathbf{v}} + \dot{\boldsymbol{\omega}} \times \mathbf{R}_P = \frac{\mathbf{F}}{m} + \left(\frac{\mathbf{R}_P \times \mathbf{F}}{I}\right) \times \mathbf{R}_P = \frac{\mathbf{F}}{m}\left(1 + \frac{mR_P^2}{I}\right),$$

which is in the direction of $\mathbf{F}$. But $\mathbf{F}$ is in the direction of $\mathbf{v}_P$; so $\mathbf{v}_P$, its change, and $\mathbf{F}$ are in the same direction which therefore does not change with time. Thus the center of mass moves like a particle in a constant parallel force field. From our experience with uniform gravitational fields, we can expect the center of mass to follow a parabolic path. To show this, we can look down on the ball in Fig. 6–1(b) which has typical initial values of $\mathbf{v}$, $\boldsymbol{\omega}$, and $\mathbf{v}_P$. Putting Y in the constant direction of $\mathbf{v}_P$ with XY the horizontal plane, we can write

$$-\mu mg = m\dot{v}_y, \qquad 0 = m\dot{v}_x.$$

Integrating, we get

$$v_y = v_{y_0} - \mu gt, \qquad y = v_{y_0}t - \tfrac{1}{2}\mu gt^2,$$
$$v_x = v_{x_0}, \qquad x = v_{x_0}t,$$

---

* We are not looking for the acceleration of the point of the body instantaneously in contact. Rather we want to see how the velocity of a contact point compares with that of its predecessor. In the terms of fluid flow and continuum theory we are looking for the local derivative, not the substantial derivative of $\boldsymbol{\omega} \times \mathbf{R}_P$, as seen from the center of mass. See Section 4–2.

which describe a parabolic path for the center of mass until slipping stops and **F** disappears.

The rotational equations become, in component form,

$$-R_P F = I\dot{\omega}_x,$$
$$0 = I\dot{\omega}_y,$$
$$0 = I\dot{\omega}_z$$

so that, with $I = \frac{2}{5}mR_P^2$,

$$\omega_x = \omega_{x_0} - \frac{5}{2}\frac{\mu g}{R_P}t,$$
$$\omega_y = \omega_{y_0},$$
$$\omega_z = \omega_{z_0}.$$

The velocity of slip is

$$v_P = v_y + R_P\omega_x = -\tfrac{7}{2}\mu g t + v_{y_0} + R_P\omega_{x_0}.$$

From this equation, we can find the time T at which slipping stops as

$$T = \frac{v_{y_0} + R_P\omega_{x_0}}{\tfrac{7}{2}\mu g}.$$

As shown in Fig. 6–1(c) at time T, we find the ball rolling in a straight line without slipping. It still has the original vertical component of angular velocity which will show up markedly if the ball strikes a cushion.

Note that in this unusual case of spherical mass symmetry, we could use advantageously a nonrotating set of axes XYZ in writing the equations of motion. In none of the remaining examples in this chapter will we again be so fortunate. ▲

EXAMPLE 6–2. To see the coupling produced by a kinematic constraint, let's look at a coin rolling in a generally wobbly fashion without slipping on a horizontal surface (Fig. 6–2). Since the coin has an axis of mass symmetry let's put X along this axis. The leaning of the coin from the vertical plane is measured by the elevation θ of X from the horizontal. The orientation of the coin's plane about a vertical axis is describable by the azimuth angle ψ between a reference horizontal direction and the vertical plane including X. Since any pair of axes through the center of mass are principal, we can, for convenience, put Z down through the point of contact P which makes Y always horizontal. Here we are tacitly assuming that the coin is very thin compared with its radius, otherwise Z would miss the point of contact.

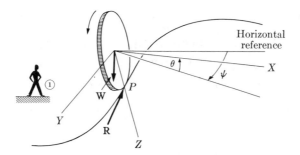

FIG. 6–2. A coin rolling without slipping.

For the kinematic constraint of no slip, we can write the vector equation

$$\mathbf{v}_P = \mathbf{v} + \boldsymbol{\omega} \times \mathbf{z}_P = 0$$

or, in scalar form,

$$v_x = -\omega_y z_P, \qquad v_y = \omega_x z_P, \qquad v_z = 0.$$

The angular motion $\boldsymbol{\Omega}$ of the axis system is due only to changes in the Euler angles θ and ψ as [Eq. (5–11)]

$$\boldsymbol{\Omega} = \frac{\overline{d\theta}}{dt} + \frac{\overline{d\psi}}{dt}$$

or, in scalar form,

$$\Omega_x = -\dot{\psi}\sin\theta, \qquad \Omega_y = \dot{\theta}, \qquad \Omega_z = \dot{\psi}\cos\theta,$$

and, because X is kept along a body axis, $\boldsymbol{\Omega}$ of the axes is related to the angular velocity $\boldsymbol{\omega}$ of the body as [Eq. (5–9)]

$$\Omega_y = \omega_y, \qquad \Omega_z = \omega_z.$$

The translational equation of the motion of the coin's center of mass in vector form is, in terms of ground reaction $\mathbf{R}$ and the weight $\mathbf{W}$,

$$\mathbf{R} + \mathbf{W} = m\mathbf{a} = m\dot{\mathbf{v}}.$$

In components along the rotating axes, this becomes three scalar equations (see Example 5–5)

$$R_x - mg\sin\theta = m(\dot{v}_x - \dot{\psi}v_y\cos\theta),$$
$$R_y = m(\dot{v}_y + \dot{\psi}v_x\cos\theta),$$
$$R_z + mg\cos\theta = m(-\dot{\theta}v_x - \dot{\psi}v_y\sin\theta).$$

Eliminating v_x and v_y by using the equations of constraint gives

$$R_x - mg \sin \theta = mz_P(-\ddot{\theta} - \dot{\psi}\omega_x \cos \theta),$$
$$R_y = mz_P(\dot{\omega}_x - \dot{\psi}\dot{\theta} \cos \theta),$$
$$R_z + mg \cos \theta = mz_P(\dot{\theta}^2 - \dot{\psi}\omega_x \sin \theta).$$

The rotational equations of motion about the center of mass are [Eq. (5–26e)]

$$\sum M_x = -z_P R_y = I_x \dot{\omega}_x,$$
$$\sum M_y = z_P R_x = I_y(\ddot{\theta} + \dot{\psi}^2 \sin \theta \cos \theta) + \dot{\psi} I_x \omega_x \cos \theta,$$
$$\sum M_z = 0 = I_y(d/dt[\dot{\psi} \cos \theta] - \dot{\psi}\dot{\theta} \sin \theta) - \dot{\theta} I_x \omega_x.$$

Note that we have six equations in the unknowns R_x, R_y, R_z, θ, ψ, ω_x, which form a set of nonlinear differential equations. You will have the opportunity in problems at the end of the chapter to look at a number of special simple solutions giving steady motion. Can you visualize one or two such motions?

As an example, we might suspect that the coin can roll in a circle at constant θ, $\dot{\psi}$, and ω_x. If we eliminate R_y from its equations, we get

$$(I_x + mz_P^2)\dot{\omega}_x - mz_P^2\dot{\psi}\dot{\theta} \cos \theta = 0,$$

which is satisfied for $\dot{\omega}_x = \dot{\theta} = 0$. Similarly, the $\sum M_z$ equation is satisfied. The equation formed by eliminating R_x,

$$I_y(\ddot{\theta} + \dot{\psi}^2 \sin \theta \cos \theta) + I_x\dot{\psi}\omega_x \cos \theta + mgz_P^2(\ddot{\theta} + \dot{\psi}\omega_x \cos \theta)$$
$$- mgz_P \sin \theta = 0,$$

reduces to

$$I_y\dot{\psi}^2 \sin \theta \cos \theta + (I_x + mz_P^2)\omega_x\dot{\psi} \cos \theta - mgz_P \sin \theta = 0.$$

For a given θ and $\dot{\psi}$, we can find the corresponding ω_x. For constant $\dot{\theta}$, ω_y is zero, which gives v_x of zero through the constraint equation. Thus

$$R_x = mg \sin \theta - m\dot{\psi}v_y \cos \theta,$$
$$R_y = 0,$$
$$R_z = -mg \cos \theta - m\dot{\psi}v_y \sin \theta.$$

If we refer $\mathbf{R}$ to horizontal and vertical directions instead of X and Z, we get

$$R_H = -m\dot{\psi}v_y = -m\dot{\psi}v, \qquad R_V = -mg.$$

Because R_H must come entirely from friction, it must not be more than μmg or slipping will occur, and the equations will no longer hold. ▲

EXAMPLE 6–3. Most of us are very familiar with the behavior of a pendulum swinging in small-amplitude planar motion from a fixed pivot. We also know that the response of the pendulum to accelerated motion of the pivot can be quite striking. Let's derive the equations of motion of a pendulum with accelerated pivot in order to demonstrate a problem in which it is convenient to use an ordinarily unacceptable moment center. The equations can also be specialized to a number of very interesting situations.

A pendulum with an axis of mass symmetry along the line from the pivot point to the center of mass is shown in Fig. 6–3(a). We will put the origin at the pivot point and again put X along the axis of symmetry. We can then choose to keep Z in the vertical plane with X so that Y remains horizontal as usual. The ordinary sinusoidal pendulum motion would be about Y. The orientation of the axes is conveniently described by the azimuth ψ to the vertical XZ-plane and the elevation θ up to Z from the horizontal plane. The angle θ is also the displacement of X from the vertical, so we must revise our usual relations between $\boldsymbol{\Omega}$ and the Euler angles to account for this new choice of θ.

If the motion $\mathbf{v}_P$ and $\mathbf{a}_P$ of the pivot point P is known to us, we need, for equations of motion, just the general moment equation (4–8)

$$\sum \mathbf{M}_{eP} = \frac{d\mathbf{H}_P}{dt} + m\ddot{\mathbf{R}}_{\text{c.m.}} \times \mathbf{a}_P,$$

with $d\mathbf{H}_P/dt$ specialized as in Eq. (5–26e) for X, an axis of mass symmetry. The only external moment about P is that due to the weight so that, in component form,

$$M_x = 0 = I_x \frac{d\omega_x}{dt},$$

$$M_y = -mgR_{\text{c.m.}} \sin \theta = I_y \frac{d\omega_y}{dt} - \Omega_x I_z \omega_z + \Omega_z I_x \omega_x - mR_{\text{c.m.}} a_{zP},$$

$$M_z = 0 = I_z \frac{d\omega_z}{dt} - \Omega_y I_x \omega_x + \Omega_x I_y \omega_y + mR_{\text{c.m.}} a_{yP}.$$

Let's assume that our pendulum has no initial absolute angular velocity about X. The first equation tells us that ω_x remains zero. With this and with $I_y = I_z = I_T$, the transverse moment of inertia, the equations become

$$\omega_x = 0,$$

$$-(mgR_{\text{c.m.}} \sin \theta - mR_{\text{c.m.}} a_{zP}) = I_T \left[\frac{d\omega_y}{dt} - \Omega_x \omega_z + \Omega_z(0) \right],$$

$$-mR_{\text{c.m.}} a_{yP} = I_T \left[\frac{d\omega_z}{dt} - \Omega_y(0) + \Omega_x \omega_y \right].$$

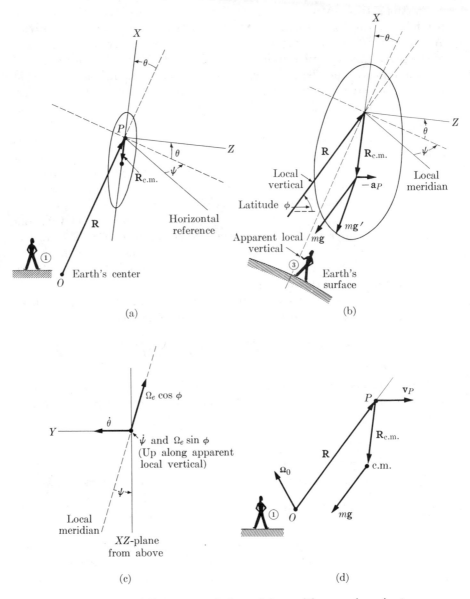

FIG. 6–3. Axially symmetrical pendulum with a moving pivot.

Note that for this special case of $\omega_x = 0$, the right-hand sides of the Y and Z equations are nothing more than $I_T \boldsymbol{\alpha}_T$, where $\boldsymbol{\alpha}_T$ is evaluated [Eq. (5–8)] for $\omega_x = 0$, $\Omega_y = \omega_y$, and $\Omega_z = \omega_z$. Returning then to vector notation, we have

$$\mathbf{R}_{\text{c.m.}} \times m\mathbf{g} - m\mathbf{R}_{\text{c.m.}} \times \mathbf{a}_P = I_T \boldsymbol{\alpha}_T,$$

or

$$\mathbf{R}_{\text{c.m.}} \times (m\mathbf{g} - m\mathbf{a}_P) = I_T \boldsymbol{\alpha}_T,$$

where $(-m\mathbf{a}_P)$ has the appearance of a D'Alembert inertia force applied at the center of mass.

If $\mathbf{a}_P$ is a constant, we can see that the pendulum behaves as if it were in an augmented gravity field $\mathbf{g} - \mathbf{a}_P$. Thus, for a point "stationary" on the surface of the rotating earth which is actually accelerated toward the axis of rotation of the earth, the vertical measured by a pendulum or plumb bob is not quite the local direction of the gravitational field. (In fact, in the literature of geodesy, $\mathbf{g}$ is often used to represent the direction of this "measured vertical.") This acceleration effect is accentuated in a vehicle moving rapidly around the earth and, for a satellite, $\mathbf{a}_P$ cancels $\mathbf{g}$.

Strictly speaking, our reference vertical direction of Fig. 6–3 is changing slowly with time, especially if we are moving over the rotating earth. The direction to which we refer the azimuth ψ may also be changing with time. If for instance we are rotating observers moving with the earth at $\boldsymbol{\Omega}_e$, we naturally measure θ and ψ from the local vertical and meridian, respectively. These reference directions are not actually fixed in inertial space but instead appear stationary to us as earthbound observers. Thus the absolute angular velocity of the XYZ-axes can be written in terms of their motion seen by us plus our own angular velocity $\boldsymbol{\Omega}_e$ as

$$\boldsymbol{\Omega} = \overline{\frac{d\psi}{dt}} + \overline{\frac{d\theta}{dt}} + \boldsymbol{\Omega}_e.$$

Since we are keeping X along the pendulum's axis of symmetry, we know (Eq. 5–9) that $\Omega_y = \omega_y$ and $\Omega_z = \omega_z$, so that the absolute angular velocity of the pendulum (for which we assumed $\omega_x = 0$) is just

$$\boldsymbol{\omega} = \boldsymbol{\Omega}_y + \boldsymbol{\Omega}_z.$$

We can now look at *the apparent effects of the earth's rotation on a lowly damped pendulum* hanging from a pivot fixed at the earth's surface. One effect is that the pendulum has a slightly modified equilibrium position. It tends to hang in the direction $\mathbf{g} - \mathbf{a}_P$ rather than $\mathbf{g}$, where $\mathbf{a}_P$ represents the centripetal acceleration $\Omega_e^2 R \cos \phi$, where ϕ is the latitude. The other most noticeable effect is that the plane of oscillation of the pendulum appears to swing steadily at a fraction of earth rate. To show this latter property of the *Foucault pendulum*, we can look at our equations of motion for this special case. Since we expect the pendulum to oscillate about the apparent local vertical $\mathbf{g}' = \mathbf{g} - \mathbf{a}_P$ as shown in Fig. 6–3(b), we might well refer θ to this apparent vertical and measure the azimuth ψ in the apparent horizontal plane. Then the apparent moment $\mathbf{R}_{\text{c.m.}} \times m(\mathbf{g} - \mathbf{a}_P)$ is entirely about Y and the equations of motion become

$$-mg'R_{\text{c.m.}} \sin \theta = I_T \left(\frac{d\omega_y}{dt} - \Omega_x \omega_z \right), \qquad 0 = I_T \left(\frac{d\omega_z}{dt} + \Omega_x \omega_y \right).$$

Referring to Fig. 6–3(c), we can show $\overline{d\psi}/dt$, $\overline{d\theta}/dt$ and Ω_e in locally (apparent) vertical and horizontal directions. Taking components along X, Y, and Z gives, for $\boldsymbol{\omega}$ of the body and $\boldsymbol{\Omega}$ of the axes,

$$\omega_x = 0, \qquad \Omega_x = (\Omega_e \sin \phi + \dot\psi) \cos \theta + \Omega_e \cos \phi \cos \psi \sin \theta,$$

$$\omega_y = \Omega_y = \dot\theta - \Omega_e \cos \phi \sin \psi,$$

$$\omega_z = \Omega_z = (\Omega_e \sin \phi + \dot\psi) \sin \theta - \Omega_e \cos \phi \cos \psi \cos \theta.$$

Assuming θ small, $\dot\theta$ much larger than either Ω_e or $\dot\psi$ and retaining only the largest terms, we get from our two equations of motion

$$I_T \ddot\theta + mg'R_{\text{c.m.}}\theta = 0, \qquad \Omega_e \sin \phi + \dot\psi = 0.$$

Thus the Foucault pendulum does oscillate about the $\mathbf{g}'$-direction while its plane of oscillation, the XZ-plane, slowly rotates around the apparent local vertical at $-\Omega_e \sin \phi$. Does this check your intuition at the poles and at the equator? What does a nonrotating observer see for the average angular motion of the axes?

In another view of the same basic pendulum arrangement, we might ask ourselves if we can *design a pendulum* such that it appears to be relatively *insensitive to accelerations of the pivot*. This sort of pendulum would be very useful in moving vehicles such as aircraft because, as the vehicle moves around the surface of the earth, the pendulum would be unaffected by local maneuverings and would still point in the direction of the local vertical $\mathbf{g}$. To explore this situation, we can adopt the viewpoint of a nonrotating observer ① at the center of the earth (Fig. 6–3d) watching the vehicle's motion. He sees the swinging of the radius vector $\mathbf{R}$ (the local vertical) to the vehicle as caused by a "horizontal" $\boldsymbol{\Omega}_0$ where, for locally horizontal motions of the vehicle and thus the pivot,

$$\mathbf{v}_P = \boldsymbol{\Omega}_0 \times \mathbf{R}.$$

The horizontal acceleration of the vehicle and thus of the pivot of the pendulum is then

$$\mathbf{a}_{P\,\text{horiz}} = \dot{\boldsymbol{\Omega}}_0 \times \mathbf{R},$$

and we are neglecting, in the vertical direction, a term of the form $\Omega_0^2 R$ which is small compared with g.

The horizontal part $\mathbf{\Omega}_H$ of the axis system's angular velocity $\mathbf{\Omega}$, if we assume that θ is very small, is essentially the same as the angular velocity $\mathbf{\Omega}_T$ of the axis system perpendicular to X. This also represents the total absolute angular velocity $\boldsymbol{\omega}$ of the pendulum itself since ω_x for the pendulum is assumed to be zero. Thus,

$$\mathbf{\Omega}_H = \mathbf{\Omega}_T = \boldsymbol{\omega} = \mathbf{\Omega}_0 + \frac{\overline{d\theta}}{dt}.$$

The angular acceleration of the pendulum is then

$$\frac{d\boldsymbol{\omega}}{dt} = \boldsymbol{\alpha}_T = \dot{\mathbf{\Omega}}_0 + \frac{\overline{d^2\theta}}{dt^2}.$$

If we represent the *small* angle θ as a vector quantity $\boldsymbol{\theta}$, the equation of motion

$$\mathbf{R}_{\text{c.m.}} \times m(\mathbf{g} - \mathbf{a}_P) = I_T \boldsymbol{\alpha}_T$$

becomes first

$$\mathbf{R}_{\text{c.m.}} \times m\mathbf{g} = I_T(\dot{\mathbf{\Omega}}_0 + \ddot{\boldsymbol{\theta}}) + \mathbf{R}_{\text{c.m.}} \times m(\dot{\mathbf{\Omega}}_0 \times \mathbf{R}),$$

and then

$$I_T \ddot{\boldsymbol{\theta}} + mgR_{\text{c.m.}}\boldsymbol{\theta} = (I_T - mR_{\text{c.m.}}R)\dot{\mathbf{\Omega}}_0.$$

For the pendulum to be insensitive to $\dot{\mathbf{\Omega}}_0$ (and thus to "horizontal" pivot acceleration), we need merely make its coefficient zero by writing

$$I_T = mRR_{\text{c.m.}}$$

or, in terms of transverse radius of gyration k_T of the pendulum about the pivot,

$$\frac{R_{\text{c.m.}}}{k_T} = \frac{k_T}{R}.$$

This condition is known as *Schuler tuning* and is of fundamental importance in inertial guidance systems for vehicles, such as aircraft and submarines. Actually such a Schuler-tuned pendulum cannot be built as a simple physical pendulum because for R about 4000 mi and a reasonable size k_T, $R_{\text{c.m.}}$ is of the order of 10^{-6} in. (The actual arrangement of such a pendulous device is discussed in Section 6–5.) The period of a Schuler-tuned pendulum thus appears to be*

$$T = 2\pi\sqrt{I_T/mgR_{\text{c.m.}}} = 2\pi\sqrt{R/g} \cong 84 \text{ min.}$$

* The major effect of the gradient of the earth's field on this period is discussed in Example 6–7.

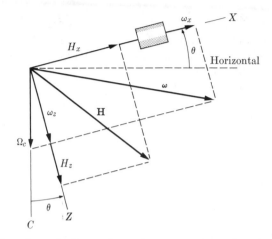

FIG. 6–4. Angular velocity and angular momentum of a steadily precessing flywheel.

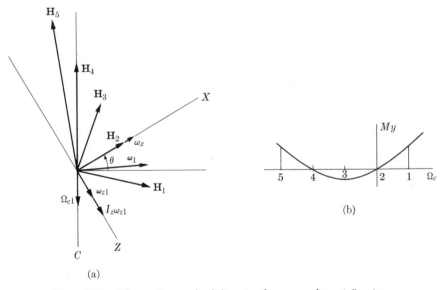

(a)

(b)

FIG. 6–5. Moments required for steady precession at 5 rates.

6–2 Forced precessions. In many problems of rotational motion, we are interested in the swinging or *precession of bodies with axial mass symmetry.* Since it is also quite usual for the component of angular velocity about the axis of symmetry to be constant in magnitude, the axial component of **H** swings but does not stretch. We have already looked at the kinematics of this kind of motion for a precessing flywheel in Example 5–4 and Fig. 5–10 where we put X along the axis of symmetry and Z in the plane formed by the X-axis and the precession vector $\mathbf{\Omega}_c$ (or $\overline{d\psi}/dt$) as shown again in Fig. 6–4 looking in along Y. We found that for θ, Ω_c, and ω_x, constant in magnitude, the angular acceleration of the flywheel is

$$\alpha_x = \alpha_z = 0,$$

$$\alpha_y = \Omega_c^2 \sin\theta\cos\theta + \omega_x\Omega_c\cos\theta,$$

where

$$\Omega_x = -\Omega_c\sin\theta \neq \omega_x,$$

$$\Omega_y = 0 = \omega_y,$$

$$\Omega_z = \Omega_c\cos\theta = \omega_z.$$

To find the moment required to produce this steady precession of the flywheel, we can use Eq. (5–26e), which was derived for axial symmetry about X. Assuming that the origin is unaccelerated so that no correction term is needed, we have

$$M_x = I_x\frac{d\omega_x}{dt},$$

$$M_y = I_y\frac{d\omega_y}{dt} - \Omega_x I_z\omega_z + \Omega_z I_x\omega_x, \qquad\text{(5–26e)}$$

$$M_z = I_z\frac{d\omega_z}{dt} - \Omega_y I_x\omega_x + \Omega_x I_y\omega_y.$$

Here, these reduce to

$$M_x = M_z = 0,$$

$$M_y = I_z\Omega_c^2\sin\theta\cos\theta + I_x\omega_x\Omega_c\cos\theta \qquad\text{(6–1a)}$$

so that only a moment about Y is needed.* Note that M_y can be formed from α_y only by multiplying the two parts of α_y by different moments of inertia. In physical terms, this comes about because the moment is related to the precession of $\mathbf{H}$ while the angular acceleration is related to the swinging of $\boldsymbol{\omega}$. The components of $\mathbf{H}$ are different from $\boldsymbol{\omega}$ by just these moments of inertia,

$$H_x = I_x\omega_x, \qquad H_y = I_y\omega_y, \qquad H_z = I_z\omega_z.$$

Thus, $\mathbf{H}$ is not only different in magnitude but also in direction from $\boldsymbol{\omega}$. (See Fig. 6–4 where ω_y is assumed to be zero and $I_x < I_z$.)

The relative sizes of $\mathbf{H}$ and $\boldsymbol{\omega}$ for five different precession rates Ω_c is shown in Fig. 6–5(a). We can see that for an Ω_c of zero, no moment is required

---

* This reduces to the simpler case of Example 5–9 for $\theta = 0$; that is, $M_y = \Omega_c I_x\omega_x$.

because $\mathbf{H}$ does not swing. For a slightly negative Ω_c, a negative M_y is needed because $\mathbf{H}$ swings in the negative Y-direction and, conversely, for Ω_{c_5}, it swings slightly positive. Note, however, for Ω_{c_4} that the resultant $\mathbf{H}$ is aligned with Ω_c and does not precess. Apparently no external moment on the flywheel is required for this case, either, even though the flywheel appears to be in steady precession. To see this analytically we can plot M_y versus Ω_c from Eq. (6–1a). As shown in Fig. 6–5(b), the relationship is a parabola such that, for the given values of θ, I_x, I_z, and ω_x, no steady precession is possible for too large a negative M_y. However, for an acceptable M_y, there appear to be two possible rates of steady precession, one fast and one slow.

Note that Eq. (6–1a) could have been written in vector form as

$$\mathbf{M}_e = \mathbf{M}_y = \Omega_c \times \mathbf{H}. \tag{6–1b}$$

because $\mathbf{H}$ is constant in magnitude and thus only swinging at Ω_c. We can also note that in terms of a rotating observer ③ riding on axis system XYZ at the rate Ω_c, the vector $\mathbf{H}$ appears motionless so that in the expression relating rates of change seen by observers ① and ③ (see Eq. 2–55),

$$\frac{d\mathbf{H}}{dt} = \frac{d'\mathbf{H}}{dt} + \Omega_c \times \mathbf{H},$$

the term $d'\mathbf{H}/dt$ vanishes for a steady precession.

EXAMPLE 6–4. To show how easily these ideas can be used to find the moments necessary for given precessions, we will look at three different situations. First, if the aircraft of Example 5–5 is still in a steady climbing turn to the right, we can immediately find the precessional moment exerted by its three-bladed propeller on the propeller shaft at the propeller's center of mass.* Recognizing that Ω_c is just the rate of turn $\dot{\psi}$, we can write from Eq. (6–1a),

$$M_{\substack{\text{on} \\ \text{shaft}}} = -M_y = -(I_z\dot{\psi}^2 \sin\theta \cos\theta + I_x\omega_x\dot{\psi}\cos\theta),$$

where perhaps we should realize ω_x is not quite the rev/min of the propeller indicated to the pilot. These indicated rev/min are relative to the pilot who is rotating at Ω and we must write

$$\omega_{x_{\text{ind}}} = \omega_x - \Omega_x = \omega_x + \dot{\psi}\sin\theta.$$

Can you estimate reasonable sizes for the moments of inertia and angular velocities in this problem and find an order of magnitude for $(-M_y)$?

---

* The propeller also normally transmits a moment to the shaft due to the action of the air on the blades. We are looking only at the "gyroscopic" moment.

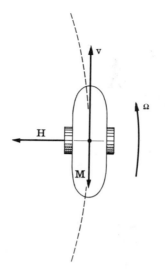

FIG. 6–6. Sidewheeler ferryboat in a steady turn.

As a second illustration we might look at the oldstyle ferryboats pro-
pelled by tremendous side paddle wheels. Even though the wheels revolved
rather slowly, their moment of inertia was so large that tremendous
moments were required to precess them when the ferryboat swung around
a turn. As shown in top view in Fig. 6–6, a steady left turn required that
a large moment (counterclockwise looking forward) be applied by the boat
to the wheels and their shaft. The only source of such a moment was the
hydrodynamic righting moment on the hull. Thus the boat had to lean
uncomfortably to the outside of the turn in order to apply the necessary
moment for precessing the paddle wheels. Can you visualize how the turn
starts and how the boat begins to lean over? How does it know when it
has leaned enough?

As a third illustration, we can watch an unsteady or oscillatory precession. Suppose an anemometer for measuring wind speed is mounted on the
top of a ship's mast while the ship is rolling violently in a gale. We might
ask whether the bending moment in the shaft at the anemometer's center
of mass is large enough to cause failure of the shaft. As an approximation,
we might say that the ship is rolling sinusoidally, but the anemometer is
spinning at a constant high rate. Using the axes shown in Fig. 6–7(a), we
can write, as a nonrotating observer ② riding with the center of mass,

$$\Omega_x = 0 \neq \omega_x = \text{constant},$$
$$\Omega_y = 0 = \omega_y,$$
$$\Omega_z = \dot{\theta} = \omega_z.$$

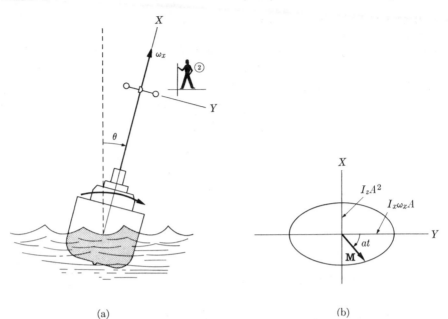

FIG. 6–7. Whirling anemometer on the mast of a rolling ship.

Since the anemometer has mass symmetry about X, we can find the moments required for the precession from Eq. (5–26e). Thus

$$M_x = 0, \qquad M_y = \dot{\theta} I_x \omega_x, \qquad M_z = I_z \ddot{\theta}.$$

With the sinusoidal rolling of the ship expressed as

$$\theta = A \sin at,$$

we have

$$M_y = I_x \omega_x A a \cos at, \qquad M_z = -I_z A a^2 \sin at,$$

where M_y undoubtedly reaches a larger maximum than M_z. Can you show that the resultant moment **M** at any instant is given by the elliptical construction in Fig. 6–7(b)? Does it seem reasonable that the precessional moment on the anemometer is large compared with the net aerodynamic moment? ▲

EXAMPLE 6–5. As two examples of the second and more difficult class of precessions in which we know only the relation of the applied moment to the motion and seek the character of the precessional motion, we can look at a charged spinning body in a uniform magnetic field and a spinning symmetrical top in a gravitational field.

Looking first at the charged body, we can assume that it is made up of particles with the same e/m (charge to mass) ratio and that in the uniform magnetic field, there will be no net external force acting on it. Thus we can assume its center of mass is at rest and an observer ① at the center of mass can say, without correction term Eq. (4–8),

$$\sum \mathbf{M}_e = \frac{d\mathbf{H}}{dt},$$

where the net external moment is approximately*

$$\sum \mathbf{M}_e = \mathbf{M} \times \mathbf{B}.$$

Here $\mathbf{M}$ is the magnetic moment of the current distribution set up by the spinning charged body, and $\mathbf{B}$ is the intensity of the uniform magnetic field.

We can relate the magnetic moment $\mathbf{M}$ to the current density $\mathbf{j}$ by integrating over the volume V of the body as (in Gaussian units)

$$\mathbf{M} = \frac{1}{2c} \int_V \mathbf{R} \times \mathbf{j} \, dV.$$

But the current density is given by the charge density and particle velocity $\mathbf{v}$ as

$$\mathbf{j} = \frac{e}{m} \rho \mathbf{v},$$

where ρ is the mass density. Thus,

$$\mathbf{M} = \frac{e}{2mc} \int_V \mathbf{R} \times \mathbf{v} \rho \, dV = \frac{e}{2mc} \mathbf{H},$$

which shows the direct relationship of the moment of momentum $\mathbf{H}$ and magnetic moment $\mathbf{M}$ characteristic of classical physics.

The equation of motion of the body now becomes simply

$$\mathbf{M}_e = \frac{d\mathbf{H}}{dt} = \frac{e}{2mc} \mathbf{H} \times \mathbf{B} = \left(-\frac{e}{2mc} \mathbf{B} \right) \times \mathbf{H}.$$

Comparison with Eq. (6–1b) shows that this is just the equation for steady precession of $\mathbf{H}$ about the direction of $\mathbf{B}$ at the angular velocity

$$\Omega = -\frac{eB}{2mc}.$$

---

* See Goldstein, Ref. 2, p. 176, for the more complete treatment after which this is patterned.

This steady precession of a spinning charged body is usually called the *Larmor precession*. (Note that we did not actually require the body to be rigid, so the result applies to any system of charged particles whose center of mass is at rest.)

Turning now to the spinning symmetrical rigid body in a uniform gravitational field, we will see that its motion can be far more complicated. Restricting ourselves to the case of the so-called *"heavy top" with one point fixed* (Fig. 6–8), which has been historically the subject of so much analysis, we will adopt the same axes and Euler angles that we have used before. (It would be more convenient and conventional to show Ω_c up and XYZ inverted, but it hardly seems worth the bother for our relatively short analysis.)

The only external moment acting on the top about the fixed point O is that due to gravity and, with our choice of axis directions, we can write,

$$\sum \mathbf{M}_e = 1 \times m\mathbf{g},$$

or

$$M_y = -mgl \cos \theta,$$
$$M_x = M_z = 0.$$

Substituting into the equations (5–26e) for bodies with axial symmetry and origin at a fixed point, we have

$$M_x = 0 = I_x \frac{d\omega_x}{dt},$$

$$M_y = -mgl \cos \theta = I_y \frac{d\omega_y}{dt} - \Omega_x I_z \omega_z + \Omega_z I_x \omega_x,$$

$$M_z = 0 = I_z \frac{d\omega_z}{dt} - \Omega_y I_x \omega_x + \Omega_x I_y \omega_y.$$

Remembering from many previous analyses that, with the symbols $\boldsymbol{\Omega}$ for the axis motion and $\boldsymbol{\omega}$ for the top, we can see that

$$\boldsymbol{\Omega} = \frac{\overline{d\psi}}{dt} + \frac{\overline{d\theta}}{dt} \qquad \Omega_y = \dot{\theta} = \omega_y,$$

$$\Omega_x = -\dot{\psi} \sin \theta \neq \omega_x, \qquad \Omega_z = \dot{\psi} \cos \theta = \omega_z.$$

Our equations of motion become, with $I_y = I_z = I_T$,

$$\omega_x = \text{constant},$$

$$- mgl \cos \theta = I_T \ddot{\theta} + I_T \dot{\psi}^2 \sin \theta \cos \theta + I_x \omega_x \dot{\psi} \cos \theta,$$

$$0 = I_T \frac{d}{dt} (\dot{\psi} \cos \theta) - \dot{\theta} I_x \omega_x - \dot{\theta} I_T \dot{\psi} \sin \theta.$$

Remembering from Eq. (6–1b) that we get steady precession when the

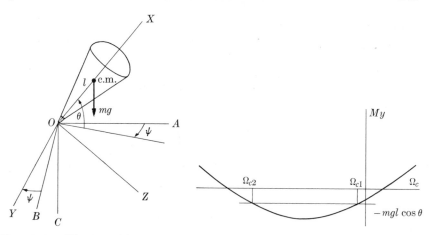

FIG. 6–8. The precession of a spin-   FIG. 6–9. The two steady preces-
ning top with its tip fixed.   sion rates for a top.

equations include no stretching of the **H** components and have the form

$$1 \times m\mathbf{g} = \boldsymbol{\Omega} \times \mathbf{H},$$

we note that $d\omega_y/dt$ and $d\omega_z/dt$ are zero when θ and $\dot{\psi}$ are constant. This, of course, corresponds to the steady precession about the vertical axis C that we looked at in some detail at the beginning of this section (see Figs. 6–4 and 6–5) where now M_y is the gravity moment.

Usually there are two possible rates of steady precession if there are any at all. To see this, look at the parabolic relation of M_y versus possible steady precession rates about C of Fig. 6–5(b) which was drawn for given I_x, I_T, θ, and ω_x. For our top, under these conditions, we can sketch the level of the gravity moment $-mgl \cos \theta$ as shown in Fig. 6–9. If it inter-sects the parabola, it indicates two possible steady precession rates, Ω_{c1} and Ω_{c2}, usually called slow and fast, respectively. If the gravity moment is too large, no steady precession is possible for the given conditions of the plot. Analytically, we can find the same precession rates from our Y-equa-tion of motion by making θ constant and replacing $\dot{\psi}$ with Ω_c. This gives

$$-mgl \cos \theta = I_T \Omega_c^2 \sin \theta \cos \theta + I_x \omega_x \Omega_c \cos \theta$$

or, solving for Ω_c,

$$\Omega_{c1,2} = -\frac{I_x \omega_x}{2 I_T \sin \theta} \pm \sqrt{\left(\frac{I_x \omega_x}{2 I_T \sin \theta}\right)^2 - \frac{mgl}{I_T \sin \theta}}.$$

Note that for given I_x, I_T, m, l, and ω_x, the maximum θ at which a steady precession is possible is the one for which the gravity moment is just tangent to the parabola in Fig. 6–9. Here the two precessional rates have merged, which is equivalent to having the radical vanish. Thus

$$\left(\frac{I_x \omega_x}{2I_T \sin\theta}\right)^2 = \frac{mgl}{I_T \sin\theta}$$

so that

$$\sin\theta_{\max} = \frac{I_x^2 \omega_x^2}{4I_T mgl}.$$

Looking at it another way, we could solve the relation for the minimum spin rate ω_x for which precession is possible at given I_x, I_T, m, l, and θ as

$$\omega_{x\min} = \frac{2}{I_x}\sqrt{I_T mgl \sin\theta}.$$

Although it seems strange, this equation shows that the top can maintain a steady precession even for $\theta = 90°$ if

$$\omega_x > \frac{2}{I_x}\sqrt{I_T mgl}.$$

Such a top spinning happily about a vertical axis is called a "sleeping top."

But this is enough of steady precessions which have to be carefully started with just the right initial conditions. Let's see what can be done with a straightforward attack on the general equations of motion.* We were able to integrate the X-equation immediately to get $\omega_x = $ constant. Turning to the Z-equation, we can show that it is a perfect differential if we first multiply it by $\cos\theta$. Thus,

$$0 = I_T\left[\cos\theta\,\frac{d}{dt}(\dot\psi\cos\theta) - \dot\psi\cos\theta\sin\theta\,\dot\theta\right] - I_x\omega_x\dot\theta\cos\theta$$

$$= I_T[\ddot\psi\cos^2\theta - 2\dot\psi\cos\theta\sin\theta\,\dot\theta] - I_x\omega_x\dot\theta\cos\theta$$

$$= I_T\frac{d}{dt}[\dot\psi\cos^2\theta] - I_x\omega_x\frac{d}{dt}(\sin\theta)$$

$$= \frac{d}{dt}[I_T\dot\psi\cos^2\theta - I_x\omega_x\sin\theta],$$

or

$$I_T\dot\psi\cos^2\theta - I_x\omega_x\sin\theta = a,$$

where a is a constant which is physically equal to H_c, the component of $\mathbf{H}$

---

* Remember that we derived equations of motion for the top using Lagrange's equations in Example 5–13.

along C. Note that the first integral could have been similarly interpreted as

$$I_x\omega_x = \text{constant} = H_x.$$

To obtain another integral of the equations of motion, we can use the general result for conservative systems that the total energy is constant.* This is made up of the potential energy V of the height of the center of mass in the gravitational field

$$V(\theta) = mgl \sin \theta,$$

and the kinetic energy of rotation, which in terms of principal moments of inertia, we found to be [Eq. (5–35c)],

$$T = \tfrac{1}{2}I_x\omega_x^2 + \tfrac{1}{2}I_T(\omega_y^2 + \omega_z^2) = \tfrac{1}{2}I_x\omega_x^2 + \tfrac{1}{2}I_T(\dot\theta^2 + \dot\psi^2 \cos^2 \theta).$$

For the total energy E, we can write

$$E = T + V = mgl \sin \theta + \tfrac{1}{2}I_x\omega_x^2 + \tfrac{1}{2}I_T(\dot\theta^2 + \dot\psi^2 \cos^2 \theta).$$

We can eliminate $\dot\psi$, by using the second integral above, to get

$$E = mgl \sin \theta + \tfrac{1}{2}I_x\omega_x^2 + \tfrac{1}{2}I_T\left(\frac{a + I_x\omega_x \sin \theta}{I_T \cos \theta}\right)^2 + \tfrac{1}{2}I_T\dot\theta^2.$$

This can be integrated for θ as a function of time but becomes involved enough to be not worth including here.†

Instead, let's use the ideas of augmented potential that we found so useful (Section 3–5, Example 3–15) in the study of the characteristics of particle motion in central force fields. Note that the first three terms of E are, at worst, functions of θ itself and thus could be thought of as parts of an augmented potential function. An observer ③ called A, rotating about axis C at the rate $\dot\psi$, would only see for kinetic energy of the top,

$$T_A' = \tfrac{1}{2}I_x\omega_x^2 + \tfrac{1}{2}I_T\dot\theta^2$$

so that he would be tempted to define the potential as

$$V_A' = V + \tfrac{1}{2}I_T\left(\frac{a + I_x\omega_x \sin \theta}{I_T \cos \theta}\right)^2.$$

Another observer ③ called B, also rotating at $\dot\psi$ about C, might say that since $\tfrac{1}{2}I_x\omega_x^2$ is a constant, he will include it in the potential and think of

---

* See the work on potentials, augmented potentials, and energy in Sections 3–3, 3–4, and 3–5, as well as Section 5–5.

† See references, such as Webster, Ref. 10, Routh, Ref. 11, and Gray, Ref. 12.

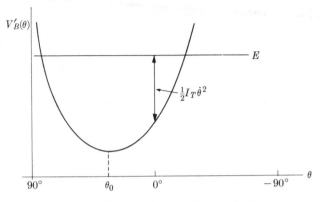

Fɪɢ. 6–10.   Energy diagram for a spinning top.

$\frac{1}{2}I_T\dot{\theta}^2$ as representing the kinetic energy of a mass m at a fixed distance of $\sqrt{I_T/m}$ out along X. He would then talk about particle motion due to changing θ with a potential function

$$V_B' = V + \tfrac{1}{2}I_x\omega_x^2 + \tfrac{1}{2}I_T\left(\frac{a + I_x\omega_x \sin\theta}{I_T \cos\theta}\right)^2$$

and a total energy E such that

$$E = V_B' + \tfrac{1}{2}I_T\dot{\theta}^2 = \text{constant}.$$

If we plot V_B' against θ, as shown in Fig. 6–10 for given m, g, l, I_x, ω_x, a and I_T, the difference between E and V_B' must represent $\tfrac{1}{2}I_T\dot{\theta}^2$. For E just large enough to intersect V_B' at its minimum value, $\dot{\theta}$ must be zero throughout the motion so that the precession must be steady. To illustrate this, we can find θ_0, the minimum point, by looking for zero slope of V_B', as

$$\frac{dV_B'}{d\theta} = 0 = mgl\cos\theta_0 + \left[\frac{a + I_x\omega_x \sin\theta_0}{I_T \cos^2\theta_0}\right]I_x\omega_x \cos\theta_0$$

$$+ \left[\frac{a + I_x\omega_x \sin\theta_0}{I_T \cos^2\theta_0}\right]^2 I_T \sin\theta_0 \cos\theta_0.$$

Substituting for the bracketed terms from our second integral above where

$$\dot{\psi} = \frac{a + I_x\omega_x \sin\theta}{I_T \cos^2\theta},$$

and, remembering that with $\theta = \theta_0 = \text{constant}$ we have called $\dot{\psi}$ the steady precession rate Ω_c, the equation becomes

$$mgl\cos\theta_0 + \Omega_c I_x\omega_x \cos\theta_0 + \Omega_c^2 I_T \sin\theta_0 \cos\theta_0 = 0.$$

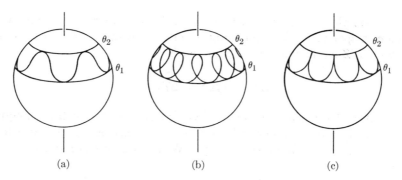

FIG. 6–11.   Nutations of the figure axis (X) of a precessing top.

This is just the quadratic expression that we solved earlier to get the two possible rates of steady precession Ω_{c1} and Ω_{c2}.

If the energy E is larger than the minimum at θ_0, the precession will be unsteady and will involve fluctuations in θ and thus in $\dot{\psi}$. However, θ can never exceed the limits on either side of θ_0 where the total energy E intersects V'_{β}. The motion of the X-axis for some of the types of periodic motion which can occur between the limiting values of θ is illustrated in Fig. 6–11. In the extensive literature on the subject, the X-axis is often called the "figure axis," $\dot{\psi}$-motion is precession, and $\dot{\theta}$-motion is "nutation." ▲

6–3 Torque-free precessions. There are two main reasons for studying the rotational motion of rigid bodies in the absence of any external torque. The first reason is that many bodies which are orbiting in gravitational fields, such as planets and man-made satellites, are to a high degree free of external torques about the center of mass. The second reason is that this short study can include the essence of an elegant geometric construction due to Poinsot, which it would be a shame to omit.

Two ideas are dominant: the kinetic energy T of rotation about the center of mass is constant, and the moment of momentum $\mathbf{H}$ is also constant. The former is true because the total energy of this conservative system is just the kinetic energy; the latter because external moments are required to produce a change in moment of momentum about the center of mass. Expressing these ideas in terms of principal axis directions for *an arbitrary rigid body*, we have

$$H^2 = I_x^2\omega_x^2 + I_y^2\omega_y^2 + I_z^2\omega_z^2, \tag{6–2a}$$

$$2T = I_x\omega_x^2 + I_y\omega_y^2 + I_z\omega_z^2, \tag{6–2b}$$

where H and T are constants of the motion.

A very simple motion satisfying Eqs. (6–2) is just pure rotation about one of the principal axes. Here the body is perfectly happy to spin around an axis such as Z as though it were fixed, with

$$H^2 = I_z^2 \omega_z^2 = 2TI_z.$$

The validity of this solution is also obvious from Euler's dynamical equations (5–26d) which we derived for axes XYZ fixed along the principal directions of a nonsymmetrical body. With no external moment, they become

$$I_x \frac{d\omega_x}{dt} = (I_y - I_z)\omega_y\omega_z,$$

$$I_y \frac{d\omega_y}{dt} = (I_z - I_x)\omega_z\omega_x, \qquad (6\text{--}3)$$

$$I_z \frac{d\omega_z}{dt} = (I_x - I_y)\omega_x\omega_y,$$

for which

$$\omega_z = \text{constant}, \qquad \omega_x = \omega_y = 0$$

is clearly a possible, but special, solution.

Although more general solutions can be obtained analytically only in cumbersome form, the essence of the solutions can be demonstrated with the help of some analytic geometry. If we express the kinetic energy in vector notation as

$$2T = \mathbf{H} \cdot \boldsymbol{\omega}, \qquad (5\text{--}35a)$$

and remember that $\mathbf{H}$ and T are constant, we can deduce that the component of the body's angular velocity $\boldsymbol{\omega}$ along $\mathbf{H}$ is also constant. Geometrically, this means that the tip of $\boldsymbol{\omega}$ always touches a particular plane perpendicular to $\mathbf{H}$ as shown in Fig. 6–12(a).

Thinking further geometrically, Eq. (6–2b) can be interpreted as the equation, in axes attached to the body, of an ellipsoid whose surface is described by the tip of the angular velocity $\boldsymbol{\omega}$ in direct analogy to our inertial ellipsoid. If we write the components of $\boldsymbol{\omega}$ temporarily in the more familiar geometric fashion of x, y, z, we have for the ellipsoid,

$$I_x x^2 + I_y y^2 + I_z z^2 = 2T.$$

The plane tangent to the ellipsoid at the point $\boldsymbol{\omega}$ is

$$(I_x \omega_{x_1})x + (I_y \omega_{y_1})y + (I_z \omega_{z_1})z = 2T,$$

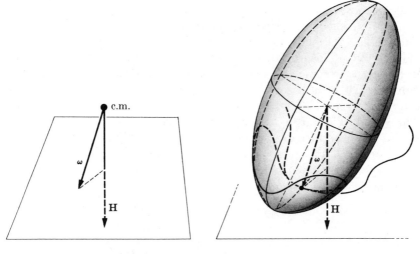

(a)   (b)

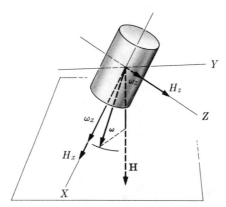

(c)

FIG. 6–12.   The classical Poinsot construction.

and the normal to the plane is parallel to a vector with components*

$$I_x\omega_{x_1}, \qquad I_y\omega_{y_1}, \qquad I_z\omega_{z_1}.$$

Thus, the normal to the ellipsoid is parallel to the constant $\mathbf{H}$ so that the tangent plane is perpendicular to $\mathbf{H}$ and must be just the plane of Fig. 6–12(a).

---

* See a text on analytical geometry, such as Section 10, Chapter 4, of Sokolnikoff and Redheffer, Ref. 5.

Since the ellipsoid is then tangent to the fixed plane throughout the motion of the body, and since the axis of rotation goes through the point of intersection, the ellipsoid appears to roll without slipping on the plane (Fig. 6–12b). This elegant construction by Poinsot has given rise to similarly elegant terminology. The "invariable plane" is perpendicular to the "invariable line" of **H** such that, during the torque-free motion of the rigid body, its "Poinsot ellipsoid" rolls without slipping on the invariable plane. The curve traced out by the ellipsoid on the invariable plane is the "herpolhode," whereas the corresponding curve on the ellipsoid is the "polhode." An alternative way of visualizing the polhode is to note that Eq. (6–2a) can also be interpreted as an ellipsoid in body axes XYZ. Although it has the same principal directions, its semi-axes are

$$H/I_x, \qquad H/I_y, \qquad H/I_z$$

rather than

$$\sqrt{2T/I_x}, \qquad \sqrt{2T/I_y}, \qquad \sqrt{2T/I_z},$$

as for the Poinsot ellipsoid. Since $\boldsymbol{\omega}$ must satisfy both Eqs. (6–2a) and (6–2b), it must follow the intersection of the two ellipsoids. Thus the polhode is just this intersection.

For the simpler case of an axially symmetric body, the polhode and herpolhode become circles, the latter about the invariable **H**. From the point of view of the top solution of Example 6–5 in the preceding section, we proved that H_c, the component of **H** along the precession axis, must be constant. But in torque-free motion, **H** itself must be constant and thus H_c is **H**. Since no components of **H** can be perpendicular to C,

$$I_y\omega_y = I_y\dot{\theta} = 0,$$

and we must have a steady precession about C without nutation [see Fig. 6–12(c) and also reexamine case 4 of Fig. 6–5]. Can you interpret this precessional motion in terms of the rolling cones of Fig. 5–8?

EXAMPLE 6–6. As a simple but illuminating illustration of torque-free precession, let's take a thin axially symmetric disk and start it to precess. If we put all of its energy in motion about the axis of symmetry X, the disk will simply spin about X as though it were fixed. If the same energy is all put in motion about a transverse diameter, the disk will be spinning at a higher angular velocity because for a thin disk

$$I_x \cong 2I_T, \qquad \omega_T \cong \sqrt{2}\,\omega_x.$$

Suppose that when we tried to get the disk spinning about X, it actually ended up with **H** along an axis a few degrees from X. Now what is the motion like? From the equations of Example 6–5 for the precession rate

Ω_c of the top, with the gravitational moment set equal to zero, and with $\theta \approx 90°$,

$$\Omega_c \cong \frac{I_x}{I_T}\omega_x \cong 2\omega_x.$$

Here the precession rate is twice the spin rate, a most unusual situation but one which has often been encountered on many thin rotating parts, such as flywheels, propellers, and even class-demonstration gyros when properly mounted for an essentially torque-free motion. Even a top may have a similar precessional motion for θ of almost 90° if it has a flat wide body and a high ω_x. Try this with a bicycle wheel spinning on the end of its short axle. Note also that a flat saucerlike space ship would be susceptible to this sort of motion if improperly set into rotation to simulate gravity. What would the motion feel like to a passenger near the rim? ▲

6-4 Gravitational torques. In most problems involving gravitational fields, we have found it quite feasible to approximate the actual field with a uniform one or, at times, a spherically symmetric field. In a similar vein, we have considered the "weight" of a body to be acting at its center of mass. There are some instances, particularly in celestial mechanics, where these approximations are not good enough and where we must recognize that an arbitrary body in a spherically symmetric field experiences a torque about its mass center. Similarly, a nonspherical body exerts a force on an attracted body which is not quite along the line joining their mass centers. Although such ideas have been almost exclusively within the province of astronomers, the growing interest in space flight and satellites has caused engineers to turn attention to them.

A model which we will find useful is shown in Fig. 6-13(a) where we have placed an arbitrarily shaped rigid body in the idealized inverse-square gravitational field of a distant particle of mass M at P. The attraction of M on an infinitesimal piece dm of the body is inversely proportional to the square of its distance from P and directed toward P, as

$$d\mathbf{F} = -\gamma M \frac{\mathbf{R}_{\text{c.m.}} + \mathbf{R}}{|\mathbf{R}_{\text{c.m.}} + \mathbf{R}|^3}\, dm.$$

The total force $\mathbf{F}$ exerted on m by M at P is then the integral

$$\mathbf{F} = -\gamma M \int_m \frac{\mathbf{R}_{\text{c.m.}} + \mathbf{R}}{|\mathbf{R}_{\text{c.m.}} + \mathbf{R}|^3}\, dm$$

with the associated moment about the center of mass of m as

$$\boldsymbol{\Gamma} = -\gamma M \int_m \mathbf{R} \times \frac{(\mathbf{R}_{\text{c.m.}} + \mathbf{R})}{|\mathbf{R}_{\text{c.m.}} + \mathbf{R}|^3}\, dm.$$

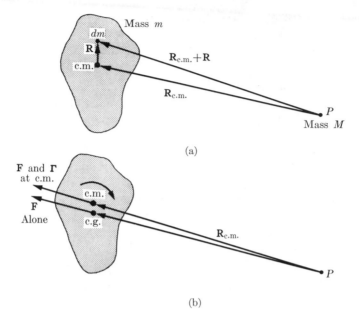

FIG. 6–13. An arbitrarily shaped mass in an inverse-square gravitational field.

To evaluate these integrals in approximate fashion, we make use of the idea that $R_{\text{c.m.}}$ is large compared with R and that the magnitude of $\mathbf{R}_{\text{c.m.}} + \mathbf{R}$ can be expressed by the law of cosines as

$$|\mathbf{R}_{\text{c.m.}} + \mathbf{R}|^2 = R_{\text{c.m.}}^2 + R^2 + 2\mathbf{R}_{\text{c.m.}} \cdot \mathbf{R}.$$

Expanding the denominator in powers of $R/R_{\text{c.m.}}$ gives

$$\frac{1}{|\mathbf{R}_{\text{c.m.}} + \mathbf{R}|^3} = \frac{1}{R_{\text{c.m.}}^3 \left(1 + \dfrac{2\mathbf{R}_{\text{c.m.}} \cdot \mathbf{R}}{R_{\text{c.m.}}^2} + \dfrac{R^2}{R_{\text{c.m.}}^2}\right)^{3/2}}$$

$$= \frac{1}{R_{\text{c.m.}}^3}\left[1 - \frac{3\mathbf{R}_{\text{c.m.}} \cdot \mathbf{R}}{R_{\text{c.m.}}^2} - \frac{3}{2}\frac{R^2}{R_{\text{c.m.}}^2} + \frac{15}{2}\left(\frac{\mathbf{R}_{\text{c.m.}} \cdot \mathbf{R}}{R_{\text{c.m.}}^2}\right)^2 + \cdots\right].$$

Substituting first into the moment expression, we get

$$\boldsymbol{\Gamma} = -\frac{\gamma M}{R_{\text{c.m.}}^3}\int \mathbf{R} \times (\mathbf{R}_{\text{c.m.}} + \mathbf{R})\left[1 - \frac{3\mathbf{R}_{\text{c.m.}} \cdot \mathbf{R}}{R_{\text{c.m.}}^2} + \cdots\right]dm,$$

which reduces to

$$\boldsymbol{\Gamma} = \frac{3\gamma M}{R_{\text{c.m.}}^5}\int \mathbf{R} \times \mathbf{R}_{\text{c.m.}}(\mathbf{R}_{\text{c.m.}} \cdot \mathbf{R})\,dm + \cdots,$$

using $\mathbf{R} \times \mathbf{R} = 0$ and the definition of the center of mass. If we choose as reference axes the central principal set of m and write each vector in terms of components along these axis directions, you can show that we will eventually get, as the lead term in the series expansion,

$$\mathbf{\Gamma} = \frac{3\gamma M}{R_{\text{c.m.}}^5} [(I_z - I_y)y_{\text{c.m.}}z_{\text{c.m.}}\mathbf{i} + (I_x - I_z)z_{\text{c.m.}}x_{\text{c.m.}}\mathbf{j}$$

$$+ (I_y - I_x)x_{\text{c.m.}}y_{\text{c.m.}}\mathbf{k}] + \cdots \qquad (6\text{-}4a)$$

for the *gravitational torque on an arbitrary body in an inverse-square field.*

In a similar manner, we can evaluate the force expression by noting first (see problems at the end of Chapter 5) that

$$\int R^2 \, dm = \int (x^2 + y^2 + z^2) \, dm$$

$$= \tfrac{1}{2} \int [(y^2 + z^2) + (z^2 + x^2) + (x^2 + y^2)] \, dm$$

$$= \tfrac{1}{2}(I_x + I_y + I_z),$$

where this sum of the moments of inertia is the trace of the inertia matrix (and thus an invariant regardless of choice of XYZ-directions), and second, that

$$R_{\text{c.m.}}^2 I_{R_{\text{c.m.}}} = x_{\text{c.m.}}^2 I_x + y_{\text{c.m.}}^2 I_y + z_{\text{c.m.}}^2 I_z$$

for the assumed principal axes XYZ, where $I_{R_{\text{c.m.}}}$ is the moment of inertia of m about $\mathbf{R}_{\text{c.m.}}$ which has the direction cosines $x_{\text{c.m.}}/R_{\text{c.m.}}$, $y_{\text{c.m.}}/R_{\text{c.m.}}$, $z_{\text{c.m.}}/R_{\text{c.m.}}$. Thus *the gravitational force on an arbitrary body* is

$$\mathbf{F} = -\gamma \frac{Mm}{R_{\text{c.m.}}^2} \left\{ \frac{\mathbf{R}_{\text{c.m.}}}{R_{\text{c.m.}}} - \frac{3}{2} \frac{\mathbf{R}_{\text{c.m.}}}{R_{\text{c.m.}}} \frac{5I_{R_{\text{c.m.}}} - [I_x + I_y + I_z]}{mR_{\text{c.m.}}^2} \right.$$

$$\left. + \frac{3}{mR_{\text{c.m.}}^2} \left(\mathbf{i} \frac{x_{\text{c.m.}}}{R_{\text{c.m.}}} I_x + \mathbf{j} \frac{y_{\text{c.m.}}}{R_{\text{c.m.}}} I_y + \mathbf{k} \frac{z_{\text{c.m.}}}{R_{\text{c.m.}}} I_z \right) + \cdots \right\}. \qquad (6\text{-}4b)$$

Actually, we could have derived the *gravitational potential V* of force $\mathbf{F}$ as

$$V = -\gamma \frac{Mm}{R_{\text{c.m.}}} \left\{ 1 + \frac{[I_x + I_y + I_z] - 3I_{R_{\text{c.m.}}}}{2mR_{\text{c.m.}}^2} + \cdots \right\}. \qquad (6\text{-}4c)$$

This force $\mathbf{F}$ and moment $\mathbf{\Gamma}$ can be thought of as being applied by M at the center of mass of m. Alternatively, we can say that $\mathbf{F}$, by definition, goes through the center of gravity of m and that $\mathbf{\Gamma}$ is the moment of $\mathbf{F}$

about the center of mass (Fig. 6–13b). Extending these ideas[*] to the attraction between two arbitrarily shaped bodies, we can show that, to this order of approximation, the moment on each body is determined by its own shape only, but the mutual force of attraction is aligned between their centers of gravity and thus is represented by the sum of the first-order correction terms.

———

An elegant derivation of MacCullagh's theorem, Eq. (6–4c), in more general form using dyadic notation and the differential operator $\nabla = \mathbf{i}(\partial/\partial x) + \mathbf{j}(\partial/\partial y) + \mathbf{k}(\partial/\partial z)$ of vector calculus is as follows. For an arbitrary body m placed in an arbitrary gravitational field described locally by its potential ϕ, the potential V of the total force $\mathbf{F}$ on m can be expanded in a Taylor form about the mass center O of m as

$$V = \int \phi \, dm = \int_m \left[\phi_0 + (\mathbf{R} \cdot \nabla)\phi \bigg|_0 + \frac{(\mathbf{R} \cdot \nabla)^2}{2!} \phi \bigg|_0 + \cdots \right\} dm$$

$$= m\phi_0 + (0) + \tfrac{1}{2}\left(\int_m \mathbf{RR} \, dm \cdot \nabla \right) \cdot \nabla\phi + \cdots.$$

Expressing the inertia tensor of m in terms of the unit tensor U as

$$I = \int_m (R^2 U - \mathbf{RR}) \, dm,$$

and with

$$(U \cdot \nabla) \cdot \nabla\phi = \nabla^2 \phi = 0,$$

for any gravitational potential ϕ in the space outside of the attracting body, the potential for $\mathbf{F}$ becomes

$$V = m\phi_0 - \tfrac{1}{2}(I \cdot \nabla) \cdot \nabla\phi|_0 + \cdots.$$

The total force $\mathbf{F}$ on m is then the gradient of V, as

$$\mathbf{F} = -\nabla V = -m\nabla\phi|_0 + \tfrac{1}{2}\nabla\{I{:}\nabla\nabla\phi\}|_0 + \cdots.$$

Similarly the gravitational moment $\boldsymbol{\Gamma}$ about the center of mass of m can be shown to be

$$\boldsymbol{\Gamma} = -\int_m \mathbf{R} \times \nabla\phi \, dm = (I \cdot \nabla) \times \nabla\phi \bigg|_0 + \cdots.$$

These expressions reduce to Eqs. (6–4) for $\phi = -\gamma M/R_{\text{c.m.}}$

———

[*] See Milne, Ref. 13, and Routh, Ref. 11.

While Eqs. (6–4) seem perfectly applicable to the interactions between distant celestial bodies, it is not immediately apparent that they can also be used for *satellites near the surface of planets* such as the earth. If we are taking into account the nonspherical nature of the earth to show that its attraction on a "near" satellite is not exactly toward the earth's center of mass, the convergence of a series based on the "small" ratio of earth size to satellite orbit radius is questionable. A close examination of Eqs. (6–4), however, shows that the series converges for a different reason in this case; namely, the earth is very nearly spherical so that numerator terms representing differences in various earth moments of inertia are very small compared with $mR_{c.m.}^2$ (where m here is the mass of the earth).

EXAMPLE 6–7. For an arbitrarily shaped unpowered satellite in orbit around the earth (without appreciable internal moving parts so that it can be considered a rigid body and high enough so that the only appreciable external forces are gravitational from the earth), we can write two vector equations of motion. For the translation of the center of mass

$$m\ddot{\mathbf{R}}_{c.m.} = -\frac{\gamma M m}{R_{c.m.}^2} \left\{ \frac{\mathbf{R}_{c.m.}}{R_{c.m.}} + \text{(correction terms)}_{\text{earth}} \right.$$

$$\left. + \text{(correction terms)}_{\text{satellite}} \right\}.$$

For rotational motion about the satellite center of mass, we have

$$\mathbf{\Gamma} = \frac{d\mathbf{H}_{c.m.}}{dt}.$$

In the force expression, let's neglect the correction terms due to oblateness of the earth and look only at those due to the asymmetry of the satellite.

Note that in both satellite force correction terms [Eq. (6–4b)] the orientation of the satellite enters through the direction of $\mathbf{R}_{c.m.}$ compared with the principal axis directions. Similarly, note that in $\mathbf{\Gamma}$, the linear position $\mathbf{R}_{c.m.}$ appears directly. It would thus appear that the translation and rotation are coupled in this problem. However, if we realize that the effect on $\mathbf{\Gamma}$ of changes in $\mathbf{R}_{c.m.}$ due to the correction terms in $\mathbf{F}$ will be of second order, we can neglect the coupling in the $\mathbf{\Gamma}$ equation if we also neglect all but the first-order terms in the series for $\mathbf{\Gamma}$. A reasonable approach would seem to be to solve the $\mathbf{\Gamma}$ equation, including $\mathbf{R}_{c.m.}$ as a known function of time from the normal orbit calculations. Then the small perturbations in the orbit can be computed using the solution for the rotational motion.

Suppose our satellite has an axis of symmetry and is carefully put into orbit so it will have no absolute angular velocity about that axis. Our problem then looks very much like those of Example 6–3 where we set up

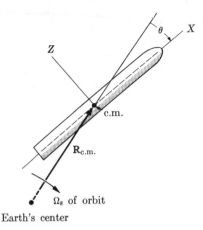

Fɪɢ. 6–14. Slender satellite oscillating in the plane of orbit about the local vertical.

the equations for the pendulum with the accelerated pivot except that here there is no pivot and the origin is at the center of mass. Yet we have a moment $\boldsymbol{\Gamma}$ much like a pendulum moment. To analyze this situation, put X, as usual, along the axis of symmetry, Y horizontal, θ from vertical to X, and ψ from the plane of the orbit to the vertical XZ-plane (Fig. 6–14). The direction cosines of $\mathbf{R}_{\text{c.m.}}$ become, for this XYZ-system,

$$\frac{x_{\text{c.m.}}}{R_{\text{c.m.}}} = \cos\theta, \qquad \frac{y_{\text{c.m.}}}{R_{\text{c.m.}}} = 0, \qquad \frac{z_{\text{c.m.}}}{R_{\text{c.m.}}} = \sin\theta,$$

so the rotational equation becomes, with $I_y = I_z = I_T$, (see Example 6–3)

$$\boldsymbol{\Gamma} = \boldsymbol{\Gamma}_y = \frac{3\gamma M}{R_{\text{c.m.}}^3}(I_x - I_T)\sin\theta\cos\theta\,\mathbf{j} = I_T\boldsymbol{\alpha},$$

$$\omega_x = 0.$$

Note that the sign of the pendulum-type gravitational moment depends on the relative sizes of I_x and I_T.

If we specialize to the case of a circular orbit so that $R_{\text{c.m.}}$ is constant and the angular velocity $\boldsymbol{\Omega}_s$ of the local vertical is, about an axis perpendicular to the orbit plane, of constant magnitude,

$$\Omega_s = \sqrt{\gamma M / R_{\text{c.m.}}^3},$$

then the angular velocity of the axes is

$$\boldsymbol{\Omega} = \boldsymbol{\Omega}_s + \frac{\overline{d\psi}}{dt} + \frac{\overline{d\theta}}{dt},$$

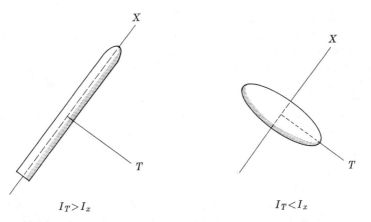

$$I_T > I_x \qquad\qquad\qquad I_T < I_x$$

FIG. 6–15. The extremes in axially symmetrical satellites.

and the angular velocity of the satellite is (again see Example 6–3)

$$\boldsymbol{\omega} = \boldsymbol{\Omega}_y + \boldsymbol{\Omega}_z,$$

or

$$\omega_x = 0,$$
$$\omega_y = \Omega_y = \dot{\theta} + \Omega_s \cos \psi,$$
$$\omega_z = \Omega_z = \dot{\psi} \sin \theta - \Omega_s \sin \psi \cos \theta.$$

If we specialize further to motion initially in the plane of the orbit by setting initial ψ and $\dot{\psi}$ equal to zero, we learn from the Z-equation that $\ddot{\psi}$ is zero too, so the motion remains in the plane of the orbit if it starts there. The Y-equation gives, after dropping higher-order terms to maintain consistency of approximation,

$$\tfrac{3}{2}\Omega_s^2(I_x - I_T) \sin 2\theta = I_T\ddot{\theta}.$$

For small θ and for $I_T > I_x$, this gives the equation

$$\ddot{\theta} + 3\Omega_s^2\left(1 - \frac{I_x}{I_T}\right)\theta = 0,$$

so that our satellite acts like a pendulum (for in-plane motion) of period

$$T = \frac{2\pi}{\Omega_s} \frac{1}{\sqrt{3}\sqrt{1 - (I_x/I_T)}}.$$

Thus a long thin satellite (Fig. 6–15) would have a period of about 50 minutes, whereas a fat saucer shape would be unstable. Note that the saucer would be willing to oscillate (in plane of orbit) about $\theta = 90°$ even though unstable at $\theta = 0$.

We should also note that the gravitational moment $\boldsymbol{\Gamma}$ is of the same order as the pendulum moment of our Schuler-tuning part of Example 6–3 in that it produces a similar period. Apparently, we should have included the gravitational moment $\boldsymbol{\Gamma}$ in that analysis. To put it differently, although Schuler tuning suggests a separation between the pivot and the "coincident" centers of mass and gravity of order 10^{-6} in., the centers may already have at least this separation due to the interaction of the nonuniformity of the earth's field and the asymmetry of the body. ▲

EXAMPLE 6–8. As another illustration of the influence of the gravitational torque $\boldsymbol{\Gamma}$, let's look at the classical precession of the slightly nonspherical earth caused primarily by the actions of the sun and the moon. In this example, the satellite (that is, the earth) is not only axially symmetrical but is spinning about its axis rapidly compared with the orbital angular velocities of one revolution per year and one per twenty-eight days. Due to the torques exerted by sun and moon, the earth's axis will tend to precess like that of a top but at a very slow rate because $\boldsymbol{\Gamma}$ is so small. In fact, the precession is so slow that the sun and moon circle the earth thousands of times during a precessional period. The torque $\boldsymbol{\Gamma}$ may then be averaged and thus the variations in the direction cosines of the earth's axis at the different seasons and phases may be eliminated.

We can assume, for simplicity in calculating an average $\boldsymbol{\Gamma}$, that the sun and moon both revolve in the same plane, the ecliptic, and the earth's axis makes an angle θ_0 with respect to the normal to this plane. The axis and the normal define a plane normal to the ecliptic. From the point of view of a nonrotating observer ② at the earth's center who watches the sun and moon circle the earth, the precession of the earth's axis is so slow that to obtain our average we can integrate from one passage to the next of the sun or moon through the normal plane. Putting X along the earth's axis

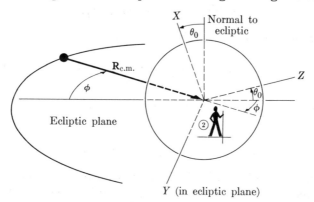

FIG. 6–16.   Gravitational torques on the oblate earth caused by the sun and the moon.

(Fig. 6–16) and Z in the normal plane forces Y to lie in the ecliptic plane. If ϕ is a measure of the circling motion of sun or moon, the direction cosines of $\mathbf{R}_{\text{c.m.}}$ are

$$\frac{x_{\text{c.m.}}}{R_{\text{c.m.}}} = -\sin\theta_0\cos\phi, \qquad \frac{y_{\text{c.m.}}}{R_{\text{c.m.}}} = \sin\phi, \qquad \frac{z_{\text{c.m.}}}{R_{\text{c.m.}}} = \cos\theta_0\cos\phi.$$

With $I_y = I_z = I_T$, we have, from Eq. (6–4a) for $\mathbf{\Gamma}$ averaged for a revolution,

$$\mathbf{\Gamma}_{\text{sun}} = \frac{3\gamma M_{\text{sun}}}{2\pi R_{\text{sun}}^3}(I_x - I_T)$$

$$\times \left[-\sin\theta_0\cos\theta_0\mathbf{j}\int_0^{2\pi}\cos^2\phi\,d\phi + \sin\theta_0\mathbf{k}\int_0^{2\pi}\sin\phi\cos\phi\,d\phi \right]$$

$$= -\frac{3}{2}\frac{\gamma M_{\text{sun}}}{R_{\text{sun}}^3}(I_x - I_T)\sin\theta_0\cos\theta_0\mathbf{j}.$$

Using this moment, and a similar one for the moon, in the Y-equation for the steady precession of the top of Example 6–5, we get (with the change $\theta_0 = \theta - \pi/2$)

$$M_y = \Gamma_{\text{sun}} + \Gamma_{\text{moon}} = -\tfrac{3}{2}(I_x - I_T)\sin\theta_0\cos\theta_0\left[\frac{\gamma M_{\text{sun}}}{R_{\text{sun}}^3} + \frac{\gamma M_{\text{moon}}}{R_{\text{moon}}^3}\right]$$

$$= -I_T\Omega_c^2\sin\theta_0\cos\theta_0 - I_x\omega_x\Omega_c\sin\theta_0.$$

As we will see, Ω_c is so small that we may neglect its square and simply get

$$\Omega_c = \frac{3}{2}\frac{I_x - I_T}{I_x}\frac{\cos\theta_0}{\omega_x}\left[\frac{\gamma M_{\text{sun}}}{R_{\text{sun}}^3} + \frac{\gamma M_{\text{moon}}}{R_{\text{moon}}^3}\right].$$

With $(I_x - I_T)/I_x$ about $\frac{1}{300}$, θ_0 of 23.5°, ω_x of 1 cycle/day, and with

$$\frac{\gamma M_{\text{sun}}}{R_{\text{sun}}^3} = \Omega_{\text{sun}}^2 = \frac{1}{365^2},$$

$$\frac{\gamma M_{\text{moon}}}{R_{\text{moon}}^3} = \frac{\gamma M_{\text{earth}}}{R_{\text{moon}}^3}\cdot\frac{M_{\text{moon}}}{M_{\text{earth}}} = \Omega_{\text{moon}}^2\frac{M_{\text{moon}}}{M_{\text{earth}}} = \frac{1}{28^2\cdot 81},$$

we have, for the precession of the earth's axis,

$$\Omega_c = 0.463\times 10^{-4} \text{ cycles/day},$$

or a period of

$$P = 21{,}300 \text{ years}.$$

This compares with a measured period of about 26,000 years.

This slow forced precession of the earth's axis about the normal to the ecliptic, often called the *precession of the equinoxes*, should not be confused with a much faster precession of the earth as though it were torque-free. If we neglect the small gravitational torques of sun and moon and think of the earth in a force-free precession of small amplitude just like the disk of Example 6–6, we have the absolute precession rate of

$$\Omega = \frac{I_x \omega_x}{I_T}.$$

We observe this precession from on the earth itself and must subtract our rate from Ω to find what we see, which is

$$\Omega' \cong \Omega - \omega_x = \frac{I_x - I_T}{I_T}\, \omega_x = \frac{1}{300}\ \text{cycles/day}.$$

The irregular precession, which has been observed, has a period of about 430 days rather than 300, with the difference ascribed to the actual non-rigid character of the earth. ▲

6–5 Gyros. One of the most intriguing demonstrations of rigid-body dynamics is to put a toy gyro through its paces. To see it stand up straight like a top or to see it precess slowly while standing on the tip of its polar axis has fascinated both children and adults for many years. Although such gyro dynamics stimulated many of the early developers of dynamics itself, the gyro remained largely a curiosity until about the turn of the century. Then for many years devices such as the gyro compass proved to be practical and useful. With the advent of the airplane and, particularly, blind flying, the development of practical gyros proceeded at a rapid pace. Gun sights and now guidance systems for aircraft, missiles, and even submarines rely heavily upon gyros which are masterpieces of design and execution.

Perhaps we should be a bit more definite as to what we should call a gyro. A very useful definition of a gyro specifies a rotating body with at least axial symmetry which spins very rapidly about that axis—so rapidly, in fact, that when computing the gyro's moment of momentum $\mathbf{H}$, it is unnecessary for practical purposes to include components of angular velocity about transverse axes. Thus in Fig. 6–17, we have put X along the gyro axis of symmetry and postulate that $H_x = I_x \omega_x$ is so large that precessional rates Ω_y and Ω_z (equal, respectively, to ω_y and ω_z for the gyro) contribute only a negligible amount to the resultant $\mathbf{H}$. Thus we can say that $\mathbf{H} = \mathbf{H}_x$ in magnitude and direction. Since gyros are maintained with constant ω_x, we have the very useful and excellent approximation that *the moment of momentum $\mathbf{H}$ of a gyro is constant in magnitude and always*

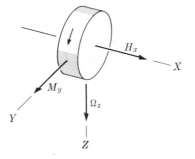

Fig. 6–17. A gyrowheel with H along its axis of symmetry; X precesses about Z when a moment is applied about Y.

aligned with its axis of symmetry or spin axis. This result avoids the difficulty of many of our previous rigid-body problems in that it is hard to keep track of the orientation of $\mathbf{H}$.

Mathematically, we can relate applied external moments to the swinging or precession of the gyro's axis and thus its $\mathbf{H}$ as [see Eq. (5–26a)]

$$\mathbf{M}_e = \boldsymbol{\Omega} \times \mathbf{H}. \qquad (6\text{–}5\text{a})$$

Since gyros are designed to have no net moments applied about the axis of symmetry and since the part of $\boldsymbol{\Omega}$ which counts in Eq. (6–5a) is just the transverse part, we can also say

$$M_y = \Omega_z H_x. \qquad (6\text{–}5\text{b})$$

Thus if we put Y along the direction of the applied torque, the precession which results is about Z. Alternatively,

$$\Omega_z = \frac{M_y}{H_x}, \qquad (6\text{–}5\text{c})$$

so that if we force a precession about Z, it will call for a torque about Y. Speaking from a more physical point of view, the application of M_y in Fig. 6–17 produces a rate of change of $\mathbf{H}$ in the Y-direction. This change corresponds to a swinging of $\mathbf{H}$ about Z.

Conceptually, gyros can be used in two basic ways. If the gyro is mounted so that no external torques are applied to it, we can call it a *free gyro* and its $\mathbf{H}$ vector should never precess. Thus the direction of $\mathbf{H}$ can in theory be used as an unvarying reference direction in inertial space, which can be carried around by the user. Actually, the gimbal mechanism or other arrangement for supporting and translating the gyro is never completely frictionless and perfectly aligned so that $\mathbf{H}$ serves as a good reference only for minutes or perhaps hours. An example is the old style

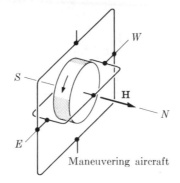

FIG. 6–18. Free gyro used as a simple gyrocompass.

simple gyro compass of Fig. 6–18 used for local maneuvering in aircraft. If the pilot points the gyro axis along the local meridian and frees it, it will serve as a compass without overshoot or lag for a short time.

The alternative to a free gyro is a *restrained gyro*. Here torques may be quantitatively related to precession rates. If the gyro is permitted a restrained freedom with respect to its case about only one transverse axis, it is called a single-degree-of-freedom gyro. If it has a restrained freedom about both transverse axes, it may be called a two-degree-of-freedom gyro. Because it is of a lesser mechanical complexity, the single-degree-of-freedom gyro has enjoyed more popularity, particularly when high precision is required.

EXAMPLE 6–9. As a first illustration of a restrained gyro with a single degree of freedom, let's look at the early aircraft rate-of-turn indicator which was so important in the early days of blind flying. As shown in Fig. 6–19(a), it consisted of a gyro wheel with axis transverse to the airplane's line of flight. The gyro was mounted so that it could swing only about the line-of-flight direction and was restrained in this swinging by a spring.

If we visualize, at first, the airplane and thus the case turning right without banking for the turn, the gyro will need a moment about the line-of-flight direction in order to precess around the turn. Since this can only be applied by the spring, which at the start of the turn is applying no torque, the gyro does not want to begin turning with the airplane. Through the case, the airplane applies a torque about a vertical axis to the reluctant gyro which responds by swinging the head of its **H** vector down. This begins to compress the spring so that the gyro begins to turn right with the aircraft. When the gyro axis has swung down far enough to obtain just the right precessional moment from the spring, it will no longer need urging by the case and will swing down no further.

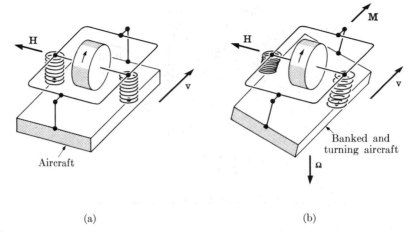

(a)   (b)

FIG. 6–19. Schematic representation of a spring-restrained rate-of-turn gyro in an aircraft.

For a steady turn, the angle of swing of the gyro axis about the line of flight is a direct measure of the rate of turn and was indicated to the pilot by a needle geared to the gyro gimbal. For a left turn, the reverse procedure results in the gyro axis tilted the opposite way. To see the effect of banking the gyro case without turning left or right, visualize yourself rotating the gyro case about the line of flight. This compresses the spring, and the gyro tries to precess about the vertical. It is restrained by the case and this restraining moment swings the gyro axis so as to diminish the spring torque. Thus if we bank the case, the gyro quickly banks a like amount. In a banked turn, then, the swinging of the gyro axis relative to the banked case will be directly related to the rate of turn.

In this simple instrument the spring torque will actually be proportional to the component of the rate-of-turn vector which is perpendicular to the gyro spin axis. Since the spin axis may not be exactly horizontal, the instrument may not measure the desired rate of turn about a vertical axis. This difficulty is related to the finite angular displacement required to compress the springs. If the torque is applied electromagnetically rather than by springs and if the torque is produced by amplifying a signal generated by small angular displacements of the gyro axis with respect to the case, our electromagnetic spring can be made very stiff. Then the gyro axis never deviates much from neutral and the gyro measures, essentially, rate of turn perpendicular to its neutral axis. Three such gyros can measure continuously the three perpendicular components of vehicle angular velocity, regardless of its orientation, and are thus very versatile. Note that the size of the applied torque can be measured here electrically without much difficulty.

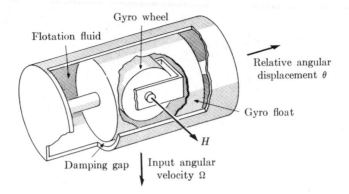

FIG. 6–20. A floated integrating gyro.

In attempting to make high precision rate-of-turn or "rate" gyros, the problem of friction in the precession axis bearings was often a limiting factor. In order to relieve the loadings on these bearings and thus reduce the friction, the gyro wheel and its immediate case is often "floated" with neutral buoyancy in a liquid bath. (See Fig. 6–20.) Of course the fluid itself tends to retard the precessional motion and introduces disturbing torques. If the clearance between inner and outer case is made very small the viscous retarding torque can be used to advantage. Here we can let the viscous torque precess the gyro about the perpendicular axis rather than using an electromagnetic torque. Whereas the electromagnetic torque was proportional to angular displacement θ about the torquing axis, the viscous torque is proportional to angular velocity $\dot{\theta}$ as

$$M_y = -k\dot{\theta} = \Omega_z H_x.$$

Thus the relative angular displacement θ inside the instrument is proportional to the integral of Ω_z, the input absolute angular velocity. Such an integrating gyro finds much use in guidance and control systems.

EXAMPLE 6–10. Even though the idea of a gyro completely free of external torques which gives a fixed inertial reference direction has not proved very practical as yet, some other approaches to the same ideal have been developed. Of considerable importance to blind flying of aircraft has been the artificial horizon, an instrument which offers the pilot a reference horizontal plane with reasonable accuracy which is automatically corrected for the changing direction of vertical as the earth rotates and as he flies around its curved surface.

As shown in Fig. 6–21(a), it consists basically of a free gyro, in an appropriate gimbal system, about which the aircraft can rotate without applying any torques. The applied forces for support and translational accelerations

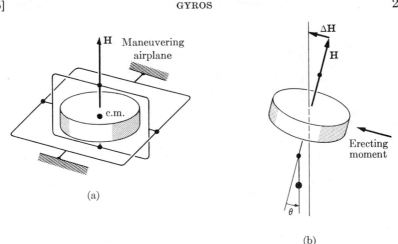

(a)

(b)

Fɪɢ. 6–21. Elements of gyro horizon.

are directed by the gimbal geometry to the gyro's center of mass. To counteract drift of the gyro axis and to put in possible slow changes in the direction of vertical, there must be some device which is responsive, like a pendulum, to the gravitational field. If the gyro is tilted slightly, as shown in Fig. 6–21(b), and this tilt is measured by a small pendulous device, an erecting torque must be generated about the perpendicular transverse axis. If this torque is made proportional to the angle of tilt, the gyro axis approaches the vertical exponentially.* Many ingenious arrangements have been devised for measuring the tilt and reliably producing the proper erecting moment. Friction, air jets, and magnetic torques have all been used.

A basic problem with the erecting mechanism is that a simple pendulous device sensitive to gravity is also sensitive to support acceleration. Thus maneuvers of the airplane create fictitious, temporary, and changing verticals to which the gyro tries to respond. If the sensitivity of the torquing device is low enough, however, the gyro will not erect appreciably to the short-term changes in the vertical caused by vehicle maneuvering, but it will respond at a satisfactory rate to the much slower true changes in the vertical. ▲

An approach to producing a portable piece of nonrotating reference space which is basically different from the free gyro is called the *stable platform*. Here gyros are combined with the servos and closed-loop systems so fundamental to the science of automatic control. As shown in Fig. 6–22, the gyros are used to sense deviations of the platform but are not expected

---

* See problems at the end of the chapter.

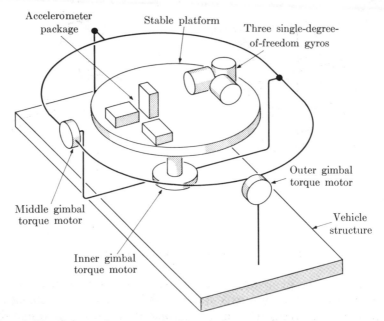

Fig. 6–22. Schematic representation of three accelerometers mounted on a stable platform.

themselves to overcome the disturbing torques. This task is given to torquing devices which are stimulated by signals from the gyros. Thus three single-degree-of-freedom gyros, operating on a simple and reliable null basis, can produce signals which will keep the platform nonrotating regardless of the angular motion of the vehicle to which it is attached.

Although this system is far superior to a single gimbal-mounted gyro, modern guidance systems demand fantastic accuracies, and this system by itself will also gradually drift off. At any instant the gyros will demand very nearly zero angular velocity, but over a period of days or weeks the orientation of the platform may change appreciably. To reset the platform periodically, star sights or other checks using external radiation may be necessary. For missiles and some aircraft applications, the uncorrected system may well be sufficient. Thus in inertial guidance for short duration missile flights, the stable platform gives the inflight instruments and the computer a basic reference system in which to carry out the guidance procedures.

For relatively longer duration guidance or navigation of long range aircraft, the stable platform can be combined with the Schuler-tuning concept to provide remarkably accurate completely self-contained inertial navigation. In simple terms, we can think of the earth as a sphere around which we are traveling at constant altitude. We can initially line up our platform

XYZ-axes in known directions such as putting one parallel to the earth's axis and another horizontal. If at a later time we can find the local vertical using a Schuler-tuned device, the orientation of the vertical with respect to the unchanged XYZ is a direct indication of our location on the spherical surface. Of course the earth is rotating with respect to XYZ while we fly so that we need a good clock to tell us elapsed time and thus angular position of the earth itself.

The Schuler-tuned device is basically a horizontal platform on which are mounted two pendulous accelerometers. Between them they measure the horizontal acceleration $\mathbf{a}_H$ of the vehicle. If the platform is to remain locally horizontal as the vehicle moves around the earth of radius $\mathbf{R}$, it must have the angular acceleration $\boldsymbol{\alpha}$ where

$$\mathbf{a}_H = \boldsymbol{\alpha} \times \mathbf{R}.$$

If the accelerometer signal is multiplied by $1/R$ and integrated twice, the output can be fed into the servos which will rotate the platform moving around the earth's curvature so that it remains horizontal. To show that this platform also acts like a pendulum, note that if it is tilted slightly by the angle ϕ, the accelerometers will not be able to differentiate the component $g \sin \phi$ of gravity from true vehicle acceleration. This extra signal which has also been integrated twice gives the error ϕ in the vertical as

$$\phi = \frac{1}{R} \iint (-g \sin \phi) \, dt \, dt.$$

Differentiating twice and setting $\sin \phi \cong \phi$, we have

$$\ddot{\phi} + \frac{g}{R} \phi = 0$$

which has a sinusoidal solution with period

$$T = 2\pi\sqrt{R/g} \cong 84 \text{ min.}$$

6–6 Vehicle motion and stability. Many of the vehicles in common use do not have that attribute so convenient in analyzing rotational motion, an axis of mass symmetry. Instead they have, almost without fail, a plane of symmetry through the center of mass and only three central principal axes, one of which is perpendicular to the plane of symmetry (see Section 5–3). Thus, if they can be approximated as rigid bodies, we will normally use Euler's dynamical equations [Eq. (5–26d)] for rotation about the center of mass. Since the estimation of the external forces and moments on a vehicle is often quite difficult, we may sometimes find it more convenient to forego the use of principal axes in the plane of symmetry to adopt a pair more suited to handling the external forces. These axes, once chosen, must move directly with the body to avoid moments and products of inertia which vary with time.

If we put Y perpendicular to the plane of symmetry so that it is a principal axis, we have available from Chapter 5

$$M_x = I_x \frac{d\omega_x}{dt} - (I_y - I_z)\omega_y\omega_z - J_{zx}\left(\frac{d\omega_z}{dt} + \omega_x\omega_y\right),$$

$$M_y = I_y \frac{d\omega_y}{dt} - (I_z - I_x)\omega_z\omega_x - J_{zx}(\omega_z^2 - \omega_x^2), \qquad (5\text{-}26\text{g})$$

$$M_z = I_z \frac{d\omega_z}{dt} - (I_x - I_y)\omega_x\omega_y - J_{zx}\left(\frac{d\omega_x}{dt} - \omega_y\omega_z\right),$$

for rotation about the center of mass, and, for its translation,

$$\sum \mathbf{F}_e = m\mathbf{a}_{\text{c.m.}} \qquad (5\text{-}25)$$

which, in terms of components along XYZ, becomes (see Section 5–2 and Example 5–5)

$$F_x = m\left(\frac{dv_x}{dt} - \omega_z v_y + \omega_y v_z\right),$$

$$F_y = m\left(\frac{dv_y}{dt} - \omega_x v_z + \omega_z v_x\right), \qquad (6\text{-}6)$$

$$F_z = m\left(\frac{dv_z}{dt} - \omega_y v_x + \omega_x v_y\right),$$

where $\mathbf{v}$ and $\boldsymbol{\omega}$ are both seen by an unaccelerated nonrotating observer.

Some of the external forces and moments are usually directly related to the motion and can be written in terms of $\mathbf{v}$, $\boldsymbol{\omega}$, their integrals and derivatives, and some are related also to the deflection of control surfaces or steering mechanisms. We will not attempt to evaluate these relations, except perhaps in simplified form in some of the problems and examples, because we do not have the space here.* We can, however, examine the form of the mathematical problem involved and gain some insight into how it can be handled.

Note that the angular velocity components enter the force equations, and the components of linear velocity enter the moment side of the moment

---

* See, for example, Etkin, Ref. 14, Perkins and Hage, Ref. 15. Also see Example 9–2 on automobile stability and Example 9–5 on the longitudinal response of an aircraft to elevator motion.

equations. The variables appear as products and powers and the problem is basically described by a set of six simultaneous nonlinear differential equations. Thus when we are interested in general large-amplitude vehicle motion, we usually have a basically nonlinear problem and the application of both digital and analog computers can be very helpful.

In many instances, however, we are primarily interested in the small amplitude motions (perturbations or disturbances) about some average or equilibrium motion which is known. Most static and dynamic stability analyses are of this nature and are extremely informative and useful. The great advantage of this *perturbation technique* is that, if the changes from equilibrium are small enough and we use them as variables, we can usually discard all the terms involving products and powers. Thus the mathematical problem is reduced to studying or solving a set of linear, often constant-coefficient, differential equations. It is not unusual for these approximate linearized equations to be in several uncoupled sets. Their solution for vehicle stability parameters and its dynamic response to control inputs is one of the subjects of the next three chapters.

EXAMPLE 6–11.   As an illustration of the reduction of the general equations of vehicle motion to several independent sets of linear differential equations, let's look at the historically significant problem of the perturbation of an aircraft from straight-line flight. Here we know that the equilibrium values of lift, weight, thrust, and drag, as well as the external moments balance out, and we want to set up as variables the deviations from equilibrium motion. Note that here the equilibrium values of ω and of $\mathbf{a}_{\text{c.m.}}$ are zero.

Let's initially put X along the equilibrium flight direction which is in the aircraft's plane of symmetry, Y out the right wing and Z down. Since the velocity in the perturbed motion will never deviate far from the X-direction, we can describe its orientation by the sideslip angle β and the angle of attack change $\Delta\alpha$ shown in Fig. 6–23. With V the equilibrium velocity, the components of actual instantaneous velocity can be written

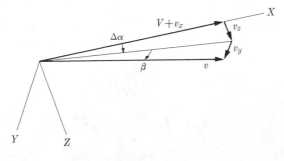

FIGURE 6–23

to first order in the perturbation variables v_x, v_y, v_z as

$$v = V + v_x,$$
$$v_y = V\beta,$$
$$v_z = V\Delta\alpha.$$

Remembering that the components of $\boldsymbol{\omega}$ are already small disturbances about zero angular velocity, we get the linearized force and moment equations,

$$F_x = m\frac{dv_x}{dt}, \qquad\qquad M_x = I_x\frac{d\omega_x}{dt} - J_{zx}\frac{d\omega_z}{dt},$$

$$F_y = mV\left(\frac{d\beta}{dt} + \omega_z\right), \qquad\qquad M_y = I_y\frac{d\omega_y}{dt},$$

$$F_z = mV\left(\frac{d(\Delta\alpha)}{dt} - \omega_y\right), \qquad M_z = I_z\frac{d\omega_z}{dt} - J_{zx}\frac{d\omega_x}{dt}.$$

Of course, similar procedures must be applied to the terms making up the external force and moment components.

Since our aircraft has an XZ-plane of symmetry, we should not be surprised to find that equations involving motion in the plane of symmetry are not coupled with those involving motion out of the plane. Thus the in-plane set, called the *longitudinal equations*, is

$$F_x = m\frac{dv_x}{dt},$$

$$F_z = mV\left(\frac{d(\Delta\alpha)}{dt} - \omega_y\right),$$

$$M_y = I_y\frac{d\omega_y}{dt},$$

where F_x, F_z, and M_y are themselves in terms only of the variables v_x, $\Delta\alpha$, and ω_y. The out-of-plane set, called the *lateral equations*, is

$$F_y = mV\left(\frac{d\beta}{dt} + \omega_z\right),$$

$$M_x = I_x\frac{d\omega_x}{dt} - J_{zx}\frac{d\omega_z}{dt},$$

$$M_z = I_z\frac{d\omega_z}{dt} - J_{zx}\frac{d\omega_x}{dt}.$$

If we are in level flight, the components of $\boldsymbol{\omega}$ are directly related to the usual Euler angles as

$$\omega_x \cong \dot{\phi},$$
$$\omega_y \cong \dot{\theta},$$
$$\omega_z = \dot{\psi}.$$

In these terms, the six variables of the problem are the three angles specifying the time history of the orientation of the XYZ-axes attached to the aircraft, the two angles designating the relative direction of the craft velocity (or tangent to flight path), and the last variable representing the magnitude of the velocity.

In using linearized equations such as these, we must remember and respect the drastic physical assumptions which made them possible. If our craft achieves fairly large roll velocities or if it goes into a spin, we can't use these linearized equations even though they are relatively easy to solve.

PROBLEMS

6–1. Do you think the curves or "hooks" exhibited by bowling balls are the parabolas predicted by the billiard-ball theory of Example 6–1? By using reasonable estimates of bowling ball and alley characteristics, determine how far a ball would go before it began rolling without slipping. Is this result dependent on ball size or density? Is it easier to curve a small ball or a large one? What total motion, normal to the alley length, do you predict?

6–2. Is it possible to strike a billiard ball such that it starts to move away and then actually rolls back toward you? What is the minimum initial amount of "underspin" which will produce this result?

6–3. Suppose a billiard ball approaches a cushion at right angles and rebounds. If it has a large component of angular velocity about a vertical axis but is rolling without slipping as it approaches the cushion, estimate quantitatively the angle of rebound as a function of coefficient of friction between ball and cushion.

6–4. (a) Show that a coin rolling steadily in a straight line is a simple solution for the general equations of motion derived in Example 6–2.

(b) Investigate the stability of this solution by writing the equations for *small* variations from this steady-state solution. Show that when products and powers of the small quantities are neglected, the equations can be reduced to a single equation of the form $\ddot{\theta} + k\theta = 0$ in which the sign of k depends on the size of the coin's angular velocity in relation to its mass properties.

(c) Estimate the critical angular velocity for a convenient coin, hoop, or disk and check your answer experimentally.

6–5. In Example 6–3, we showed that an earthbound observer would see the plane of the Foucault pendulum swing about the local vertical at $\dot{\psi} = -\Omega_{\text{earth}} \sin \theta$, where θ is the latitude. What would a nonrotating observer say the plane of oscillation was doing?

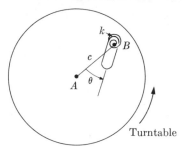

FIGURE 6–24

6–6. In the light of all the pendulum analysis of Example 6–3, look again at the simple pendulum in an airplane which is making a steady horizontal turn (see Problem 3–19) and try to write its equations of motion. Can you make reasonable assumptions which make the equations tractable, linear, or even meaningful? What can you learn about the possible motions of the pendulum?

6–7. Suppose a turntable (Fig. 6–24) that can be rotated freely about a vertical axis A has mounted in it, at a radius c, a vertical axis B. A body is free to swing about this axis B, restrained only by a torsion spring of stiffness k. If the turntable is held fixed, the body can oscillate sinusoidally in the horizontal plane according to the equation $I_B\ddot{\theta} + k\theta = 0$. Although this simple oscillatory motion would normally be disturbed by swinging the turntable about A, find a criterion for designing the spring-restrained body such that the simple oscillatory motion is, for small θ, unaffected by arbitrary angular motion of the turntable about A.

6–8. For the steadily precessing flywheel of Fig. 6–4 which requires a moment as indicated in Fig. 6–5(b) for given θ and ω_x, sketch the curve of M_y versus Ω for a slightly smaller θ, and then for a slightly smaller ω_x.

6–9. Carefully examine the process by which the ferryboat of Example 6–4 enters the turn. Relate the changing angle of lean to the increasing rate of turn by writing separate equations for the paddle wheels and the ferryboat.

6–10. We have all watched a figure skater start to spin, with arms outstretched, about essentially a fixed vertical axis. When she pulls her arms in close, her rate of spin becomes very high. Estimate *quantitatively* whether or not the skater is in a stable motion in the sense of the fully erect rapidly spinning "heavy top."

6–11. Suppose the "heavy top" of Example 6–5 and Fig. 6–8 is on a *frictionless* horizontal floor. What changes must we make in writing the equations of motion compared with Example 6–5? Will the minimum ω_x for which the top can spin with X vertical be larger or smaller than when the point of the top is fixed?

6–12. (a) What horizontal force must be applied at the tip of the precessing top of Fig. 6–8 to maintain its steady precession?

(b) If we think of the tip being in a small hole in a surface which is accelerating linearly along the direction of axis A at the constant rate $\mathbf{a}_T$, is there a set of precessions that would appear steady to an observer ② riding on the surface? [*Hint:* If you must, see Example 3–6 for an idea of how to look at this problem.]

6–13. For the three-bladed propeller of Example 6–4 in a steady climbing turn, estimate the gyroscopic moment M_y by estimating the inertial properties of the propeller and the necessary angular velocities. Would you expect a larger or smaller M_y on the turbine of a jet aircraft in the same turn? How about the gyroscopic moment required for a wheel on a car in a turn? How about on a locomotive?

6–14. Suppose we want to calculate the bending moment at the hub end of a *single* blade on a propeller spinning at constant rev/min on an airplane executing a rapid nose-up maneuver. Do not attempt an explicit solution, but write down in detail the equations of motion you would use and the various steps necessary to arrive at the desired bending moment. Assume that the varying aerodynamic loads on the blade are given to you.

6–15. As discussed in Example 6–6, suppose a saucer-like space ship is given an angular momentum H which is inadvertently about 10° out of alignment with the axis of symmetry. If a crewman at 20 ft radius was supposed to have experienced a steady "artificial gravity" of $\frac{1}{2}g$, what unsteady acceleration will he now feel?

6–16. In throwing a football, it is customary to give it an angular velocity about its axis of geometric symmetry, as well as giving it the proper translational motion. You have probably noticed that an expert's throw results only in a steady spin about the axis of symmetry, whereas the novice frequently achieves a persistent wobbling rotational motion, or even an end-over-end motion. Assuming that the surrounding air exerts no significant moments about the center of mass of the football, discuss the possible steady rotational motions (including steady precessions) which the football may exhibit.

6–17. Derive Eq. (6–4b) for the gravitational force on an arbitrarily shaped body in a simple inverse-square field.

6–18. Prove that, to first order, the gravitational moment Γ about the center of mass of an arbitrarily shaped body equals the moment of the corresponding force F as

$$\Gamma = -R_{c.m.} \times F.$$

6–19. Suppose the case of our simple rate-of-turn gyro of Fig. 6–19 is suddenly rotated by ϕ about the horizontal axis (this corresponds to a sudden bank angle, but no turn). Find an expression for the way in which the gyro axis approaches the angle ϕ as a function of time.

CHAPTER 7

SYSTEM DYNAMICS

In the preceding chapters we have been concerned primarily with the motion of particles and rigid bodies, and these idealized concepts were of great practical use. However, in many problems of dynamics we must deal realistically with more complicated systems which may be idealized or approximated by *interconnected sets of particles, rigid bodies, and even flexible bodies.* Quite often, as in many servos and control systems, our mechanical systems may be closely *interrelated with electrical, hydraulic, and pneumatic systems,* and we will want to study the performance of the complete systems.

In this chapter, we will attempt to illustrate some of the systematic approaches to dynamics of systems which have been developed in this rapidly evolving field. Because each of the approaches is a broad subject by itself, you must remember that we can only look briefly at the simpler aspects.*

7–1 Distinguishing characteristics. We should recognize at the outset that all physical systems, when examined carefully and in detail, are extremely complicated. There are actually no particles, no linear systems, no systems with but a single degree of freedom. It is only after we have discarded what we consider irrelevant and have simplified, idealized, and approximated that we can even attempt to formulate mathematical statements of physical problems. Thus, even exact solutions to the mathematical formulations can be only approximate solutions of the physical problems. However, if we do an intelligent job, we may often be able to represent the essential and interesting characteristics of a physical problem in rather simple mathematical form.

We might well ask what have been the more useful mathematical forms in the general field of dynamics of systems, especially mechanical systems. Although some problems appear quite naturally as integral equations and as integro-differential equations, by far the most usual form is the differential equation. If time is the only independent variable, we will have in general *a set of simultaneous ordinary differential equations.* We have

---

* Periodic, pulse, and random signals and their transmission, the Laplace transform technique, system performance and stability, orthogonality in self-adjoint and nonself-adjoint systems, system optimization, and variational principles are treated in Chapters 8 through 11.

already encountered many such sets in the previous chapters in both particle and rigid-body dynamics. If there is more than one independent variable, such as in the dynamics of a fluid, an elastic beam, or an electromagnetic field, we will encounter *partial differential equations.* Our differential equations are linear if each term contains at most only the first power of a dependent variable or one of its derivatives. If any terms have higher powers or cross products, the equation is nonlinear. The character of our system's equations determines whether we call it *a linear system or a nonlinear system.* Linear systems, that is, systems describable by linear differential equations, may be further subdivided into systems whose equations have only *constant coefficients* and those with coefficients which are *functions of the independent variable.*

You may wonder why we are so worried about the particular mathematical form of our problems. In all cases, we are simply looking for the system's time-varying behavior. Yet, as we will see, the general behavior depends very strongly on the form of the equations. Thus the type of question which we can ask of a system and the approach to evaluating its characteristics differ markedly between linear and nonlinear systems. Sometimes it is informative to look for the *general behavior characteristics* of a system, whereas at other times it is more reasonable to find *specific system responses.* To put it differently, when we are working with linear constant-coefficient systems we will normally deal with simple exponentials and their close relatives, the circular and hyperbolic sines and cosines. With variable-coefficient systems, we often find instead the functions named for Legendre, Bessel, Mathieu, and others. With nonlinear systems, we may hear of Van der Pol or Poincaré, limit cycles, and hard oscillations.

If we should count the number of books on dynamics of systems and separate them into those dealing with linear systems and those dealing with nonlinear systems, we would discover a great preponderance in the linear category. Many elegant and powerful techniques have been developed to a very high degree of perfection for the analysis of linear systems, and, in fact, most engineering systems seem susceptible to the linear approach. This is somewhat of a chicken and egg situation because the ease of analysis of linear systems often causes engineers to design systems which are linear, at least over small ranges. From an historical point of view, much of the basic power of linear system analysis stems from the work, around 1750, of Euler and Lagrange leading to the idea of *general superposition* for linear systems. A vigorous development of the linear theory has continued right up to the present day.

By comparison, the first systematic study of nonlinear systems comparable to Euler's work was not carried out until about 1870 by Poincaré who was principally interested in celestial mechanics. About 1920, Van der Pol stimulated further interest by his study of oscillations in electron-tube circuits, and considerable systematic development has since taken place primarily in the Soviet Union. The recent advent of analog and digital computers has further stimulated interest in nonlinear systems and promises to open completely new horizons in a field as yet little understood.

7–2 Linear systems. Even though many times before you have analyzed the motion of simple systems such as a pendulum and a spring-supported mass, you are perhaps now better prepared to appreciate the assumptions and approximations normally made to describe these systems as linear with constant coefficients. The familiar pendulum equation (see Fig. 7–1)

$$\ddot{\theta} + \frac{l}{g}\,\theta = 0$$

is restricted to small θ, a point mass, a weightless inextensible string, and no friction or other dissipation of energy. In the following sections, we will indicate the effects of removing such assumptions. Before proceeding in general terms, however, let's develop some basic ideas by looking at a familiar situation.

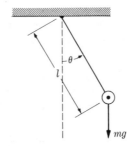

FIG. 7–1. A simple pendulum.

EXAMPLE 7–1. The familiar, simple mass-spring system is sketched in Fig. 7-2(a). It is, as usual, made up of a rigid mass presumed to move frictionlessly only in vertical translation so that it has only one degree of freedom and thus requires only one coordinate. (Just try starting such a system in simple vertical motion without any swinging, wobbling, or twisting of the mass, to say nothing of superimposed high-frequency oscillations of the coils themselves.) Is it a linear system? In addition, are the coefficients of x and its derivatives constant in the mathematical formulation of the problem? The conversion from a physical to a mathematical problem requires the proper statement of the applicable physical principle, in this case Newton's second law. This assures us that the coefficient of $\ddot{x}$ is a constant, the mass m, but what about the spring force? As shown in Fig. 7–2(b), it is normally a somewhat complicated function

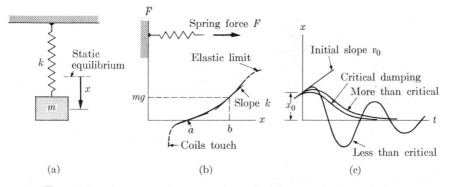

(a)   (b)   (c)

FIG. 7–2.   A mass-spring system restricted to vertical translation.

of the length of the spring. Unless the spring is uniformly made, its characteristic will nowhere be exactly straight. To be sure, for small amplitudes, it seems reasonable to approximate the characteristic with its tangent, but do we take the tangent at point a or b? If it is not clear to you that we should take it at b and that we then get

$$m\ddot{x} + kx = 0,$$

please do some serious thinking about it in terms of small displacements from static equilibrium. We should also note that we have neglected the mass of the spring as well as its weight in our usual high-handed fashion.*

As you know, the solution to this differential equation is sinusoidal in nature and can be written as

$$\left.\begin{aligned} x &= C \cos (\omega_0 t + \psi), \quad \text{or} \\ x &= C \sin (\omega_0 t + \phi), \quad \text{or} \\ x &= A \cos \omega_0 t + B \sin \omega_0 t, \end{aligned}\right\} \omega_0 = \sqrt{k/m}.$$

Can you specify the relations between the various pairs of constants?* The solution tells us that the mass oscillates at constant amplitude C where the two constants of integration can be evaluated by specifying two independent facts about the motion, usually the position and velocity at a specific (initial) time. Mathematically, we expect a second-order differential equation to have two constants of integration.

Suppose we admit that the amplitude of the oscillation actually dies out slowly with time. We may suspect that in this case it is due to air resistance largely proportional to velocity squared. In another situation, it might be caused by a sliding or Coulomb friction force of constant magnitude

---

* See the problems at the end of the chapter.

always opposing the direction of motion. Still another possible physical mechanism is structural damping within the material of the spring which often appears as a force proportional in magnitude to the displacement x but "in phase with" the velocity. None of these causes of amplitude decay leads to a linear differential equation. However, if we presume a viscous air-damping force directly proportional to $\dot{x}$, we get the linear equation

$$m\ddot{x} + f\dot{x} + kx = 0.$$

Since you may not be quite so familiar with this equation, let's solve it by the normal procedure of assuming a somewhat too general solution of what we believe to be an appropriate form. If it doesn't work, we will soon find out, and if it does, we will know that quite quickly too. Although we could try slowly subsiding sines and cosines, let's try, instead, a simple exponential because we know circular functions are related to exponentials with imaginary exponents and because differentiating an exponential does not change its form.

Assuming that $x = Ce^{\alpha t}$ and substituting, we can cancel the common factor $Ce^{\alpha t}$ since we are not interested in $C = 0$, and $e^{\alpha t}$ is not zero. This leaves

$$m\alpha^2 + f\alpha + k = 0$$

so that α can only have the two values

$$\alpha = -\frac{f}{2m} \pm \sqrt{(f/2m)^2 - (k/m)}.$$

Clearly there are two principal cases: when the radical is real and when it is imaginary, separated by the borderline situation when $(f/2m)^2$ just equals k/m. If we say that this borderline value of damping coefficient f is a "critical" value f_c, where then

$$f_c = \sqrt{4km},$$

we have for *less than critical damping* the complex conjugate values

$$\alpha = a \pm ib, \qquad a = -f/2m, \qquad b = \sqrt{(k/m) - (f/2m)^2},$$

and for *more than critical damping*, we have the real values

$$\alpha_1 = -\frac{f}{2m} - \sqrt{(f/2m)^2 - (k/m)},$$

$$\alpha_2 = -\frac{f}{2m} + \sqrt{(f/2m)^2 - (k/m)}.$$

Note that for zero damping, we get $a = 0$ and $b = \omega_0$ so that the solution

$$x = C_1 e^{+i\omega_0 t} + C_2 e^{-i\omega_0 t}$$

must correspond to the simple sinusoidal solutions above. Using this idea, we can write the general solution for *less than critical damping* as

$$
\begin{aligned}
x &= C_1 e^{(a+ib)t} + C_2 e^{(a-ib)t} \\
&= e^{at}(C_1 e^{ibt} + C_2 e^{-ibt}) \\
&= e^{at} C \cos{(bt + \psi)} \\
&= e^{-(f/2m)t} C \cos{(\sqrt{(k/m) - (f/2m)^2}\, t + \psi)},
\end{aligned}
$$

which is the decaying oscillation that we expected (Fig. 7–2c). For *more than critical damping*, we get simply the sum of two decaying exponentials

$$
\begin{aligned}
x &= C_1 e^{\alpha_1 t} + C_2 e^{\alpha_2 t} \\
&= C_1 e^{[-(f/2m)-\sqrt{(f/2m)^2 - (k/m)}]t} + C_2 e^{[-(f/2m)+\sqrt{(f/2m)^2 - (k/m)}]t}.
\end{aligned}
$$

For the *critically damped* borderline case, we get*

$$x = (C_1 + C_2 t)e^{-(f/2m)t}.$$

Note also that for large damping and a relatively small mass, our differential equation tends toward the first-order system described by

$$f\dot{x} + kx = 0,$$

where, trying $x = Ce^{\alpha t}$, we get a single root $\alpha = -k/f$. Can a first-order system have an oscillatory response whatever the initial conditions? ▲

Single-degree-of-freedom mechanical systems (as well as electrical *RLC*-circuits) are usually characterized by a second-order differential equation although, occasionally, they may be adequately represented by a first-order equation. If the system can be assumed linear and with constant coefficients, we can write, with x as the single coordinate, the three forms

First order $\qquad\qquad\qquad\qquad\qquad \dot{x} + \beta x = 0,$ $\quad$ (7–1a)

Second order (conservative) $\qquad\qquad \ddot{x} + \omega_0^2 x = 0,$ $\quad$ (7–1b)

Second order (general) $\qquad\qquad \ddot{x} + 2\zeta\omega_0\dot{x} + \omega_0^2 x = 0.$ $\quad$ (7–1c)

---

* For repeated roots, see the problems at the end of this chapter, Chapter 9, and your text on differential equations.

If we assume a solution in each case of the exponential form

$$x = Ce^{\alpha t},$$

we find that α must have the values, respectively, of

$$\alpha = -\beta, \tag{7-2a}$$

$$\alpha = \pm i\omega_0, \tag{7-2b}$$

$$\alpha = -\zeta\omega_0 \pm \sqrt{(\zeta\omega_0)^2 - \omega_0^2}. \tag{7-2c}$$

The corresponding solutions are (see Example 7-1)

$$x = Ce^{-\beta t}, \tag{7-3a}$$

$$x = C \cos (\omega_0 t + \psi), \tag{7-3b}$$

and the pair of equations written as

$$x = Ce^{-\zeta\omega_0 t} \cos (\sqrt{1 - \zeta^2}\, \omega_0 t + \psi), \qquad \zeta < 1,$$

$$x = C_1 e^{-(\zeta+\sqrt{\zeta^2-1})\omega_0 t} + C_2 e^{-(\zeta-\sqrt{\zeta^2-1})\omega_0 t}, \qquad \zeta > 1, \tag{7-3c}$$

for less than and more than critical damping, respectively. Here we have used ω_0 for the circular or reduced frequency of the undamped oscillation and ζ as the ratio of the damping coefficient f to the critical damping f_c as defined in Example 7-1. The common name for the dimensionless quantity ζ is *the damping ratio*.

For a system of two degrees of freedom, such as two particles in recti-linear motion, one particle in planar motion or a two-loop electrical circuit, we will normally have a pair of simultaneous second-order differential equations in the coordinates x_1 and x_2 which, if linear with constant co-efficients, might look like

$$\ddot{x}_1 + a\dot{x}_1 + bx_1 + c\dot{x}_2 + dx_2 = 0,$$

$$\ddot{x}_2 + e\dot{x}_2 + fx_2 + g\dot{x}_1 + hx_1 = 0. \tag{7-4}$$

If we assume solutions of the form*

$$x_1 = C_1 e^{\alpha t},$$

$$x_2 = C_2 e^{\alpha t}, \tag{7-5}$$

---

* You might expect α to be different in x_1 and x_2. If you assume different α's, you will only discover that they actually are the same in both solutions. Try it in a simpler case. See problems at the end of the chapter.

we get, after substitution,

$$(\alpha^2 + a\alpha + b)x_1 + (c\alpha + d)x_2 = 0,$$

$$(g\alpha + h)x_1 + (\alpha^2 + e\alpha + f)x_2 = 0.$$

For solutions other than the trivial ones $x_1 = x_2 = 0$, the determinant of the coefficients must be equal to zero.* Thus,

$$\begin{vmatrix} \alpha^2 + a\alpha + b & c\alpha + d \\ g\alpha + h & \alpha^2 + e\alpha + f \end{vmatrix} = 0. \qquad (7\text{–}6a)$$

Expanding the determinant gives the fourth-degree *characteristic equation* in α,

$$(\alpha^2 + a\alpha + b)(\alpha^2 + e\alpha + f) - (g\alpha + h)(c\alpha + d) = 0,$$

which has the general form

$$a_1\alpha^4 + a_2\alpha^3 + a_3\alpha^2 + a_4\alpha + a_5 = 0, \qquad (7\text{–}6b)$$

where all of the coefficients are real. Such an algebraic equation, although it may be tedious to factor, always has roots of the typical forms in Eq. (7–2) so that both x_1 and x_2 must contain time functions such as those in Eq. (7–3). These are basically simple exponentials or sinusoidal oscillations of exponentially varying amplitude with the special case of constant amplitude sine waves. The fourth-degree polynomial in α [Eq. (7–6b)] thus contains four real roots corresponding to four exponential time functions, or one or more of the pairs of real roots might instead be an imaginary pair or a complex conjugate pair. These latter pairs correspond to the simple sine function and the exponentially changing sine function, respectively.

Since the roots of the characteristic equation seem to determine the character of the time functions in the solution, we might try interpreting them graphically. We will need a complex plane because they are not always real quantities. The locations of typical roots are indicated in Fig. 7–3(a) and the corresponding time functions in Fig. 7–3(b). Note that roots which have a positive real part, that is, are to the right of the imaginary axis, always correspond to time functions which grow exponentially with time. Any system which has such a time function among its characteristic responses is called *an unstable system* because its output is unbounded.

---

* This is equivalent to eliminating x_2 between the equations and then setting the coefficient of x_1 equal to zero. See your differential equations text or, for instance, Section 36, Chapter 1 of Sokolnikoff and Redheffer, Ref. 5. See Sections 5–1 and 5–3 of this text.

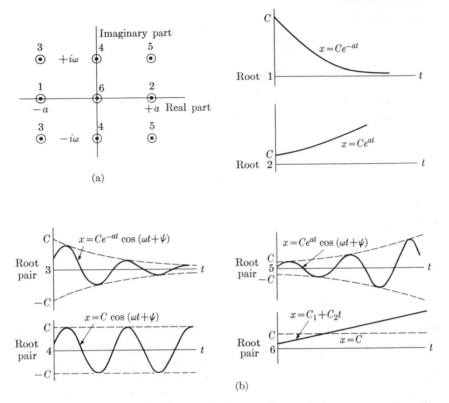

Fig. 7-3. Roots of the characteristic equation and the corresponding time responses.

On the other hand, if *all* the roots lie in the left half-plane, the system will always return to its equilibrium condition after being disturbed and is thus termed *a stable system*. A root pair on the imaginary axis corresponding to a constant amplitude sinusoidal response is really a mathematical border-line case and is not realizable physically. However, such a pair often results from the neglect of small system damping in setting up the mathematical counterpart of the physical system.* (The meaning of zero roots and repeated roots will become clearer in studying Section 9–1.) Also, a system with many degrees of freedom leads to a characteristic equation of high degree which is very tedious to factor into the many roots α_i. Sometimes methods for checking system stability by insuring that no roots have positive real parts, without actually carrying out the complete factorization, can be very useful (as indicated later in Section 9–1).

---

* As we will see, systems which characteristically generate sinusoidal oscillations, such as audio-oscillators, are basically nonlinear devices.

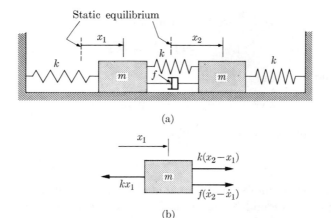

Fig. 7–4. A system with two degrees of freedom.

EXAMPLE 7–2. To illustrate the behavior of systems with multiple degrees of freedom while keeping the algebraic manipulations to a minimum, we can look at the somewhat idealized mass-spring-damper system of Fig. 7–4(a). If we assume that the masses slide without friction and that the springs and viscous damper are linear and weightless, we can write Newton's second law for each mass. Measuring the displacements of the masses from the static equilibrium positions (corresponding to minimum potential energy), we get

$$m\ddot{x}_1 = -kx_1 + k(x_2 - x_1) + f(\dot{x}_2 - \dot{x}_1),$$
$$m\ddot{x}_2 = -kx_2 - k(x_2 - x_1) - f(\dot{x}_2 - \dot{x}_1),$$

where the forces on the first mass are indicated in Fig. 7–4(b) at an instant for which $x_2 > x_1$ and $\dot{x}_2 > \dot{x}_1$. These latter assumptions are quite arbitrary and either or both could be reversed without any net effect on the equations. Try it and see!

If we substitute

$$x_1 = C_1 e^{\alpha t}, \qquad x_2 = C_2 e^{\alpha t},$$

and collect terms, we get

$$(m\alpha^2 + f\alpha + 2k)x_1 - (f\alpha + k)x_2 = 0,$$
$$-(f\alpha + k)x_1 + (m\alpha^2 + f\alpha + 2k)x_2 = 0.$$

Setting the determinant of the coefficients of x_1 and x_2 equal to zero and expanding, we get the characteristic equation in α as

$$(m\alpha^2 + f\alpha + 2k)^2 - (f\alpha + k)^2 = 0.$$

To simplify the algebra, we break the first term into two parts as

$$[(m\alpha^2 + k) + (f\alpha + k)]^2$$

and expand to obtain

$$(m\alpha^2 + k)[m\alpha^2 + k + 2(f\alpha + k)] = 0.$$

The four roots are, assuming small f,

$$\alpha = \pm i\sqrt{k/m}, \quad -f/m \pm i\sqrt{(3k/m) - (f/m)^2}.$$

(Note that in a more complicated and unsymmetrical situation, this factoring process could be quite difficult.) The corresponding time solutions are

$$
\begin{aligned}
x_1 &= C_{11} \cos (\sqrt{k/m}\, t + \psi_{11}) \\
&\quad + C_{12} e^{-(f/m)t} \cos (\sqrt{(3k/m) - (f/m)^2}\, t + \psi_{12}), \\
x_2 &= C_{21} \cos (\sqrt{k/m}\, t + \psi_{21}) \\
&\quad + C_{22} e^{-(f/m)t} \cos (\sqrt{(3k/m) - (f/m)^2}\, t + \psi_{22}).
\end{aligned}
$$

That these are actually the solutions may be checked by trying them in the original differential equations. We would expect to get two pairs of roots from two second-order equations, but we seem to have twice the expected number of "constants of integration." The substitution of these solutions into the differential equations verifies this by requiring relations between corresponding pairs of constants. Thus, either the set in x_1 or the set in x_2 may be considered arbitrary. In this problem the relations come out to be simply

$$
\begin{aligned}
C_{11} &= C_{21}, \quad C_{12} = -C_{22}, \\
\psi_{11} &= \psi_{21}, \quad \psi_{12} = \psi_{22}.
\end{aligned}
$$

The natural motion of this simplified system seems to be made up of two components, an undamped oscillation at $\sqrt{k/m}$ and a damped oscillation at $\sqrt{3k/m - (f/m)^2}$. Note that we can define two new coordinates q_1 and q_2 as one-half the sum and difference of x_1 and x_2 to get

$$
\begin{aligned}
q_1 &= \tfrac{1}{2}(x_1 + x_2) = Q_1 \cos (\sqrt{k/m}\, t + \psi_1), \\
q_2 &= \tfrac{1}{2}(x_1 - x_2) = Q_2 e^{-(f/m)t} \cos (\sqrt{(3k/m) - (f/m)^2}\, t + \psi_2),
\end{aligned}
$$

where

$$
\begin{aligned}
Q_1 &= \tfrac{1}{2}(C_{11} + C_{21}) = C_{11}, \quad \psi_1 = \psi_{11} = \psi_{21}, \\
Q_2 &= \tfrac{1}{2}(C_{12} - C_{22}) = C_{12}, \quad \psi_2 = \psi_{12} = \psi_{22}.
\end{aligned}
$$

Application of the same linear transformation of coordinates to the differential equations themselves produces

$$m\ddot{q}_1 + kq_1 = 0,$$
$$m\ddot{q}_2 + 2f\dot{q}_2 + 3kq_2 = 0.$$

Note that this particular transformation* has produced independent rather than simultaneous or coupled equations of motion and has separated the modes of system response. ▲

7–3 Forced linear systems. So far in our analysis of linear systems with constant coefficients, we have looked only at the motions characteristic of the systems after being disturbed at an initial instant. We will often be interested in their *response to continued excitation*, such as that of a vehicle to the driver's input or that of a circuit to an applied time-varying voltage. In the previous example we might want to know the system response to an external force $F(t)$ applied to the first mass. This would result in $F(t)$ appearing on the right-hand side of our first equation, and our set of equations would no longer be homogeneous; that is, not all of the terms would contain a dependent variable or its derivative.

Study of such *nonhomogeneous equations* indicates, as we will see, that the solutions must contain additional terms usually called *particular solutions*. The form and number of the particular solutions will depend directly on the form and number of the external excitations or forcing functions. We will also find that if we study just a simple second-order system under the action of external excitation we should be able to apply the results to more complicated systems.†

---

* See Sections 9–2 and 9–3 for a general look at such transformations for both conservative and nonconservative systems. The analogies between this transformation and the coordinate rotations for finding the single equivalent axes of Section 5–1 and the principal axes of inertia of Section 5–3 are explored in detail.

† If in the previous two-degrees-of-freedom example we had applied an external force $F(t)$ to the first mass and then tried the transformation to q_1 and q_2, we would have obtained

$$m\ddot{q}_1 + kq_1 = \tfrac{1}{2}F(t),$$
$$m\ddot{q}_2 + 2f\dot{q}_2 + 3kq_2 = \tfrac{1}{2}F(t).$$

Thus the system can be represented by two independent second-order equations each with its own forcing function. In this simple symmetrical case, half of the applied force excites the undamped mode and half the damped mode. See Section 9–2 for the more general situation.

Let's think of applying a sinusoidal forcing function $P \cos \omega t$ to a general second-order system [see Eqs. (7–1c), (7–2c), (7–3c)] so that the equation of motion is*

$$\ddot{x} + 2\zeta\omega_0\dot{x} + \omega_0^2 x = \frac{P}{m} \cos \omega t. \tag{7–7}$$

Our general solution should still contain two constants of integration and, of course, should give just $(P/m) \cos \omega t$ when substituted into the left-hand side. Since the solution x_h to the homogeneous equation [Eq. (7–3c)] has two such constants and gives zero when substituted, it would seem necessary for the particular solution x_p to merely produce $(P/m) \cos \omega t$. Thus with

$$x = x_h + x_p, \tag{7–8a}$$

let's try a particular solution x_p of the form

$$x_p = A \cos \omega t + B \sin \omega t,$$

where ω is the forcing frequency,† not the natural frequency ω_0. Substituting to find appropriate values of A and B, we have, after collecting coefficients,

$$(-A\omega^2 + 2\zeta\omega_0\omega B + \omega_0^2 A) \cos \omega t$$
$$+ (-B\omega^2 - 2\zeta\omega_0\omega A + \omega_0^2 B) \sin \omega t = \frac{P}{m} \cos \omega t.$$

Equating the coefficients of sin and cos separately to zero because they cannot cancel each other, we get the algebraic equations, in A and B,

$$(\omega_0^2 - \omega^2)A + 2\zeta\omega_0\omega B = \frac{P}{m},$$

$$-2\zeta\omega_0\omega A + (\omega_0^2 - \omega^2)B = 0.$$

Thus,

$$A = \frac{(\omega_0^2 - \omega^2)P/m}{(\omega_0^2 - \omega^2)^2 + (2\zeta\omega_0\omega)^2}, \qquad B = \frac{2\zeta\omega_0\omega P/m}{(\omega_0^2 - \omega^2)^2 + (2\zeta\omega_0\omega)^2}.$$

Alternatively, we could have expressed x_p as $C_p \cos(\omega t + \psi_p)$ where

---

* In our general form, we divided through by the coefficient of the acceleration term, which in a mass-spring-dashpot system is just m. The dimensions of P/m are those of acceleration.

† Here we use the term frequency for ω and ω_0 which are in rad/sec and should properly be called reduced or circular frequency. It is a common practice and a source of confusion to the unwary.

$C_p = \sqrt{A^2 + B^2}$ and $\psi_p = \tan^{-1}(-B/A)$ so that

$$x_p = \frac{P/m}{\sqrt{(\omega_0^2 - \omega^2)^2 + (2\zeta\omega_0\omega)^2}} \cos(\omega t + \psi_p),$$

$$\psi_p = \tan^{-1}\left(\frac{-2\zeta\omega_0\omega}{\omega_0^2 - \omega^2}\right) = \tan^{-1}\left[\frac{-2\zeta(\omega/\omega_0)}{1 - (\omega/\omega_0)^2}\right], \qquad (7\text{–}8b)$$

and the full solution, written for less-than-critical damping, is

$$x = Ce^{-\zeta\omega_0 t} \cos(\sqrt{1 - \zeta^2}\, \omega_0 t + \psi)$$

$$+ \frac{P/k}{\sqrt{[1 - (\omega/\omega_0)^2]^2 + [2\zeta(\omega/\omega_0)]^2}} \cos(\omega t + \psi_p). \qquad (7\text{–}8c)$$

Note that it consists of a "transient" part x_h that dies out and a "permanent" part x_p that does not. We will look at this solution more closely and those for "step" and "ramp" forcing functions after the next example. In a given situation, of course, the constants C and ψ are determined by two independent boundary (initial) conditions.

A very important property of linear systems was illustrated above where we simply added the solution to the homogeneous equation to the particular solution to obtain a new solution. In a similar fashion, we can find the complete solution for a different forcing function if we know the appropriate particular solution. If the system is subjected simultaneously to both forcing functions, the complete solution is then merely the sum of the homogeneous and the two particular solutions.* This additive property is one of the reasons linear systems are so easily analyzed and is called *the principle of superposition*. It encourages the process of finding general solutions. For nonlinear systems, we will sorely miss this principle and will not be able to talk in terms of general solutions, even in relatively simple cases.

EXAMPLE 7–3. A simple illustration of a first-order system with a constant for a forcing function is the motion of Millikan's oil drop in Example 3–17. Here the differential equation for the vertical velocity v of the drop is

$$\dot{v} + \frac{9}{2}\frac{\mu}{R^2\rho_{\text{oil}}}\, v = \frac{3}{4}\frac{neE}{\pi R^3\rho_{\text{oil}}} - \left(1 - \frac{\rho_{\text{air}}}{\rho_{\text{oil}}}\right)g$$

$$= (n - 1)\left(1 - \frac{\rho_{\text{air}}}{\rho_{\text{oil}}}\right)g,$$

---

* See the problems at the end of the chapter.

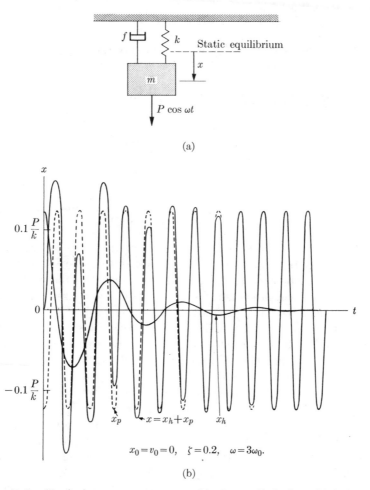

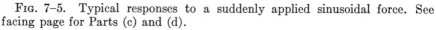

(b)

FIG. 7–5. Typical responses to a suddenly applied sinusoidal force. See facing page for Parts (c) and (d).

where the right-hand side represents the sum of the electrostatic and net buoyancy forces when the electrostatic field E is adjusted to give no net force on a drop with a single charge ($n = 1$).

The homogeneous solution is, from Eq. (7–3a),

$$v_h = Ce^{-(9/2)(\mu/R^2\rho_{\text{oil}})t},$$

and the particular solution is just a constant as

$$v_p = \frac{2}{9}\frac{R^2\rho_{\text{oil}}\,g}{\mu}\,(n-1)\left(1 - \frac{\rho_{\text{air}}}{\rho_{\text{oil}}}\right).$$

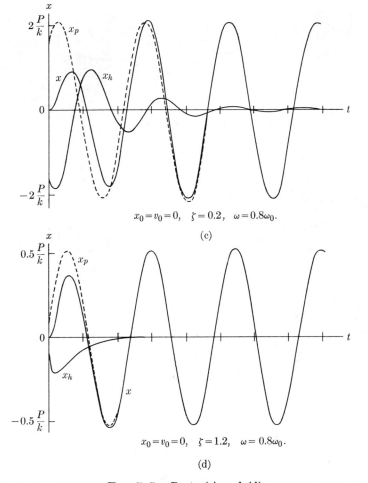

$$x_0 = v_0 = 0, \quad \zeta = 0.2, \quad \omega = 0.8\omega_0.$$

(c)

$$x_0 = v_0 = 0, \quad \zeta = 1.2, \quad \omega = 0.8\omega_0.$$

(d)

FIG. 7–5. Parts (c) and (d).

With the initial velocity v_0 at $t = 0$ equal to the terminal velocity of magnitude V in the absence of any field E, as

$$v_0 = -V = -\frac{2}{9} \frac{R^2 \rho_{\text{oil}} g}{\mu} \left(1 - \frac{\rho_{\text{air}}}{\rho_{\text{oil}}} \right),$$

we can solve at $t = 0$ for C, the constant of integration, as

$$v_0 = (v_h + v_p)_0 = C + v_p,$$

$$C = v_0 - v_p = nv_0.$$

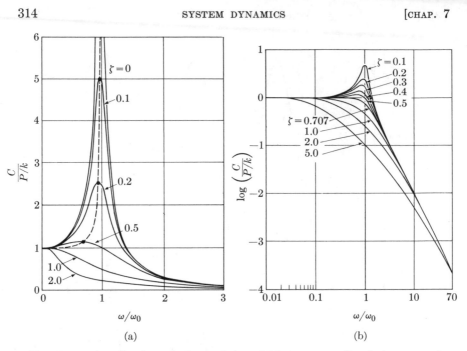

FIG. 7-6. Amplitude and phase of sinusoidal response. See facing page for Parts (c) and (d).

The complete solution is then

$$v = nv_0 e^{-(9/2)(\mu/R^2\rho_{\text{oil}})t} + (1 - n)v_0$$

$$= \frac{2}{9}\frac{R^2\rho_{\text{oil}}\,g}{\mu}\left(1 - \frac{\rho_{\text{air}}}{\rho_{\text{oil}}}\right)[(n - 1) - ne^{-(9/2)(\mu/R^2\rho_{\text{oil}})t}],$$

as written in Example 3–17 and plotted for various n in Fig. 3–21. ▲

We have already derived the complete response of a simple second-order system to *a sinusoidal input*. The system (see Eq. 7–7) was characterized by its undamped natural frequency ω_0 and the ratio ζ of its damping to critical damping. The input was characterized by its amplitude* P/m and

---

* This rather awkward form of forcing amplitude as force per unit mass disappears if we complete our shift to dimensionless parameters. Thus, if we use P/k as a reference displacement, define x' as $x/(P/k)$, define t' as $\omega_0 t$ so that $dt' = \omega_0\,dt$, Eq. (7–7) can be written in the elegant form,

$$\frac{d^2x'}{dt'^2} + 2\zeta\frac{dx'}{dt'} + x' = \cos\left(\frac{\omega}{\omega_0}\right)t'.$$

Although simple in appearance, this form tends to hide the physical parameters that we must watch to keep our feet on the ground at this stage of our experience.

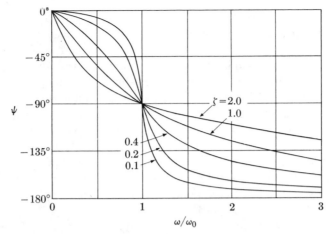

(c)

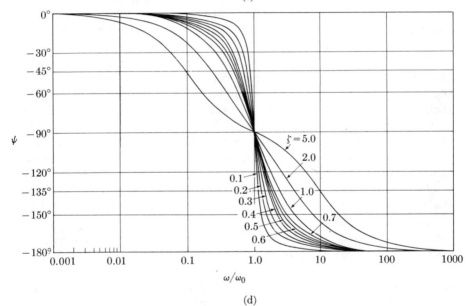

(d)

FIG. 7–6.   Parts (c) and (d).

its frequency ω, as well as two initial conditions. The output depends on all these quantities, as shown in Fig. 7–5 where the responses for a variety of damping ratios and forcing frequencies are plotted. Note that, in each case, the homogeneous "transient" part of the solution dies out with advancing time and plays the role of providing the transition from the specified initial conditions to the simple sinusoidal particular solution with its well-defined amplitude, phase, and frequency.

In many instances, we are less interested in detailed responses than in the general variation of response of our system to changes in a parameter such as forcing frequency ω. By plotting the coefficient of the particular solution [Eq. (7–8b)] against forcing frequency ω, we can evaluate the influence of this parameter for our given system. By also plotting curves for other systems with different damping ratios f/f_c and making the abscissa frequency ratio ω/ω_0, we can generalize the plot to include all simple second-order systems. This has been done in Fig. 7–6(a). Such "frequency-response" curves are fundamental not only in the study of mechanical systems but also of linear electrical circuits and in many other areas. It is often convenient to use logarithmic scales (Fig. 7–6b) for amplitude ratio and frequency ratio. The corresponding plots of phase angle [Eq. (7–8b)] are shown in Fig. 7–6(c) and 7–6(d).

Simple, nonperiodic inputs, which are very often used to explore the response characteristics of a system, are the *step, ramp, and impulse functions* illustrated in Figs. 7–7(a), (b), and (c). These are usually taken to have unit amplitude, slope, and area, respectively, and, when applied to a second-order linear system initially at equilibrium, have the responses depicted in Figs. 7–7(d), (e), and (f). The response to a step function looks very similar to the homogeneous responses of Fig. 7–2(c), except that here the initial slope is zero. Actually the application of a constant force can be thought of as simply changing the static equilibrium position of the system (as discussed for gravity in Figs. 7–2(a) and 7–2(b) and in problems at the end of the chapter). With a redefined displacement coordinate, the response to the step function becomes merely the homogeneous response to a negative initial displacement.*

The *response to an impulse* is a very useful basic response even though the impulse is quite an idealization of an actual physical input. Although we never experience an infinite force for an infinitesimal time, a system may experience an applied force over a very short period. Of course, short for one system may be only a few microseconds, whereas another may find that even several seconds is quite short compared with its basic response capabilities. Thus if a, in Fig. 7–7(c), is very small compared with $1/\omega_0$ for a system, the impulse is applied before the system has a chance to move appreciably, and only the size of the total impulse, which is the area under the curve, affects the resulting motion. Following this line of reasoning further for a simple mass-spring-dashpot system, we can say that during the time a the spring force and damping force are negligible compared with $1/a$ so that the impulse is transferred entirely into momentum. For a unit impulse, the velocity at time a is $1/m$. From this

---

* This and the solution to the ramp input are problems at the end of the chapter. Note that the ramp input is merely the integral of the step input.

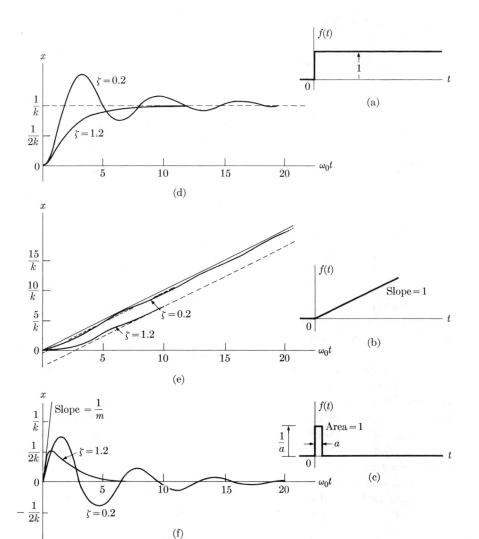

FIG. 7–7.　Response to unit step, ramp, and impulse inputs.

time on, no force is applied, so the solution is simply the homogeneous one [Eq. (7–3c)] for zero initial displacement and an initial velocity of $1/m$ as shown in Fig. 7–7(f). If we call the impulse response $h(t)$, we can write it explicitly for a simple underdamped second-order system by evaluating the homogeneous response,

$$x = Ce^{-\zeta\omega_0 t}\cos\left(\sqrt{1-\zeta^2}\,\omega_0 t + \psi\right), \tag{7–3c}$$

at t equal to zero. Thus,

$$x_0 = 0 = C \cos \psi,$$

$$v_0 = \frac{1}{m} = \left[\frac{dx}{dt}\right]_{t=0} = [-\zeta\omega_0 C e^{-\zeta\omega_0 t} \cos (\sqrt{1 - \zeta^2}\,\omega_0 t + \psi)$$

$$- \sqrt{1 - \zeta^2}\,\omega_0 C e^{-\zeta\omega_0 t} \sin (\sqrt{1 - \zeta^2}\,\omega_0 t + \psi)]_0$$

$$= -\zeta\omega_0 C \cos \psi - \sqrt{1 - \zeta^2}\,\omega_0 C \sin \psi.$$

For $\cos \psi = 0$, we can say $\psi = -90°$, and thus

$$C = \frac{1}{m\omega_0\sqrt{1 - \zeta^2}}$$

so that the response to a unit impulse is

$$h(t) = \frac{e^{-\zeta\omega_0 t}}{m\omega_0\sqrt{1 - \zeta}} \sin (\sqrt{1 - \zeta^2}\,\omega_0 t). \tag{7-9}$$

EXAMPLE 7-4. To illustrate the response of a simple linear system to an applied force $F(t)$ in an unusual but very useful situation, we can merely accelerate the previously fixed support of our mass-spring-dashpot system and call the relative motion between mass and support the output of the system. Since this output $x(t)$, for proper system properties, is closely related to support acceleration $A(t)$, the device is often called *an accelerometer*. It may have a variety of physical forms, such as the pendulous, floated accelerometer in which small-amplitude rotation of an offset mass about a nearly frictionless pivot is substituted for the linear displacement x. Nevertheless, the device in Fig. 7-8(a) is an excellent idealized model of a real accelerometer.

If we measure x from the zero-spring-force position of the mass (and if all motion is horizontal to prevent the gravity field from producing a deflection), we can write Newton's second law for the mass in the X-direction, as

$$\sum F_x = -kx - f\dot{x} = m[\ddot{x} - A(t)],$$

assuming x positive to the left, relative to the case, but A positive to the right. Then

$$m\ddot{x} + f\dot{x} + kx = mA(t)$$

or

$$\ddot{x} + 2\zeta\omega_0\dot{x} + \omega_0^2 x = A(t).$$

Thus if the case is subjected to a step input in acceleration of unit magnitude, we would expect a response $x(t)$ (see Fig. 7-7d) as shown in Figs 7-8(b) and 7-8(c) for a slightly underdamped system ($\zeta = 0.7$).

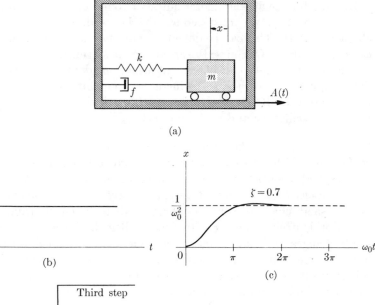

(a)

(b)

(c)

(d)

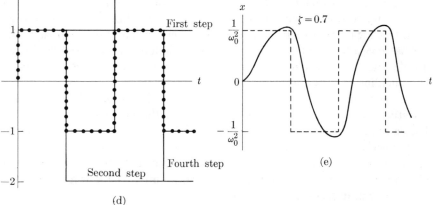

(e)

FIG. 7–8. The response of an accelerometer to a step input in acceleration and to a square wave input for which $\omega = \frac{2}{3}\omega_0$.

To keep the instrument from accelerating out of sight to the right, let's reverse the acceleration A at $t = t_1$. If we maintain the reversed acceleration until $t_2 = 2t_1$, the case will be at rest, and we can repeat the process. This acceleration-time history is sketched in Fig. 7–8(d). Note that it can be built up by the addition or superposition of step functions, the first of which is of unit magnitude. Since we are dealing with a linear system, we can find the response to each step separately and then add them to get the complete response as shown in Fig. 7–8(e).

In order for the accelerometer output x to match more closely the input acceleration $A(t)$, we must reduce the lag with which x follows sharp changes in $A(t)$. This can be done by increasing the spring stiffness so that ω_0 is much larger. Of course this means the basic sensitivity $1/\omega_0^2$ is reduced so that a more sensitive displacement measuring device must be used. Also the damping constant f must be increased to maintain the desirable damping ratio of 0.7. If just the spring is stiffened, the response will be faster but quite oscillatory and lowly damped. ▲

So far, we have looked almost entirely at linear systems with constant coefficients. Although such systems are of great importance to the engineer and applied scientist, we will often encounter *linear systems with time-varying coefficients*. This will be particularly true of problems where we look at small changes from equilibrium, when the equilibrium or average condition is itself changing with time. Then the linear equations for the small changes will have varying coefficients. As an example of such a linear system, consider the small amplitude pendulumlike motion of a non-spherical satellite of the earth. If its center of mass is in a circular orbit, we get a simple pendulum equation such as Eq. (7–1b) (see Example 6–7) with constant coefficients. If the satellite is following an ellipse, however, the gravity torque varies with the orbit radius and thus in a known fashion with time. Similar differential equations occur in many other areas with a spatial coordinate rather than time as an independent variable; for example, the torsional deformation of a nonuniform wing in an airstream or the buckling of a nonuniform column.

In the systems with constant coefficients, we have seen that the crucial question to be asked is that of stability. Is the system stable and thus basically satisfactory for engineering use? All we need to know to answer this question are the constant coefficients themselves. With time-varying coefficients the situation is not quite the same, particularly when coefficients may change sign. To illustrate this, we might look at a simple first-order system described by the equation

$$\dot{x} + \beta(t)x = 0. \tag{7–10a}$$

The solution can be written as

$$\log \frac{x}{x_0} = -\int_0^t \beta(t)\,dt \tag{7–10b}$$

or

$$x = x_0 e^{-\int_0^t \beta(t)\,dt}, \tag{7–10c}$$

where x_0 is the initial value of x. If β is always positive, x will decrease and eventually vanish. If β is always negative, x will grow without limit. These systems fit our previous ideas of stable and unstable systems.

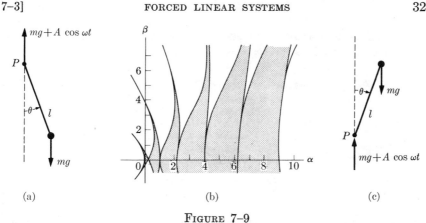

FIGURE 7–9

Suppose $\beta(t)$ is generally positive except between t_1 and t_2. Then x will diminish up to t_1, grow from t_1 to t_2, and then diminish again. It is difficult to define stability in such a case, and we must ask instead whether the actual system performance is satisfactory in the particular situation that we are studying. If t_1 and t_2 are fairly close together, the increase of x in this range may not be at all troublesome; that is, we may go through the "unstable range" quickly enough to avoid an unacceptable condition. It depends on the initial conditions and the limits of permissible operation of the system.

Linear equations with varying coefficients, nevertheless, have solutions which satisfy the principle of superposition and can still be divided into homogeneous and particular parts. Many such equations, particularly those of second order, have been studied intensively* and yield extensively tabulated solutions such as Bessel functions. However, many dynamics problems involving a set of linear equations with time-varying coefficients do not come within the scope of such work and must be handled largely with the help of analog and digital computers† or by various approximate analytical techniques, which we do not have the space or time to consider here.

EXAMPLE 7–5. An interesting class of linear systems with nonconstant coefficients which has been thoroughly studied is characterized by coefficients varying periodically with time. A simple yet characteristic example is the basic pendulum modified so that an oscillatory vertical force $A \cos \omega t$ can be applied at the pivot in addition to the constant force mg which provides static equilibrium. The pivot point is presumed to be free to move vertically but not horizontally (see Fig. 7–9a).

---

* See reference books on differential equations, such as Chapter 2, Sections 13, 14, and 22 of Ref. 9.

† See Tsien, Ref. 17, p. 177.

If we still assume small amplitude response, the vertical acceleration of the pivot point P will be $(A/m) \cos \omega t$ so that we can write [Eq. (4–8)]

$$\sum \mathbf{M}_P = \frac{d\mathbf{H}_P}{dt} + m\mathbf{R}_{\text{c.m.}} \times \mathbf{a}_P,$$

$$-mgl\theta = ml^2\ddot\theta + ml\left(\frac{A}{m} \cos \omega t\right)\theta,$$

which becomes

$$\ddot\theta + \left(\frac{g}{l} + \frac{A}{ml} \cos \omega t\right)\theta = 0.$$

Such an equation with a periodic coefficient is known as Hill's equation. It becomes a Mathieu equation when the periodicity is simply sinusoidal, which is just our case. With the substitution $\tau = \omega t$, we can put it in the standard form

$$\frac{d^2\theta}{d\tau^2} + (\alpha + \beta \cos \tau)\theta = 0,$$

where

$$\alpha = \frac{g/l}{\omega^2} = \left(\frac{\omega_0}{\omega}\right)^2, \qquad \beta = \frac{A}{ml\omega^2}.$$

Upon investigation,* it can be shown that the pendulum motion may be periodic (in terms of Mathieu functions) at the same frequency or at one-half the frequency of the applied force. Somewhat surprisingly perhaps, it may also be divergent or unbounded for large values of time. The stability of the motion depends on the relative values of α and β, as shown in Fig. 7–9(b) where the regions of stable solutions are shaded.

If we look instead at the inverted pendulum of Fig. 7–9(c), we will still get a Mathieu equation but with α negative. Although the response of such an inverted pendulum is normally divergent, note that for certain combinations of α and β, the solutions are stable. This phenomenon is often called parametric damping and is one of the more interesting aspects of this general class of problems which goes under the name of *parametric excitation.* ▲

7–4 Nonlinear conservative systems. If we remember that linear systems constitute a very special class of systems and that all other systems are called nonlinear, it is not surprising that we find it difficult to speak with any generality about nonlinear systems. It is easier instead to

---

* See Stoker, Ref. 18, Chapter 6; Tsien, Ref. 17, p. 166, and your text on differential equations.

mention important properties of linear systems upon which we can no longer depend. Thus the characteristic motions will no longer be expressible in terms of simple exponentials, sines and cosines, or even Bessel, Legendre, or Mathieu functions. Neither can we depend on the principle of superposition. If we know the system responses to each of two inputs or forcing functions, we cannot say that the response to the sum of the inputs is simply the sum of the individual responses.

Despite the recent exploitation of the general descriptive concepts pioneered by Poincaré* and the progress made in defining various concepts of stability, nonlinear system analysis is in the early throes of development, and the era of purposeful design of nonlinear systems is just dawning. Of course, in some narrow areas such as in electronic oscillator design and in signal modulation and wave shaping, the engineer has a wealth of experience to draw on, but this is generally not the case.

To explore the field of nonlinear systems in just a few pages, we will look primarily at single-degree-of-freedom systems and will usually concentrate on their oscillatory behavior. Somewhat in parallel with our development of linear systems, in this section we will look first at conservative systems, then second-order systems with nonlinear damping, in both cases without any forcing functions. The equations will not contain time explicitly and are often called *autonomous*. Unfortunately, the analysis techniques useful for autonomous systems are not applicable to the *nonautonomous or forced systems* (as we will see in Section 8–4). This forcing may be "internal," such as the parametric excitation of Example 7–5, or it may be the more familiar "external" type.

As the first part of our general look at nonlinear systems, let's try those *conservative second-order systems* characterized by the differential equation

$$m\ddot{x} + f(x) = 0. \tag{7–11}$$

We have studied far more complicated systems of this sort in two and three degrees of freedom such as for satellite orbits and precessing tops, so we should not be frightened by Eq. (7–11) but rather curious. In terms of our simple spring-mass system, we can think of the nonlinearity being represented in the spring characteristic $f(x)$. In Fig. 7–10(a), the characteristic of a "hard" spring is sketched where the spring force builds up more rapidly than the linear force. Remembering that for a linear spring, Fig. (7–10b), the frequency of the characteristic period response is independent of amplitude, it seems reasonable to expect higher frequencies for large amplitudes with a hard spring. This dependence of frequency on amplitude is very characteristic of nonlinear systems and is indicated in

---

* See Poincaré, Ref. 16.

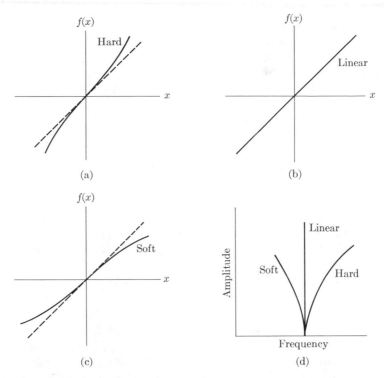

FIG. 7–10. Nonlinear spring characteristics and the corresponding variations of natural frequency with amplitude of oscillation.

Fig. 7–10(d). Similarly, the "soft" spring produces a periodic response whose frequency is lower, the larger the amplitude. If the spring is "soft" enough to produce a reversal of slope, we may approach zero frequency and even lose the oscillatory character of the motion. In any case, we can expect exactly sinusoidal motion only for the linear spring characteristic.

EXAMPLE 7–6. To illustrate these ideas in a familiar situation, we can look again at a simple pendulum but this time one not restricted to small amplitudes. If we think of the concentrated mass m, in Fig. 7–11(a), connected to the frictionless pivot by a weightless rigid bar, we get the equation of motion

$$ml^2\ddot{\theta} + mgl \sin \theta = 0.$$

Here we have a soft spring with a sinusoidal characteristic (Fig. 7–11b) and from experience, we know that the period gets larger, the closer the amplitude comes to π.

For this conservative system, we expect that a simple integration of the equation of motion will give us the appropriate form of the principle of

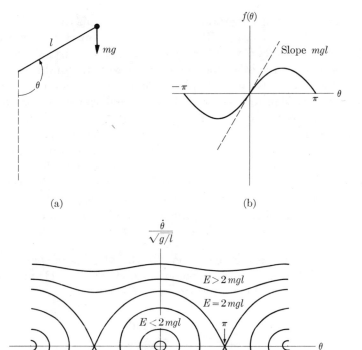

(a)   (b)

(c)

FIG. 7–11. A simple pendulum at large amplitudes.

conservation of mechanical energy E.* Thus,

$$ml^2\dot{\theta}\frac{d\dot{\theta}}{d\theta} + mgl\sin\theta = 0,$$

$$\frac{ml^2}{2}\dot{\theta}^2 - mgl\cos\theta = \text{constant} = E - mgl,$$

where E is arbitrarily defined to approach zero for very small amplitudes of oscillation.

---

* See Sections 3–4 and 5–5.

A further attempt at integration, even in this simple case, involves us in elliptic integrals. A more fruitful approach recognizes that the energy equation relates the two variables, position and velocity, which can be plotted one against the other for various values of the total energy. This $\theta\dot{\theta}$-plane (Fig. 7–11c) is called *the phase plane* and the curves of constant energy are not difficult to interpret. Thus the small contours near the origin must be nearly circles because for small amplitudes the motion is just simple harmonic; if θ is represented by a sine, $\dot{\theta}$ is a cosine, and the radius in the phase plane is $\sqrt{\theta^2 + (\dot{\theta}/\sqrt{l/g})^2}$, which is a constant. For larger total energy E, we get periodic motions of larger amplitude until we try an amplitude of 180°, when the period becomes indefinitely large. For still larger energies, the motion is no longer oscillatory in the sense that $\dot{\theta}$ periodically changes sign. Instead, the pendulum goes round and round in the initial direction and never comes to rest. ▲

The forming of the energy equation and the plotting of *constant energy contours in the phase plane* can be demonstrated for Eq. (7–11) representing our general conservative nonlinear system. We can write

$$mv\,\frac{dv}{dx} + f(x) = 0,$$

$$\frac{mv^2}{2} - \frac{mv_0^2}{2} = -\int_0^x f(x)\,dx = -(F(x) - F(x_0)),$$

or

$$\frac{mv^2}{2} + F(x) = E, \tag{7–12}$$

where the sum of the kinetic energy $\frac{1}{2}mv^2$ and potential energy $F(x)$ equals the total energy E. Using v and x as coordinates, Eq. (7–12) can be plotted on the phase plane for a particular $F(x)$ and various levels of total energy E, as in Fig. 7–12. Note how the shape of the potential energy curve $F(x)$ is related to the phase-plane plots with the velocity zero when $F(x)$ equals the total energy E and a maximum when $F(x)$ is smallest. Thus total energy levels E_1, E_2, E_3, and E_4 give rise to the four sets of curves drawn in the phase plane. Notice the closed regions and the points of stable and unstable static equilibrium. Remember that we are not restricting ourselves to small amplitudes about an equilibrium but are exploring the larger patterns of possible motion.

In nonlinear, conservative systems, just as in linear, it is difficult to talk clearly about dynamic stability. Here again the lack of energy-dissipating terms in the equations is usually the result of an approximation. Note that a small disturbance which changes the energy level will in general

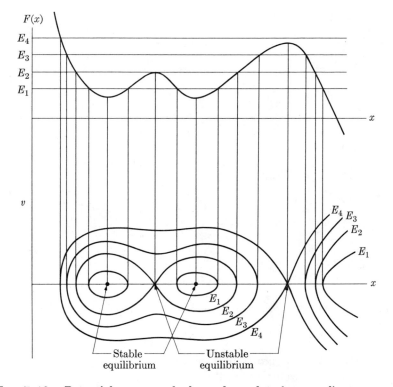

FIG. 7–12. Potential energy and phase-plane plots for a nonlinear conservative system.

shift our motion from one curve in the phase plane to a neighboring one. The motion will not return to the original curve. In fact, since even the period for traversing neighboring closed curves is different, the shifting from one curve to a neighboring one results in an everchanging time lag between the new motion and the original one.

We do not have space here to explore the basis of the elegant classical theory of dynamics for just such conservative systems developed by men like Hamilton and Jacobi. In this sophisticated approach, the total energy E is closely related to the Hamiltonian* and for systems with many degrees of freedom, the phase plane generalizes to phase space. Similarly the displacement-velocity coordinates become displacement-momentum generalized coordinates. These techniques, although not of too great use to the engineer, have been very important to the physicist in his approach to quantum theory.

---

* See Chapter 11 or an advanced dynamics text, e.g., Goldstein, Ref. 2.

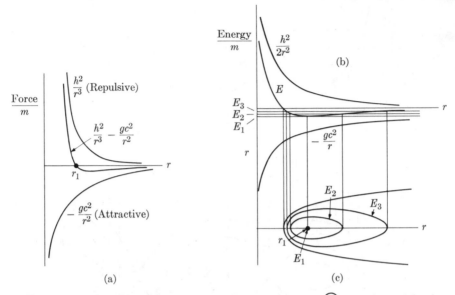

FIG. 7–13. Satellite orbits as seen by an observer ③ rotating with the position vector.

EXAMPLE 7–7. To gain some experience with interpreting phase-plane plots, let's look at two problems that we have studied previously, the satellite in orbit and the precessing top. In both cases, the systems have more than one degree of freedom, but since the potential energy can be written in terms of a single coordinate, the problems can be cast into our nonlinear form in one coordinate.

Looking first at a satellite of mass m orbiting the earth, we see that the basic equations in polar coordinates are (see Section 3–7)

$$m(\ddot{r} - r\dot{\theta}^2) = \frac{-mgc^2}{r^2},$$

$$\frac{d}{dt}(mr^2\dot{\theta}) = 0,$$

where mg is the gravitational force on m at radius c. The angular variable can be eliminated easily to make the problem appear one dimensional as

$$\ddot{r} - \frac{h^2}{r^3} + \frac{gc^2}{r^2} = 0,$$

with

$$h = \frac{H}{m} = r^2\dot{\theta} = \text{constant},$$

where h is the angular momentum per unit mass and h^2/r^3 and gc^2/r^2 can be thought of as forces in the r-direction. In this sense the equation governs the purely radial motion seen by an observer ③ rotating with r at the instantaneous rate $\dot\theta = h/r^2$. For a particular choice of h and gc^2, the nonlinear force variation with r is plotted in Fig. 7–13(a).

We can integrate to get the energy equation as

$$\tfrac{1}{2}\dot r^2 + \frac{h^2}{2r^2} - \frac{gc^2}{r} = E,$$

which is plotted in Fig. 7–13(b). Note that the rotating observer sees a contribution to the potential energy from the rotational part of the motion.* The corresponding set of phase-plane curves is sketched in Fig. 7–13(c). The closed curves correspond to the actual elliptical orbits around the earth which our rotating observer sees as oscillatory motion out against the gravitational force and in against the $1/r^3$ "repelling" force about the point where they balance. The balance point at E_1 corresponds to an actual circular orbit. Can you see the phase-plane curves corresponding to escape energies? Remember that we get different sets of curves in the phase plane for different values of angular momentum h. Remember also that the period of the closed orbits is directly related to the size of the semimajor axis which is the average of the extreme values of r for a closed curve in this phase-plane picture.

Turning now to the "heavy top" of Example 6–5 and Fig. 6–8, we were able to form an energy equation for unsteady motion in terms of the single coordinate θ, the elevation of the axis of symmetry X above the horizontal, as,

$$E = mgl \sin\theta + \tfrac{1}{2}I_x\omega_x^2 + \tfrac{1}{2}I_T\left(\frac{a + I_x\omega_x \sin\theta}{I_T \cos\theta}\right)^2 + \tfrac{1}{2}I_T\dot\theta^2.$$

Here the first term on the right represents the potential energy of the height of the center of mass in the gravitational field, the second term is the kinetic energy associated with the constant spin rate ω_x about the axis of symmetry, and the next two terms are the contributions of the kinetic energy about the Z- and Y-axes, respectively. The next to the last term could have been written $\tfrac{1}{2}I_T(\dot\psi \cos\theta)^2$, but it took on a more complicated form when the azimuth rate $\dot\psi$ was eliminated by the equation

$$a = \text{constant} = I_T\dot\psi \cos\theta - I_x\omega_x \sin\theta.$$

An observer rotating at $\dot\psi$ about the vertical and watching just the motion of the X-axis as θ changes would logically include all the terms except

---

* See Section 3–5 for a discussion of augmented potentials. See also Fig. 3–23.

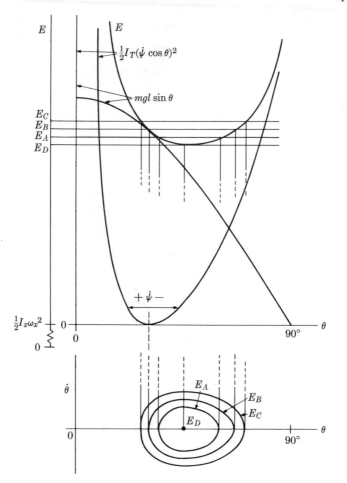

FIG. 7–14.   Energy and phase-plane plots for the nutations of the heavy top of Fig. 6–11.

$\frac{1}{2}I_T\dot{\theta}^2$ in the "potential energy" of the θ-motion.   In Fig. 7–14, we have plotted energy and phase-plane curves for a typical heavy top.   Can you see that energy levels E_A, E_B, and E_C correspond to the nutational motions of Fig. 6–11(a), 6–11(b), and 6–11(c), respectively?   Energy E_D corresponds to steady precession at constant θ.   ▲

7–5 Nonlinear systems with damping.   To study nonlinear systems with damping by using the idea of phase-plane plots, we might first see what the phase plane looks like for our familiar damped linear system whose differential equation is

$$\ddot{x} + 2\zeta\omega_0\dot{x} + \omega_0^2 x = 0. \qquad (7\text{–}1c)$$

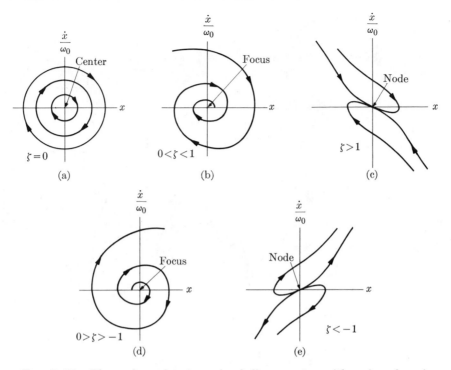

FIG. 7–15.   Phase-plane plots for a simple linear system with various damping ratios.

In terms of the phase-plane coordinates x and $\dot{x}$, we can write the pair of equations

$$\frac{d\dot{x}}{dt} = -2\zeta\omega_0\dot{x} - \omega_0^2 x, \qquad \frac{dx}{dt} = \dot{x}.$$

Eliminating time and using the more convenient variable $\dot{x}/\omega_0$, we have the differential equation for the phase-plane curves,

$$\frac{d(\dot{x}/\omega_0)}{dx} = -2\zeta - \frac{x}{\dot{x}/\omega_0}. \qquad (7\text{–}13)$$

Typical transient responses are plotted in the phase plane in Figs. 7–15(a), 7–15(b), and 7–15(c) for an undamped, underdamped, and overdamped system.   For completeness, the two negatively damped cases are also plotted (Figs. 7–15d and 7–15e).   The latter correspond to what we have called unstable systems because the motion grows without any limit.   Note that plots (a), (b), and (d) correspond to oscillatory cases, with (a) quite similar to some of the curves in the preceding figures for nonlinear conservative systems.

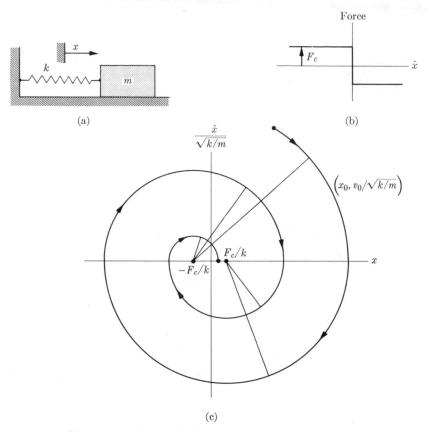

FIG. 7–16. Coulomb friction in a mass-spring system.

In all parts of Fig. 7–15, the origin corresponds to a singular point representing stable or unstable equilibrium depending on whether the damping is positive or negative. For the undamped case, the origin is called *a center;* for the overdamped cases, (c) and (e), it is called a *node,* and for the underdamped cases, (b) and (d), it is called a *focus.* This idea of classifying singularities turns out to be particularly helpful for handling nonlinear systems. Also, as we shall see, the curves of Fig. 7–15 are the building blocks for constructing phase-plane plots for *piecewise linear systems* in which the response is built up with segments of linear response curves suitably joined together. This is typical of many systems incorporating switching devices and relays.

EXAMPLE 7–8. To illustrate the use of the phase-plane plots for linear systems on a step by step basis, we might look at our mass-spring system without the dashpot but with sliding or Coulomb friction (Fig. 7–16a). A reasonable approximation to this sort of friction force is that it opposes the direction of the motion but is constant in magnitude (Fig. 7–16b). Thus it changes sign whenever the velocity $\dot{x}$ does. The differential equation can be written as

$$m\ddot{x} + F_c \frac{\dot{x}}{|\dot{x}|} + kx = 0,$$

but a more useful form is

$$m\ddot{x} + kx = \pm F_c,$$

where the sign is chosen opposite to that of $\dot{x}$. Thus while $\dot{x}$ is positive, we have a negative force applied, and vice versa. The response to a constant negative force is, however, just a response as in Fig. 7–15(a) with the center transferred to $x = -F_c/k$, the new equilibrium position. When the velocity reaches zero, the direction of the friction force reverses so that for the next interval the effective center of the circular arc response is at $+F_c/k$. As shown in Fig. 7–16(c), the motion in the phase plane is a succession of semicircular arcs of decreasing size until eventually the mass stops close enough to equilibrium so that the spring force is smaller than F_c. Can you sketch x as a function of time and compare it with the oscillatory decay of the underdamped linear system? How much does the amplitude decrease in one cycle? If the mass-spring system above also had some viscous (that is, linear) damping, the phase-plane response would be made up of similarly displaced sections of the spiral responses in Fig. 7–15(b).

As a generalization of the above example involving the switching of the friction force when the sign of the velocity changes, let's devise a switch for a mass-spring-dashpot system which reverses the sign of a constant applied force F when $ax + b\dot{x}$ goes through zero. This is called *linear switching*,* and the shift from the left to the right equilibrium point takes place when the phase-plane curve reaches the line $ax + b\dot{x} = 0$ rather than the line $\dot{x} = 0$, which is the x-axis. Such a switching line is shown in Fig. 7–17(a) with the switch connected so as to change from the left equilibrium point to the right one as we cross the switching line from left to right. A possible motion of our system (assumed underdamped on a linear basis) connects appropriate sections of diminishing spirals as shown in (a) until finally the curve does not intersect the switching line but spirals in to one of the foci.

A pair of curves critical to the behavior of this system are those just tangent to the switching line (Fig. 7–17b) because curves of smaller amplitude are no longer subject to the switching action. As a matter of interest,

---

* See Tsien, Ref. 17, p. 145, for an interesting exposition of relay servo-mechanisms.

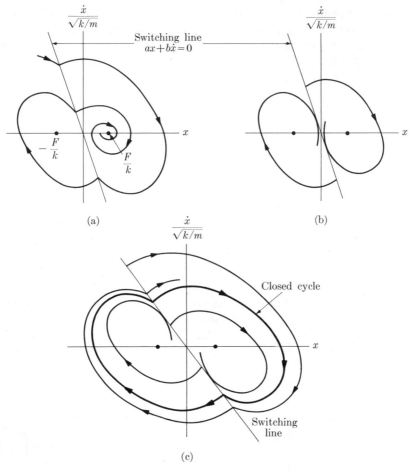

FIGURE 7–17

let's try a somewhat different switching line for the same basic system as shown in Fig. 7–17(c). Again we sketch the critical curves but notice that the end of each curve intersects the switching line beyond (instead of inside of) the beginning of the next critical curve. Thus it would appear that a system response starting just outside a critical curve will increase in amplitude as a result of the switching procedure. Actually, it will approach the closed cycle shown, a plausible result which we will not prove in detail. Note, however, that if we start with large amplitude motion, the construction indicates a response decreasing in size and again approaching the closed cycle.

You may wonder how a damped system can maintain a steady oscillation just because a switch has been introduced. Actually, the switching action implies the application of a constant force. In the Coulomb friction example, the force always opposed the motion and dissipated mechanical energy as heat. In this case, the force travels further with the motion than against it and thus puts energy into the motion. In the closed cycle, it adds energy just equal to that dissipated by the viscous dashpot. Thus we have implied that there is an energy source available to produce the requisite applications of force. ▲

Many nonlinear systems of considerable practical importance can be represented by second-order differential equations which are "nearly linear"; that is *the nonlinear terms are quite small*. As we shall see, this does not necessarily mean that their apparent characteristics are close to those of the linear systems we have studied. Yet, we must remember that our linear systems are really idealizations of actual systems which are never exactly linear, even for small amplitudes. As pointed out by Tsien,* we must be particularly aware of the nonlinearity of the "nearly linear" system when its damping is small and we are near resonance. Here we may expect strong effects from small nonlinear terms; in particular, we can get self-sustained oscillations of definite frequency and amplitude.

Historically, Rayleigh studied an equation with a small nonlinear term, in working with acoustic phenomena, which can be written

$$\ddot{x} - (A - B\dot{x}^2)\dot{x} + x = 0.$$

However, much of the important pioneering work was done later by Van der Pol in the study of oscillations in vacuum tube circuits in which the basic equation has the form†

$$\ddot{x} - \mu(1 - x^2)\dot{x} + x = 0. \tag{7–14}$$

Considering μ to be small, we certainly expect a basic oscillatory character for such a system, but is it stable or unstable, or can we even use these terms? For small amplitude ($x^2 < 1$), we would seem to have a negative damping coefficient so that the amplitude of our oscillatory motion should increase. However, for large amplitude ($x^2 > 1$), the damping is positive, so there would seem to be some amplitude at which the motion would neither increase nor decrease. Van der Pol found this by experiment,‡ when he obtained the time history shown in Fig. 7–18(a) (for $\mu = 0.1$). He also found that the steady oscillation was represented by an almost

---

* Tsien, Ref. 17, p. 162.

† Rayleigh's equation reduces to this form by a differentiation and change of variable $y = \sqrt{3B/A}\ \dot{x}$.

‡ See Minorsky, Ref. 19, p. 113.

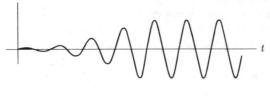

(a)

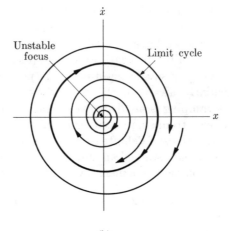

(b)

FIG. 7–18.   Responses of systems described by Van der Pol's equation.

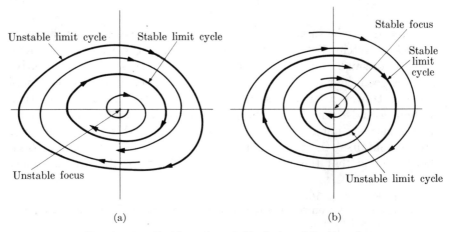

(a)   (b)

FIG. 7–19.   Stable and unstable foci and limit cycles.

circular curve in the phase plane (Fig. 7–18b). This curve is called a *limit cycle* after the terminology of Poincaré whose earlier extensive analytical techniques and proofs were shown by Andronow,* to be closely related to Van der Pol's problem. The general descriptive techniques of Poincaré classify the origin of the phase plane in this problem as an unstable focus (see also Fig. 7–15 for linear systems). Note the outward spiralling of the motion from the origin to the "stable" limit cycle. Similarly, initial large-amplitude motion spirals in toward the limit cycle.

Van der Pol obtained his phase-plane curves by the method of isoclines in the following kind of procedure. Writing Eq. (7–14) in terms of the phase-plane variables x and $\dot{x}$ as [see Eq. (7–13)]

$$\frac{d\dot{x}}{dt} = \mu(1 - x^2)\dot{x} - x, \qquad \frac{dx}{dt} = \dot{x},$$

and then eliminating time, he obtained

$$\frac{d\dot{x}}{dx} = \mu(1 - x^2) - \frac{x}{\dot{x}}. \tag{7–15}$$

It is possible to plot slopes $d\dot{x}/dx$ at many points in the plane. If enough slopes are plotted, we can easily follow from a given initial point along a solution curve because at each point we have a good idea of the direction in which to proceed. Note that for $x = \pm 1$, the slopes for any $\dot{x}$ are perpendicular to the radius from the origin. The term isocline refers to lines in the $x\dot{x}$-plane along which $d\dot{x}/dx$ is a constant. In this problem, the equation of the isoclines is

$$\mu(1 - x^2) - \frac{x}{\dot{x}} = a, \tag{7–16}$$

where a represents the constant value of $d\dot{x}/dx$ along a particular isocline.

In more complicated systems, the phase plane may contain other types of singular points such as nodes and saddles.† There may be limit cycles, that is, closed curves, which are unstable as well as stable. In Fig. 7–19(a), we have surrounded our stable limit cycle of Fig. 7–18(b) with another limit cycle which can be termed unstable. Note that curves beginning in its neighborhood spiral away from it. Figure 7–19(b) is the reverse picture. Here the unstable limit cycle surrounds a stable focus so that any motion originating within the limit cycle spirals into the center. Observe that a motion beginning outside of the unstable limit cycle spirals toward the larger stable limit cycle. Thus, to start this system going in a steady oscillation, we must have an initial disturbance large enough to give initial condi-

---

* See the excellent book by Andronow and Chaikin, Ref. 20.
† See problems at the end of the chapter.

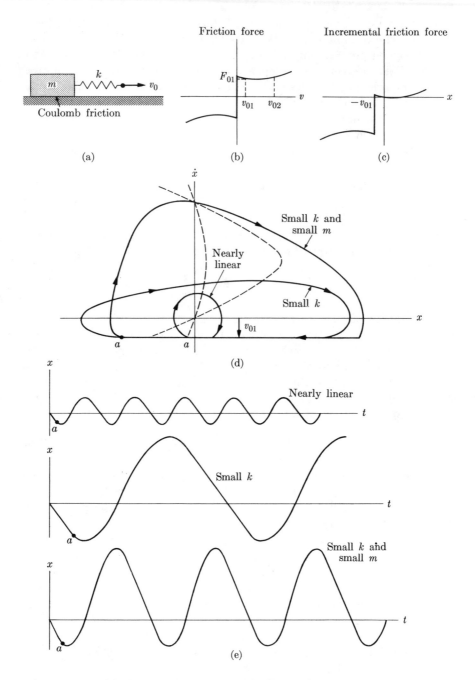

FIG. 7–20.   Limit cycles associated with the negative slope in the Coulomb friction characteristic.

tions outside of the inner limit cycle. You may have noticed that many pendulum clocks have this characteristic. If you try to start them too gently, the motion dies out. If you are more insistent the clock will stabilize on its "design" limit cycle.* Such a system is often termed *hard*, whereas that of Fig. 7–19(a) is termed *soft*. (Do not confuse these designations with the "hard" and "soft" spring of Fig. 7–10.)

EXAMPLE 7–9. Although many of the important and useful applications of this approach to nearly linear systems are in the realm of electric circuitry which abounds in nonlinear elements, such as diodes, transistors, saturable core inductors, triodes, etc., we will look first at a simple mechanical system which is close to our experience. Let's again concentrate on a spring-mass system with Coulomb friction like that of Example 7–8 and Fig. 7–16, except that we will move the end of the spring at a constant horizontal velocity as shown in Fig. 7–20(a). I think most of us have seen such a system oscillate or "chatter" when we tried to maintain a slow speed v_0. However, the mass slides steadily when we insist on maintaining a faster speed.

To explain this behavior, we must make a better approximation of the friction-force characteristic than we did in Fig. 7–16. Actually, the magnitude of the friction force can be less at low speeds than at rest or at high speeds (Fig. 7–20b). If we maintain a velocity v_{01}, the "equilibrium" friction force is on a part of the curve which has a negative slope. A higher velocity v_{02} corresponds to a positive slope. Possibly the first case represents unstable equilibrium and the second, stable. If so, we get a limit-cycle type of oscillation such as is actually observed.

Choosing the speed v_{01}, let's change coordinates (that is, unaccelerated observers) so the end of the spring appears stationary and the floor moves to the left at constant v_{01}. If we also measure incremental spring deflection from the extended position where the spring force just balances F_{01}, we can redraw the friction-force characteristic as in Fig. 7–20(c). This certainly seems to represent unstable equilibrium because locally a positive speed $\dot{x}$ corresponds to a negative "retarding" force, and vice versa. In physical terms, if the mass m achieves a negative velocity of magnitude v_{01}, it is actually at rest on the "moving" floor and the friction force can have any value over a large range as shown. Once the mass is at rest relative to the floor, the static friction can balance the spring force until enough time has elapsed so that the spring force reaches a value larger than the maximum attainable friction force. The mass then begins sliding forward under the urging of the spring force and the diminishing friction

---

* See Minorsky, Ref. 19, p. 424, Andronow and Chiakin, Ref. 20, p. 118, and problems at the end of the chapter.

force. The velocity which is then positive, may be brought to zero and a negative value by the spring force as the displacement x goes through a positive maximum.

For a nearly linear system in which the peak friction forces are always much smaller than the peak spring and inertia forces, the phase-plane plot* is shown in Fig. 7–20(d). Note that the velocity $\dot{x}$ never is less than $-v_{01}$ and that the curve is nearly circular. The response is thus almost sinusoidal, as shown in Fig. 7–20(e), where the "flat spot" corresponds to the period that the mass spends at rest relative to the floor. Remember that during this time, the static friction force is changing so as to just balance the spring force. Can you draw a time history of friction force for this motion?

For a system with a weaker spring, the breakaway point a where the spring force exceeds the maximum static friction will occur at larger displacement x. The corresponding phase-plane plot in Fig. 7–20(d) is far less like a circle and the corresponding time history is much less sinusoidal. Observe that the proportion of the total period that the mass spends at rest relative to the floor is greatly increased. Notice also that if the mass m is now made very small (without changing the friction characteristics, please), the speed at which the spring moves the mass around the curved portion of the phase-plane plot is greatly increased, whereas the time spent at $-v_{01}$ is almost unchanged. For this system which is far from nearly linear, the time response is shown in Fig. 7–20(e). Such an oscillation which is made up of several portions with entirely different behavior characteristics on each is usually called a *relaxation oscillation*.

You may have objected on practical grounds to keeping the friction characteristic unchanged while drastically reducing both the mass and stiffness. However, by doing so, we were able to look at systems ranging from nearly linear to highly nonlinear in which Coulomb friction is the nonlinear element. Other systems which are susceptible to very similar analyses are the oscillations of a pendulum on a slowly rotating shaft (Froude's pendulum), the bowing of a violin string (analyzed by Rayleigh), the chatter of brake shoes on linings, and the screeching of chalk on the blackboard (demonstrated by many teachers). ▲

The problem of discussing *the stability of nonlinear systems* is far more complicated than for linear systems in which instability is represented by any root of the characteristic equation with a positive real part. In terms of Fig. 7–3, any root in the right half-plane corresponds to an exponentially divergent time response. For nonlinear systems, we have been speaking

---

* See problems at the end of the chapter for the construction of these curves for which, initially, k/m is assumed equal to unity.

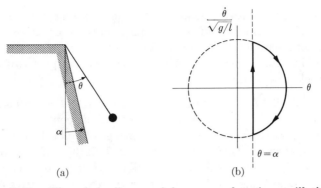

FIG. 7–21. The rebounding pendulum as a relaxation oscillation.

of stable foci and limit cycles without carefully defining what we mean by stability. Particularly for nearly linear systems, the work of Poincaré, expanded and developed quite recently, primarily by the Russians, is quite thorough and elaborate. However, the stability analysis of highly nonlinear systems, particularly when forced externally, is quite another matter and is understood only in some rather special situations. We do not have the space in this chapter to do more than touch on the ideas of stability at a number of points.

However, an important idea concerning stability is already quite evident. For nonconservative systems, both linear and nonlinear, to be unstable in any fashion, there must be a source of available energy which can be fed into the motion. Under the assumptions of linear theory, the amplitude builds up indefinitely. In nonlinear systems, there may be unstable and stable regions, limit cycles, and the like. Thus, an airplane whose motion is disturbed by a gust may begin to oscillate with increasing amplitude if improperly designed or loaded, obtaining its energy from the kinetic energy of the approaching airstream. This can be predicted by linear theory. On the other hand, the steady ticking of a clock requires the potential energy of a wound spring or a raised weight, but this maintenance of a steady oscillation is a nonlinear process.

Turning now to *the very nonlinear system* and the *relaxation oscillations* of which it sometimes is capable, we saw in the last example that the oscillations seemed to be made up of several distinct portions. This is perhaps more clearly demonstrated by the system of Fig. 7–21(a) in which we have a ball on a string in elastic collision with a wall. We can handle quite easily the pendulum part of the motion, but the details of the elastic collision are quite different. We find it useful to merely state that momentum and energy are conserved during the collision, which for practical purposes takes place instantaneously. The corresponding phase-plane plot is sketched in Fig. 7–21(b). This treatment of part of the motion in discontinuous fashion is directly analogous to the handling of shock waves in supersonic flow. Note that if our system is not conservative, the oscillations will not be maintained unless there is an external source of energy. Thus a child bouncing a rubber ball must apply an impulse with her hand at the top of each bounce.

EXAMPLE 7–10. As a traditional example of a relaxation oscillator, we can look at a simple resistance-capacitance circuit containing a neon discharge tube as shown in Fig. 7–22(a). Such a gas-filled tube has the current voltage characteristic $I_N(V)$, shown in Fig. 7–22(b). If the tube is conducting at a relatively high voltage, it will continue to conduct as the voltage decreases (although with decreasing current transmitted) until the point B is reached. For lower voltages, the conduction ceases abruptly. If the voltage is raised, the conduction will not start until D is reached when the tube is again suddenly operating at A.

The differential equations for the circuit are

$$E - (i_C + i_N)R - V = 0,$$

$$i_C = C \frac{dV}{dt},$$

$$i_N = \begin{cases} I_N(V) & \text{for } i_N > i_{N_D}, \\ 0 & \text{otherwise.} \end{cases}$$

Eliminating the currents, we get the first-order equation in V,

$$\frac{dV}{dt} = \frac{1}{RC}[E - V - RI_N(V)]$$

during conduction, and

$$\frac{dV}{dt} = \frac{1}{RC}[E - V]$$

when the tube is extinguished. The conduction equilibrium point occurs when dV/dt is zero so that

$$I_N(V) = \frac{E - V}{R}.$$

This condition is shown in Fig. 7–22(b) as the intersection O of the curves $I_N(V)$ and $(E - V)/R$. Note that we have chosen circuit elements such that O is on the negative slope or "negative resistance" part of the curve. (Can you show that if the intersection O was made between A and B, the operating point would be stable there?)

Let's suppose we connect the battery to the circuit at $t = 0$ when V is zero. The tube is nonconducting and, solving the second differential

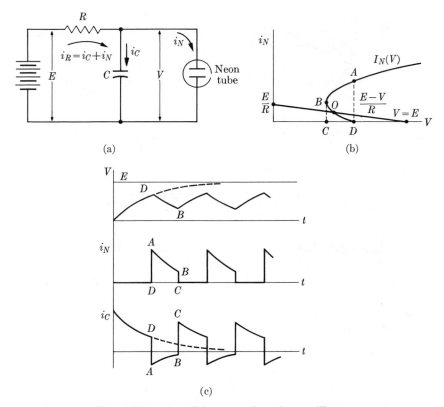

Fig. 7–22.   A well-known relaxation oscillator.

equation, we obtain

$$V = E(1 - e^{-t/RC}), \qquad i_R = i_C = \frac{E - V}{R}, \qquad i_N = 0.$$

When V reaches D, however, the tube begins to conduct. The voltage on the capacitance cannot change very rapidly, but since we have postulated no inductance in our circuit, the current can change in a discontinuous fashion. Thus we jump to point A at the same value of V. Now

$$i_C = i_R - i_N = \left[\frac{E - V}{R} - I_N(V)\right] = C\frac{dV}{dt}$$

with $I_N(V)$ larger than $(E - V)/R$. Thus dV/dt is negative and V decreases, in roughly an exponential form, until we reach point B when conduction stops. Once again, V rises exponentially to D, etc.

The time histories of V, i_N, and i_C are shown in Fig. 7–22(c). Note that they are hardly sinusoidal. Note also that the system did not spiral in

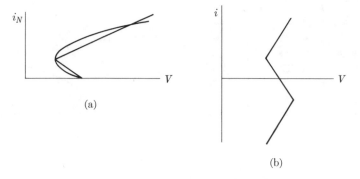

FIG. 7–23. Piecewise linear characteristics which suggest approximate but analytical procedures.

toward a limit cycle like our nearly linear systems but rather got right down to business as soon as it reached the operating range. The effect of small inductance can be included,* but it changes the vertical lines into segments with very large slope. By analogy, look at Fig. 7–20(e) and visualize that reducing m to zero changes the steep portions of the response to vertical discontinuities, and the second-order system degenerates to a first-order system similar to this neon oscillator. ▲

Very often the essential features of a system can be calculated if the nonlinear element is approximated by a series of straight lines, *the piecewise linear approximation.* The neon tube characteristic becomes that of Fig. 7–23(a). The advantages of this approach are expounded by Zimmerman and Mason† who show how characteristics with a negative resistance portion, as in Fig. 7–23(b), can be obtained with elements, such as transistors and triodes.

In analogy with the development of linear system analysis of Section 7–2 where we studied homogeneous equations in which time did not appear explicitly, we have looked only at *similarly autonomous nonlinear systems* in these sections. This has enabled us to use the phase plane extensively with Poincaré's limit cycles and other descriptive techniques. If we look at *nonautonomous nonlinear systems* in which time appears, for example, through a periodic external forcing function, the situation becomes less well understood. The phase plane is no longer useful, and the calculations become more complicated. Still, for nearly linear systems, the explicit introduction of time involves no essential difficulty. (We will defer looking at nonautonomous nonlinear systems until Section 8–4.)

---

* See Zimmerman and Mason, Ref. 21, p. 446.

† Ref. 21, p. 431 ff.

PROBLEMS

7–1. (a) Derive carefully the equation of vertical translation of the mass-spring system of Fig. 7–2(a), showing that the coordinate of the small-amplitude motion should be measured from b in Fig. 7–2(b).

(b) Suppose that the spring weighs about $\frac{1}{10}$ of mg. Can you include this fact in your equation of motion in an approximate but reasonable fashion? [See Example 3–8 and Fig. 3–10(d).]

7–2. In analyzing the mass-spring system of Fig. 7–2(a), we assumed the mass could only translate vertically, the spring was massless, etc. How many independent coordinates would we need to describe possible motions of an actual mass hanging from an actual spring? What specific assumptions must we make to justify our analysis? How reasonable are they? Hang a mass on a spring and check your ideas.

7–3. Write the differential equation of motion for a simple mass-spring system subject to each of the following common kinds of damping: (a) viscous damping, proportional to velocity; (b) coulomb damping, constant in magnitude but of opposite sign to the velocity; (c) square law damping, proportional to velocity squared; (d) structural damping, proportional to amplitude but "in phase with" the velocity. Which of these equations are tractable mathematically? Why?

7–4. The differential equation $m\ddot{x} + kx = 0$ is usually accompanied by two initial conditions $x(t_0) = x_0$, $\dot{x}(t_0) = v_0$. (a) Can you obtain an explicit solution if these conditions are specified at a later time t_1? (b) Can x_0 and $\ddot{x}_0$ be used as independent initial conditions? (c) Can $x(t_0)$ and $x(t_1)$ be used as a pair of conditions? What if $t_1 - t_0 = 2\pi\sqrt{m/k}$? Give reasons for your answers.

7–5. A mass-spring damper system has a damping ratio less than unity. If set into oscillation by releasing the mass at an initial displacement x_0 and with zero initial velocity, find the ratio of the amount of the first overshoot to x_0 in terms of the damping ratio.

7–6. In Example 7–1, it is stated that the solution to the equation $m\ddot{x} + kx = 0$ can be written in the three forms $x = C \cos(\omega_0 t + \psi)$, $x = C \sin(\omega_0 t + \phi)$, and $x = A \cos \omega_0 t + B \sin \omega_0 t$. (a) Find the relations between the pairs of constants of integration. (b) Assuming that the position and velocity at $t = 0$ are x_0 and v_0, relate the pairs of integration constants to these initial conditions.

7–7. Demonstrate that the differential equation $m\ddot{x} + f\dot{x} + kx = 0$ has the solution $x = (C_1 + C_2 t)e^{-(f/2m)t}$ for the critically damped case where $f = \sqrt{4mk}$ by assuming a trial solution of the more general form $x = y(t)e^{-(f/2m)t}$ and evaluating $y(t)$.

7–8. Derive the equations of motion of the two simple pendulums connected by the relatively light linear spring as shown in Fig. 7–24. (a) Assume motion

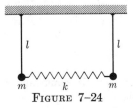

FIGURE 7–24

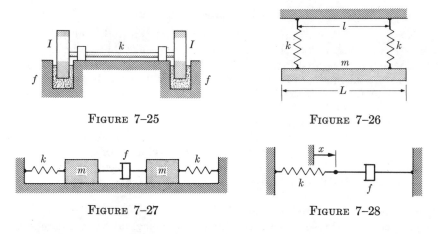

FIGURE 7-25　　　　　　　　　FIGURE 7-26

FIGURE 7-27　　　　　　　　　FIGURE 7-28

in the plane of the diagram only. (b) If we permit small out-of-plane as well as small in-plane motions, are the equations for the out-of-plane motions coupled with those for in-plane motions or are they independent? (c) Evaluate the natural frequencies which characterize this system.

7-9. (a) Derive the equations of rotational motion of the two flywheels connected by a shaft of low torsional stiffness k in Fig. 7-25. The flywheels dip into viscous fluid which contributes torsional moments proportional to angular velocity as $f\dot\theta$.

(b) Is there a critical value of damping constant f for this system?

7-10. Derive the differential equations for motion of the rigid bar supported elastically as shown in Fig. 7-26. (a) Consider only motions in the plane of the diagram. (b) Assuming the springs are replaced by wires of length s, consider only motions out of the plane of the diagram.

7-11. Demonstrate that the differential equations of motion derived in Example 7-2 are not dependent on the assumptions that $x_2 > x_1$ and $\dot x_2 > \dot x_1$ at the instant of observation. Try different assumptions and see if you obtain the same equations of motion.

7-12. Show that the two simultaneous differential equations of motion of Example 7-2 are equivalent to the single fourth-order equation,

$$m^2\ddddot{x}_1 + 2mf\dddot{x}_1 + 4mk\ddot{x}_1 + 2fk\dot{x}_1 + 3k^2x_1 = 0,$$

obtained by eliminating x_2 and its derivatives, and also to the four first-order equations

$$m\dot v_1 = -2kx_1 + kx_2 - fv_1 + fv_2,$$
$$m\dot v_2 = kx_1 - 2kx_2 + fv_1 - fv_2,$$
$$\dot x_1 = v_1,$$
$$\dot x_2 = v_2.$$

7-13. Show that the characteristic equation obtained from the alternative forms in the previous problem is the same that was obtained in Example 7-2.

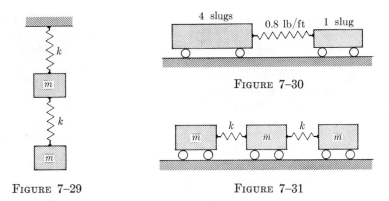

FIGURE 7–30

FIGURE 7–29

FIGURE 7–31

Would the characteristic roots have been the same if x_1 had been eliminated to form a fourth-order equation in x_2?

7–14. Two equal masses on a frictionless surface are connected by a viscous damper, and each is restrained by a spring as shown in Fig. 7–27. Find the motion of the system when it starts from rest with one mass initially displaced a distance x_0 from its equilibrium position, and the other mass initially at its equilibrium position. Consider only simple rectilinear motion.

7–15. A massless spring is connected to a massless damper as shown in Fig. 7–28. Show that the rate of change of potential energy of the system equals the rate at which the damper dissipates energy.

7–16. The mass-spring system illustrated in Fig. 7–29 is free to move only linearly in the vertical direction. When the system is in static equilibrium under the attraction of gravity, the springs, of course, are under some tension. Suppose the *lower mass* is very slowly raised until the *lower spring* has no tension. If the lower mass is then suddenly released find a complete expression for the subsequent motion of the *upper mass*. [*Note:* Please define the origins of your coordinates carefully.]

7–17. Calculate the natural frequency of any free oscillation of which the system shown in Fig. 7–30 is capable.

7–18. For the three mass system of Fig. 7–31, (a) write the differential equations of motion; (b) for $m = 2$ slugs and $k = 10$ lb/ft, find the natural frequencies of the system; (c) for the initial conditions of unstretched springs, center mass stationary, and end masses moving apart at 1 ft/sec, find the expression for the motion of the left end mass as a function of time.

7–19. Referring to the context of Eq. (7–8b), show that $C_p = \sqrt{A^2 + B^2}$ and that $\psi_p = \tan^{-1}(-B/A)$.

7–20. By substituting the general solutions derived in Example 7–2 into the differential equations, show that the disposable constants must be related as $C_{11} = C_{21}, C_{12} = -C_{22}, \psi_{11} = \psi_{21}$, and $\psi_{12} = \psi_{22}$.

7–21. Find, analytically, the response [shown in Fig. 7–7(d)] of a damped second-order system to a step input.

7–22. Find, analytically, the response [shown in Fig. 7–7(e)] of a damped second-order system to a ramp input.

7–23. Note that the step input (see Fig. 7–7) is simply the integral over time of the impulse input and that the ramp is the integral of the step. Would you expect the same to be true of the responses of the second-order system to these inputs? Try it and see.

7–24. Demonstrate the principle of superposition by showing that the particular solutions for step and ramp inputs to a simple second-order system become, when added together, the particular solution for an input of a ramp superimposed on a step.

7–25. If we remember that the angular deflection θ of the spring-restrained needle on an ordinary voltmeter corresponds to the rotation of a coil in a fixed magnetic field, it is not difficult to obtain the following equation relating instantaneously the needle deflection and the applied voltage:

$$A\ddot{\theta} + B\dot{\theta} + C\theta = V(t).$$

For $A = 100$ volt-sec^2/radian, $B = 30$ volt-sec/radian, $C = 2$ volts/radian. (a) Calculate and sketch the response of this meter to a sudden applied voltage of 1 volt. (b) Suppose that the voltage was removed after $\frac{1}{4}$ of a second. Find the complete response of the needle from $t = 0$ to $t \to \infty$.

7–26. A system has the differential equation

$$\frac{du}{dt} + bu(t) = v(t),$$

where $u(t)$ is the output and $v(t)$ the input. Find the response of the system to a unit step function input when the system is initially at rest.

7–27. The electric circuit illustrated in Fig. 7–32 contains a capacitor C, a resistor R, and an inductor L. A voltage E is applied across the terminals. The equation governing the current i flowing in this circuit reads

$$L\frac{d^2i}{dt^2} + R\frac{di}{dt} + \frac{1}{C}i = \frac{dE}{dt}.$$

Suppose that no current flows up to time $t = 0$ when a voltage $E = E_0 \cos \omega t$ is suddenly applied. Using what you know about single-degree-of-freedom systems, describe in a few short sentences how the current through the circuit will behave. Find that particular value of ω which will cause the current to reach the largest amplitude after the sinusoidal voltage has been acting for some time.

7–28. At $t = 0$ the closing of a switch impresses a constant voltage E of 100 v on the capacitance-resistance circuit illustrated in Fig. 7–33. The behavior of the system is described by the equation

$$\frac{1}{C}\int_0^t i\,dt + Ri = 100$$

and by the initial condition $i = 0$ for $t < 0$. Find i as a function of time.

7–29. Figure 7–34 represents a pressure gauge that is subjected to atmospheric pressure. Suddenly an explosion blast causes a pressure disturbance

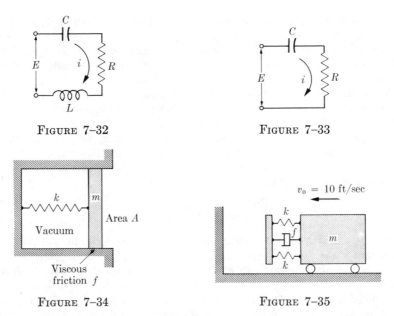

FIGURE 7–32   FIGURE 7–33

FIGURE 7–34   FIGURE 7–35

from atmospheric pressure which can be represented by $P_0 e^{-at}$. (a) Derive the differential equation for the motion of the piston. (b) Solve this differential equation and determine the constants (assume damping less than critical damping). (c) Give a rough plot of the displacement of the piston as a function of time.

7–30. Consider an ordinary mercury thermometer immersed in ice water. It reads 0°C. If it is suddenly transferred to a bath of boiling water, the thermometer will eventually read 100°C. It can be shown that the instantaneous reading T of the thermometer can be described by the simple differential equation

$$B \frac{dT}{dt} + T = F(t),$$

where $F(t)$ in this case is simply the constant (step function) 100, and where B is a known constant. Find the transient and permanent parts of the solution and sketch the complete response versus time.

7–31. Our familiar mass-spring-dashpot system is at rest at $t = 0$ when it is subjected to an impulse of 2 lb-sec. Assume $m = 1$ slug, $k = 1$ lb/ft, $f = 4$ lb/ft/sec. (a) What is the damping ratio of this system? (b) Calculate and sketch the system's response to the impulse.

7–32. The mass of Problem 7–31 is acted upon by an external force $F_a \sin \omega_f t$, applied at the initial instant, at which time the mass is at rest. (a) Write the relation for the subsequent motion with all arbitrary constants evaluated. (b) Write the relation for the motion if the external force is considered to have been applied initially in the remote past.

7–33. A mass m (Fig. 7–35) traveling at 10 ft/sec runs into a fixed wall at time $t = 0$. It is protected by a massless bumper connected to m by two springs and a viscous damper. For the parameters $m = 1$ slug, $k = 10$ lb/ft, and $\zeta = 0.1$, (a) What is the maximum displacement to the left experienced by mass m and when does it occur? (b) Will the mass and bumper bounce away again? Explain carefully, indicating how you would find the instant it left contact and its final velocity.

7–34. An aircraft rate-of-climb meter consists primarily of an elastic bellows of fixed length divided by a diaphragm whose displacement moves the needle of the meter. Air at static pressure from the pitot tube is permitted to flow freely to one side of the bellows but must go through a capillary tube to reach the other. In a climb, the static pressure decreases and, since the flow out of only one side of the bellows is retarded, the diaphragm and thus the needle move. The system can be represented by the differential equation

$$\dot{\theta} + R\theta = A\dot{h},$$

where θ represents needle displacement, h is airplane altitude, and A and R are constants. Find the response of the instrument in an airplane which after flying at constant altitude pulls up at $t = 0$ into a steady climb at rate B so that $h = h_0 + Bt$.

7–35. Suppose the accelerometer of Fig. 7–8(a) is placed on an inclined plane and allowed to slide down the plane. Looking carefully at the effects of gravity on the seismic mass m as well as on the accelerometer itself, find the response $x(t)$ of the instrument, (a) if the plane is frictionless, and (b) if the friction coefficient $\mu = \frac{1}{2} \tan \theta$ (where θ is the angle of the plane's inclination).

7–36. Suppose that it has been determined experimentally that a certain mercury thermometer responds exponentially to a sudden change in temperature. It is also noted that it takes three seconds for the exponent in the response to reach unity. If this thermometer is subjected suddenly to a linearly rising temperature (which had been constant) of 10 degrees per second, find the subsequent *error* in the thermometer reading.

7–37. Find the response of the second mass of the system of Fig. 7–4 and Example 7–2 if a unit impulse is applied to the first mass at $t = 0$.

*7–38. (a) Derive, but do not solve, the equations of vertical motion for the system illustrated in Fig. 7–36, defining carefully the origins for your coordinates. The applied force $F = F_0(1 - e^{-t})$.

(b) How many initial conditions are needed for a complete statement of this problem?

(c) For large t what are the positions of the masses?

7–39. Consider the torsional system illustrated in Fig. 7–37 where a flywheel with large moment of inertia I_2 is connected to a flat disk of small moment of inertia I_1 by means of a weightless rod of torsional spring constant k rad/ft-lb. The disk dips into a viscous bath which exerts a retarding torque proportional to the disk angular velocity. (This might represent an engine connected to a propeller in a sticky fluid.) Assume that the large flywheel I_2 is subjected to a steady torque Q_0 at $t = 0$ when the system is at rest. (a) Derive the differential equations for this system. (b) Assume I_1 is small enough to be considered equal to zero and then solve for θ_1 and θ_2 as functions of time.

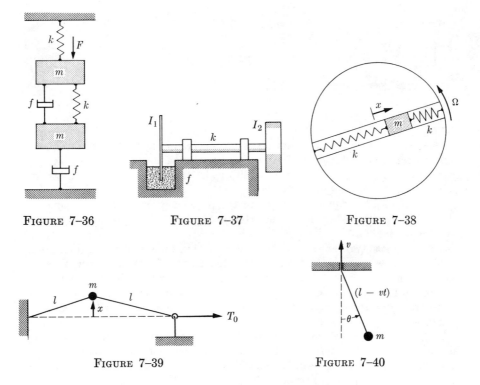

FIGURE 7–36   FIGURE 7–37   FIGURE 7–38

FIGURE 7–39   FIGURE 7–40

7–40. A turntable rotating about a vertical axis has an elastically restrained mass sliding in a frictionless slot as shown in Fig. 7–38. Assuming the spring forces are equal and opposite at $x = 0$, write the equation of motion for the slider for a constant value of Ω. Is there a critical value of Ω?

7–41. In the preceding problem, assume that Ω is a sinusoidal function of time as $\Omega = \Omega_0 \cos at$. Derive the equation of motion of the slider and try to identify it as a Hill or Mathieu equation. For what ranges of Ω_0 and a is the motion stable?

7–42. (a) Find the natural frequency of a mass m mounted as shown in Fig. 7–39 on a string of constant tension T_0.

*(b) Derive the equation of transverse motion for the mass if the tension is made to vary as $T = T_0 (1 + \epsilon \cos \omega t)$. Under what conditions is the small amplitude motion stable? Can you visualize a sinusoidal response of the mass at a frequency of $\omega/2$? Explain carefully.

*7–43 Suppose the string supporting a mass as a simple pendulum (Fig. 7–40) is being withdrawn through a hole as shown at the constant rate v. Show that the equation for the pendulum motion is

$$(l - vt)\ddot{\theta} - 2v\dot{\theta} + g \sin \theta = 0.$$

For small θ and for $vt \ll l$ will the amplitude increase or decrease? What can you say if v is negative?

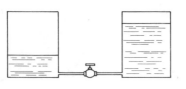

FIGURE 7-41   FIGURE 7-42

7-44. In Example 6-7, we studied pendulum-like motions in the orbital plane of a satellite in circular orbit. Find the differential equation governing the corresponding motion when the orbit is elliptical. Is the equation still linear for small amplitude pendulum motion?

7-45. Reduce the equation derived in the previous problem to correspond to the nearly circular twenty-four hour orbit of Fig. 3-27. Can you find a solution for this special case?

7-46. Suppose two tanks are connected by a thin tube as shown in Fig. 7-41. If the valve is opened, the fluid levels will change. Make whatever physical assumptions seem reasonable to permit yourself to write a simple equation of motion for the system. Carefully list these assumptions. Did you obtain a linear first-order equation? If not, what further assumptions will result in such an equation?

7-47. Consider the changes in level of the water in the U-tube manometer shown in Fig. 7-42. Is this system's transient behavior characterized by an essentially linear or nonlinear differential equation? Is it second order or first order? Do you expect oscillations in level? Explain carefully.

7-48. Verify that Eq. (7-13) gives the phase-plane plots of Fig. 7-15 for various damping ratios. Construct some of the curves graphically, using isocline procedures if necessary.

7-49. In Example 3-15, we studied the motion of a mass attracted to a fixed origin by a spring of stiffness k. Using the ideas of augmented potential and the plots of Fig. 3-19, sketch the phase-plane plots $(\dot{r}, r)$ for various values of angular momentum. Compare your results with those of Fig. 7-13 for a mass under gravitational attraction.

*7-50. Suppose the horizontal axis of a simple pendulum is made to rotate about the vertical at the rate Ω and thus forces the plane of the pendulum to rotate as shown in Fig. 7-43. (a) Show that the differential equation of the motion is

$$\ddot{\theta} - \Omega^2 \left(\cos \theta - \frac{g}{\Omega^2 a} \right) \sin \theta = 0.$$

(b) Find the energy equation for this conservative system. (c) Sketch the essential features of the phase-plane plot for this system and identify energies corresponding to small oscillations about an equilibrium position, larger irregular oscillations, and nonoscillatory continuous rotations.

7-51. Suppose the flow through the valve of Problem 7-46 is characterized by a pressure drop proportional to fluid velocity squared. For slow changes in fluid height the differential equation approximating the behavior of the system is

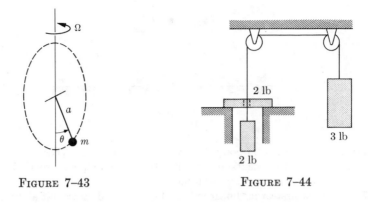

FIGURE 7–43   FIGURE 7–44

$\dot{h}^2 - kh = 0$ where h is the difference in fluid height in the two tanks. (a) Plot phase-plane curves for this system for different initial values of h. (b) Find a solution for $h(t)$ analytically.

7–52. In order to see a saddle point, plot the phase plane curves for the equation $\ddot{x} - x = 0$ and look carefully at the neighborhood of the origin. For comparison, can you find any saddle points in Fig. 7–11?

7–53. Label the singularities occurring in Figs. 7–12, 7–17(a) and 7–17(b) as centers, saddles, stable or unstable nodes or foci.

7–54. Show by the method of isoclines that $\ddot{x} + x = 0$ gives circles in the phase plane.

7–55. Show that Rayleigh's equation,

$$\ddot{x} - (A - B\dot{x}^2)\dot{x} + x = 0,$$

can be transformed into Van der Pol's equation (Eq. 7–14).

7–56. Plot phase-plane curves for Van der Pol's equation for $\mu = 0.1$ using the isocline technique. Show that the limit cycle can be approached from outside and inside.

7–57. If the mass-spring system of Fig. 7–16(a) has some viscous as well as coulomb damping, how will the phase-plane plot of Fig. 7–16(c) change? Sketch it for $\zeta \sim 0.2$.

7–58. Suppose that for the pendulum bouncing against the wall in Fig. 7–21(a) the collisions are not perfectly elastic. How does this change the phase-plane plot for the motion?

7–59. If the 3-lb weight in Fig. 7–44 is released from a high position, it will accelerate down until the rising 2-lb weight picks up the stationary 2-lb weight. The system will oscillate, alternately picking up and leaving the upper 2-lb weight. Assuming no appreciable mass in the pulley, sketch a phase-plane curve for the motion of the 3-lb weight. Also plot the motion as a function of time.

7–60. Replot the motions of Fig. 7–20(e) from the viewpoint of a stationary observer.

7–61. Draw the phase-plane limit cycle corresponding to a small girl maintaining the bouncing of a rubber ball by hitting it lightly at the top of each bounce.

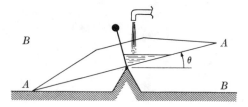

FIGURE 7–45

7–62. If the operating point 0 of the neon tube circuit (Fig. 7–22) is between A and B on the tube characteristic, is the system stable for small disturbances? Is it stable following a large disturbance?

7–63. Can a first-order linear system be subjected to an initial condition such that its transient response is oscillatory? How about a first-order nonlinear system? Explain. [*Hint:* See Example 7–10.]

*7–64. As a first approximation to an ordinary pendulum clock, assume that it consists of three elements: (1) an oscillatory dissipative pendulum system, (2) a source of energy such as a mainspring, and (3) an escapement which periodically permits the mainspring to apply an impulse to the pendulum system. If we assume that the pendulum is a second-order linear system with small viscous damping and that the escapement applies a fixed impulse once each cycle when θ is zero, show that the clock will stabilize on a particular limit cycle in the phase plane. According to this analysis the final motion of the pendulum is not controlled by the manner in which the clock was started, is it?

*7–65. Add a small amount of coulomb friction to the pendulum system of the previous problem and show in the phase plane that a clock started too gently will stop. Also show that if started vigorously enough, the clock will achieve a stable limit cycle.

7–66. A mechanical system which acts very much like an electronic multivibrator circuit is the two-tank teeter-totter shown in Fig. 7–45. It has two "stable" positions, AA and BB, and shifts suddenly between them whenever a critical condition is reached. Sketch the phase-plane trajectory for this system and also sketch the time history $\theta(t)$. Note that an oscillation of definite frequency is associated with a steady source of energy.

REFERENCES

REFERENCES

1. H. P. Robertson, *Modern Physics for the Engineer*, L. N. Ridenour, ed. New York: McGraw-Hill, 1954.

2. H. Goldstein, *Classical Mechanics*. Reading, Mass.: Addison-Wesley, 1950.

3. G. B. Thomas, Jr., *Calculus and Analytic Geometry*. 3rd ed. Reading, Mass.: Addison-Wesley, 1960.

4. D. W. Sciama, *The Unity of the Universe*. New York: Doubleday, 1959.

5. I. S. Sokolnikoff and R. M. Redheffer, *Mathematics of Physics and Modern Engineering*. New York: McGraw-Hill, 1958.

6. L. Page, *Introduction to Theoretical Physics*. 3rd ed. Princeton, New Jersey: Van Nostrand, 1952.

7. K. S. Ehricke, *Space Flight*. Princeton, New Jersey: Van Nostrand, 1960.

8. H. W. Seifert, *Space Technology*. New York: Wiley and Sons, 1959.

9. R. L. Bisplinghoff, H. Ashley, and R. L. Halfman, *Aeroelasticity*. Reading, Mass.: Addison-Wesley, 1955.

10. A. G. Webster, *Dynamics of Particles and of Rigid, Elastic, and Fluid Bodies*. 2nd ed. New York: Dover, 1959.

11. E. J. Routh, *Advanced Dynamics of a System of Rigid Bodies*. 6th ed. New York: Dover, 1955.

12. A. Gray, *Treatise on Gyrostatics and Rotational Motion*. New York: Macmillan, 1918.

13. E. A. Milne, *Vectorial Mechanics*. New York: Interscience Publications, 1948.

14. B. Etkin, *Dynamics of Flight*. New York: Wiley and Sons, 1959.

15. C. D. Perkins and R. E. Hage, *Airplane Performance, Stability, and Control*. New York: Wiley and Sons, 1949.

16. H. Poincaré, *Les Methodes Nouvelles de la Mecanique Celeste*. 3 vols. New York: Dover, 1957.

17. H. S. Tsien, *Engineering Cybernetics*. New York: McGraw-Hill, 1954.

18. J. J. Stoker, *Nonlinear Vibrations in Mechanical and Electrical Systems*. New York: Interscience Publications, 1950.

19. N. Minorsky, *Introduction to Nonlinear Mechanics*. Ann Arbor, Michigan: Edwards, 1947.

20. A. A. Andronow and C. E. Chaikin, *Theories of Oscillations*. Princeton, New Jersey: Van Nostrand, 1949.

21. H. J. Zimmerman and S. J. Mason, *Electronic Circuit Theory*. New York: Wiley and Sons, 1959.

22. F. Hilderbrand, *Methods of Applied Mathematics*. New York: Prentice-Hall, 1952.

APPENDIX

APPENDIX A

MATRICES

A–1 Matrix algebra. Any of us who have worked with sets of *simultaneous algebraic equations* have felt the need of a systematic technique for manipulating such equations. Matrices, which can be considered a step beyond determinants, have evolved with just this need in mind. A typical set of equations, such as

$$
\begin{aligned}
a_{11}x_1 + a_{12}x_2 + a_{13}x_3 &= y_1, \\
a_{21}x_1 + a_{22}x_2 + a_{23}x_3 &= y_2, \\
a_{31}x_1 + a_{32}x_2 + a_{33}x_3 &= y_3,
\end{aligned}
\tag{A–1a}
$$

involves the quantities x_1, x_2, x_3 and y_1, y_2, y_3, as well as the coefficients a_{ij} which relate them. In our standard form [Eq. (A–1a)] the a's and x's are intermixed, whereas in the form

$$
\begin{bmatrix}
a_{11} & a_{12} & a_{13} \\
a_{21} & a_{22} & a_{23} \\
a_{31} & a_{32} & a_{33}
\end{bmatrix}
\begin{Bmatrix} x_1 \\ x_2 \\ x_3 \end{Bmatrix}
=
\begin{Bmatrix} y_1 \\ y_2 \\ y_3 \end{Bmatrix},
\tag{A–1b}
$$

the *square matrix* containing the a's is distinct from the *column matrix* of the x's.

The multiplication of such matrices is simply the procedure which makes Eqs. (A–1a) and (A–1b) entirely equivalent. Thus, the first row of the square matrix is combined with the column of x's by multiplying corresponding terms and then summing. Similarly, the second and third rows are each combined with the column of x's to obtain the terms on the left-hand side of Eq. (A–1a). Notice that one *matrix equation*, which can also be written in the shorthand form

$$
[a]\{x\} = \{y\},
\tag{A–1c}
$$

represents a whole set of ordinary algebraic equations. You may also be familiar with the *summation notation* for this same set of equations,

$$
\sum_{j=1}^{3} a_{ij}x_j = y_i, \qquad i = 1, 2, 3,
\tag{A–1d}
$$

in which the summation sign itself is often omitted with the understanding that a summation is to be carried out over any subscript which is repeated in a product.

361

Somewhat more generally, we can have the array of terms

$$[a] = \begin{bmatrix} a_{11} & a_{12} & a_{13} & \cdots & a_{1n} \\ a_{21} & a_{22} & a_{23} & \cdots & a_{2n} \\ a_{31} & & & \cdots & \\ \vdots & & & & \\ a_{m1} & a_{m2} & & \cdots & a_{mn} \end{bmatrix}, \qquad (A\text{–}2)$$

which is called a *matrix of m rows and n columns* of elements. A matrix with but a single column is often distinguished by braces { }, whereas a single row matrix may be symbolized by half-brackets ⌊ ⌋.

Two matrices are said to be *equal* when they are of the same size and corresponding pairs of elements are equal. Similarly, the *addition* or *subtraction* of matrices involves simply addition or subtraction of corresponding elements.

EXAMPLE.

$$\begin{bmatrix} 1 & 2 & 3 \\ 2 & -3 & 4 \end{bmatrix} + \begin{bmatrix} 4 & -5 & 6 \\ 5 & 6 & 7 \end{bmatrix} = \begin{bmatrix} 5 & -3 & 9 \\ 7 & 3 & 11 \end{bmatrix}.$$

Scalar multiplication of a matrix can be thought of as successive additions of itself so that each element is multiplied by the number.

EXAMPLE.

$$2 \begin{bmatrix} 1 & 2 & 3 \\ 2 & -3 & 4 \end{bmatrix} = \begin{bmatrix} 2 & 4 & 6 \\ 4 & -6 & 8 \end{bmatrix}.$$

The *product* $[c]$ of two matrices $[a]$ and $[b]$ is defined only when they are *conformable;* that is, when the number of columns of $[a]$ equals the number of rows of $[b]$. Thus

$$[a][b] = [c] \qquad (A\text{–}3a)$$

may have the form

$$\begin{bmatrix} a_{11} & a_{12} & a_{13} \\ a_{21} & a_{22} & a_{23} \end{bmatrix} \begin{bmatrix} b_{11} & b_{12} \\ b_{21} & b_{22} \\ b_{31} & b_{32} \end{bmatrix} = \begin{bmatrix} c_{11} & c_{12} \\ c_{21} & c_{22} \end{bmatrix}, \qquad (A\text{–}3b)$$

where, for example, the element

$$c_{12} = \lfloor a_{11} \quad a_{12} \quad a_{13} \rfloor \begin{Bmatrix} b_{12} \\ b_{22} \\ b_{32} \end{Bmatrix} = a_{11}b_{12} + a_{12}b_{22} + a_{13}b_{32}. \qquad (A\text{–}3c)$$

In general c_{ij} is formed by multiplying the ith row with the jth column. Note that the reverse product $[b][a]$ will give a 3×3 matrix with nine elements. This shows that matrix multiplication is *not generally commutative*. It is, however, *associative and distributive*, so we can write

$$[a][b] \neq [b][a],$$

$$[a]([b][c]) = ([a][b])[c], \tag{A--4}$$

$$[a]([b] + [c]) = [a][b] + [a][c].$$

EXAMPLES.

$$\lfloor 1 \quad -3 \quad 5 \rfloor \begin{Bmatrix} -2 \\ 4 \\ 6 \end{Bmatrix} = (1 \times -2) + (-3 \times 4) + (5 \times 6) = 16,$$

$$\begin{bmatrix} 3 & -1 & 2 \\ 1 & 0 & -2 \\ 2 & 1 & 0 \end{bmatrix} \begin{Bmatrix} 1 \\ -2 \\ 1 \end{Bmatrix} = \begin{Bmatrix} 7 \\ -1 \\ 0 \end{Bmatrix},$$

$$\begin{bmatrix} 1 & 2 & -3 \\ 2 & -1 & 3 \end{bmatrix} \begin{bmatrix} 1 & 2 \\ 0 & 1 \\ -1 & 3 \end{bmatrix} = \begin{bmatrix} 4 & -5 \\ -1 & 12 \end{bmatrix},$$

$$\begin{bmatrix} 1 & 2 \\ 0 & 1 \\ -1 & 3 \end{bmatrix} \begin{bmatrix} 1 & 2 & -3 \\ 2 & -1 & 3 \end{bmatrix} = \begin{bmatrix} 5 & 0 & 3 \\ 2 & -1 & 3 \\ 5 & -5 & 12 \end{bmatrix}.$$

A matrix may be *partitioned* into smaller submatrices by horizontal and vertical lines.

EXAMPLE.

$$\begin{bmatrix} 4 & \vdots & 0 & 1 \\ 1 & \vdots & -1 & 2 \\ \cdots & & \cdots & \cdots \\ -3 & \vdots & 2 & 4 \end{bmatrix} = \begin{bmatrix} [a] & \vdots & [b] \\ \cdots & & \cdots \\ [c] & \vdots & [d] \end{bmatrix}, \tag{A--5}$$

where

$$\{a\} = \begin{Bmatrix} 4 \\ 1 \end{Bmatrix}, \qquad [b] = \begin{bmatrix} 0 & 1 \\ -1 & 2 \end{bmatrix}, \qquad [c] = [-3], \qquad \lfloor d \rfloor = \lfloor 2, 4 \rfloor.$$

In general, partitioned matrices can be added, subtracted, and multiplied as though the submatrices were ordinary matrix elements. It is of course necessary, during multiplication, that the partitioned matrices satisfy the conformability requirement.

An important manipulation of our original set of algebraic equations involves solving for the quantities x_1, x_2, x_3. In *determinant* notation, we have learned to write by Cramer's rule

$$x_1 = \frac{\begin{vmatrix} y_1 & a_{12} & a_{13} \\ y_2 & a_{22} & a_{23} \\ y_3 & a_{32} & a_{33} \end{vmatrix}}{\begin{vmatrix} a_{11} & a_{12} & a_{13} \\ a_{21} & a_{22} & a_{23} \\ a_{31} & a_{32} & a_{33} \end{vmatrix}} = \frac{y_1 A_{11} + y_2 A_{21} + y_3 A_{31}}{|a|}. \quad \text{(A–6a)}$$

Here $|a|$ must not be zero and the A's are *cofactors* or signed minors. Thus

$$A_{ij} = (-1)^{i+j} M_{ij}, \quad \text{(A–6b)}$$

where M_{ij} is formed by removing the ith row and jth column from $|a|$ as

$$A_{21} = -M_{21} = - \begin{vmatrix} a_{12} & a_{13} \\ a_{32} & a_{33} \end{vmatrix}. \quad \text{(A–6c)}$$

Note that we can put Cramer's rule [Eq. (A–6a)] into matrix form for all x's simultaneously as

$$\begin{Bmatrix} x_1 \\ x_2 \\ x_3 \end{Bmatrix} = \frac{1}{|a|} \begin{bmatrix} A_{11} & A_{21} & A_{31} \\ A_{12} & A_{22} & A_{32} \\ A_{13} & A_{23} & A_{33} \end{bmatrix} \begin{Bmatrix} y_1 \\ y_2 \\ y_3 \end{Bmatrix}. \quad \text{(A–7)}$$

The matrix of cofactors above can be formed from the matrix $[a]$ by replacing each a_{ij} by its cofactor A_{ij} and then transposing or interchanging rows and columns as

$$\begin{bmatrix} a_{11} & a_{12} & a_{13} \\ a_{21} & a_{22} & a_{23} \\ a_{31} & a_{32} & a_{33} \end{bmatrix} \rightarrow \begin{bmatrix} A_{11} & A_{12} & A_{13} \\ A_{21} & A_{22} & A_{23} \\ A_{31} & A_{32} & A_{33} \end{bmatrix} \rightarrow \begin{bmatrix} A_{11} & A_{21} & A_{31} \\ A_{12} & A_{22} & A_{32} \\ A_{13} & A_{23} & A_{33} \end{bmatrix}.$$

This last step is often visualized as flipping the matrix about its main diagonal. The matrix of cofactors is often called the *adjoint matrix**

---

* Sometimes the term "adjoint matrix" is reserved for the matrix whose elements are the complex conjugates of those of $[a]$ after its rows and columns are transposed. See Goldstein, Ref. 2, p. 105.

Adj a, so Eq. (A–7) becomes

$$\{x\} = \frac{1}{|a|} \text{ Adj } a \{y\}. \tag{A–8}$$

Comparing this form with our original set of equations,

$$[a]\{x\} = \{y\}, \tag{A–1c}$$

we apparently have been able to solve for $\{x\}$ by manipulating the square matrix $[a]$. If we define, in analogy with the ideas of division or inversion, the *inverse matrix* $[a]^{-1}$ as

$$[a]^{-1} = \frac{\text{Adj } a}{|a|} = \frac{[A_{ji}]}{|a|}, \tag{A–9}$$

we can write Cramer's rule as

$$\{x\} = [a]^{-1}\{y\}. \tag{A–10}$$

Do not forget that in forming this inverse or reciprocal matrix, the cofactors must be transposed across the main diagonal and that $|a| \neq 0$.

EXAMPLE.

$$2x_1 + 3x_2 = 1, \quad 4x_1 + 7x_2 = 3,$$

$$\begin{bmatrix} 2 & 3 \\ 4 & 7 \end{bmatrix} \begin{Bmatrix} x_1 \\ x_2 \end{Bmatrix} = \begin{Bmatrix} 1 \\ 3 \end{Bmatrix},$$

$$[a] = \begin{bmatrix} 2 & 3 \\ 4 & 7 \end{bmatrix}, \quad |a| = 14 - 12 = 2,$$

$$\text{Adj } a = \begin{bmatrix} 7 & -3 \\ -4 & 2 \end{bmatrix}, \quad [a]^{-1} = \begin{bmatrix} \frac{7}{2} & -\frac{3}{2} \\ -\frac{4}{2} & 1 \end{bmatrix},$$

$$\begin{Bmatrix} x_1 \\ x_2 \end{Bmatrix} = \begin{bmatrix} \frac{7}{2} & -\frac{3}{2} \\ -2 & 1 \end{bmatrix} \begin{Bmatrix} 1 \\ 3 \end{Bmatrix} = \begin{Bmatrix} -1 \\ 1 \end{Bmatrix}.$$

Various techniques for inverting a matrix $[a]$ to form $[a]^{-1}$, which are particularly suitable to machine computation, are available but cannot be included here. However, the inverse matrix has some important general properties which we should know. Let's evaluate the product

$$[a][a]^{-1} = \frac{1}{|a|} \begin{bmatrix} a_{11} & a_{12} & a_{13} \\ a_{21} & a_{22} & a_{23} \\ a_{31} & a_{32} & a_{33} \end{bmatrix} \begin{bmatrix} A_{11} & A_{21} & A_{31} \\ A_{12} & A_{22} & A_{32} \\ A_{13} & A_{23} & A_{33} \end{bmatrix}.$$

Note that each of the main diagonal terms of the product matrix will be simply an expansion of $|a|$ in cofactors along a different row of $|a|$. The off-diagonal terms each correspond to expansions of determinants, which have two equal rows and are therefore zero. Thus

$$[a][a]^{-1} = \begin{bmatrix} 1 & 0 & 0 \\ 0 & 1 & 0 \\ 0 & 0 & 1 \end{bmatrix} = [1], \qquad (A\text{–}11)$$

where $[1]$ is called the unit or *unitary matrix*. In a similar fashion, we can demonstrate the commutative property of this particular product and arrive at the result

$$[a]^{-1}[a] = [1] = [a][a]^{-1}. \qquad (A\text{–}12)$$

EXAMPLE (from above).

$$[a] = \begin{bmatrix} 2 & 3 \\ 4 & 7 \end{bmatrix}, \qquad [a]^{-1} = \begin{bmatrix} \frac{7}{2} & -\frac{3}{2} \\ -2 & 1 \end{bmatrix},$$

$$[a][a]^{-1} = \begin{bmatrix} 2 & 3 \\ 4 & 7 \end{bmatrix} \begin{bmatrix} \frac{7}{2} & -\frac{3}{2} \\ -2 & 1 \end{bmatrix} = \begin{bmatrix} 1 & 0 \\ 0 & 1 \end{bmatrix},$$

$$[a]^{-1}[a] = \begin{bmatrix} \frac{7}{2} & -\frac{3}{2} \\ -2 & 1 \end{bmatrix} \begin{bmatrix} 2 & 3 \\ 4 & 7 \end{bmatrix} = \begin{bmatrix} 1 & 0 \\ 0 & 1 \end{bmatrix}.$$

With these properties of a square matrix, we can formally "solve" our original equation (A–1c) by premultiplying both sides by the inverse as

$$[a]^{-1}[a]\{x\} = [a]^{-1}\{y\},$$

which from Eq. (A–12) becomes simply

$$\{x\} = [a]^{-1}\{y\}.$$

A–2 Simple orthogonal transformations. A particularly simple and useful matrix relates or transforms vectors and tensors when expressed in terms of orthogonal axis directions. Such an *orthogonal transformation matrix* (as shown in Chapters 2 and 5) is made up of the nine direction cosines

$$\begin{bmatrix} \alpha_{11} & \alpha_{12} & \alpha_{13} \\ \alpha_{21} & \alpha_{22} & \alpha_{23} \\ \alpha_{31} & \alpha_{32} & \alpha_{33} \end{bmatrix}, \qquad (A\text{–}13)$$

which relate the three directions of an axis system with the three directions of a rotated axis system. In the usual case with each axis system consisting of three mutually perpendicular directions, the nine direction cosines are not entirely independent but are related by six equations. These can be formed by writing (in either axis system) the scalar equations corresponding to the six relations (see the problems at the end of Chapter 5)

$$\mathbf{i} \cdot \mathbf{i} = \mathbf{j} \cdot \mathbf{j} = \mathbf{k} \cdot \mathbf{k} = 1,$$

$$\mathbf{i} \cdot \mathbf{j} = \mathbf{j} \cdot \mathbf{k} = \mathbf{k} \cdot \mathbf{i} = 0.$$

Typical equations are

$$\alpha_{11}^2 + \alpha_{12}^2 + \alpha_{13}^2 = 1,$$

$$\alpha_{11}\alpha_{21} + \alpha_{12}\alpha_{22} + \alpha_{13}\alpha_{23} = 0,$$

and the complete set can be written as

$$\begin{bmatrix} \alpha_{11} & \alpha_{12} & \alpha_{13} \\ \alpha_{21} & \alpha_{22} & \alpha_{23} \\ \alpha_{31} & \alpha_{32} & \alpha_{33} \end{bmatrix} \begin{bmatrix} \alpha_{11} & \alpha_{21} & \alpha_{31} \\ \alpha_{12} & \alpha_{22} & \alpha_{32} \\ \alpha_{13} & \alpha_{23} & \alpha_{33} \end{bmatrix} = [\alpha][\alpha]' = [1]. \quad \text{(A–14a)}$$

Here [ ]' stands for the *transposed matrix* in which all the terms are flipped across the main diagonal.

Equation (A–14a) is often called an *orthogonality relation* and can easily be shown to be commutable to give an alternative set of orthogonality relations, such as

$$[\alpha]'[\alpha] = [1]. \quad \text{(A–14b)}$$

Comparison of Eq. (A–14) with our definition of an inverse matrix in Eq. (A–12) shows that for the orthogonal transformation matrix $[\alpha]$, the inverse and transpose are identical,

$$[\alpha]' = [\alpha]^{-1}.$$

Since forming the transpose is such an easy operation, here its equivalence to the inverse makes the handling of many manipulations involving the direction cosine matrix very simple. A further property* of $[\alpha]$ is that its determinant is always unity as

$$|\alpha| = 1 \quad \text{(A–15)}$$

There are two distinct geometrical interpretations associated with the matrix $[\alpha]$, which itself defines a rotation of definite magnitude about a

---

* See Goldstein, Ref. 2, p. 96 ff. for a more complete treatment of orthogonal transformations.

particular axis. If $\{y\}$ represents the components of a vector in $Y_1 Y_2 Y_3$, then with

$$\{x\} = [\alpha]\{y\}, \tag{A–16}$$

the column matrix $\{x\}$ represents the new components in $Y_1 Y_2 Y_3$ of the vector after it has been rotated positively about the axis characteristic of $[\alpha]$. The second interpretation of Eq. (A–16) is that $\{x\}$ represents the new components of the original vector on an axis system $X_1 X_2 X_3$ rotated negatively from $Y_1 Y_2 Y_3$. These interpretations are shown in Figs. 5–5(b) and 5–5(a), respectively, for

$$[\alpha] = \begin{bmatrix} \cos\theta & -\sin\theta & 0 \\ \sin\theta & \cos\theta & 0 \\ 0 & 0 & 1 \end{bmatrix},$$

which corresponds to a rotation θ about axis Y_3. Note that $[\alpha]$ corresponds to the $[\theta]'$ of Chapters 2 and 5 and to $[\gamma]'$ of Chapter 5. Thus the θ and γ matrices are defined to exploit the second of these interpretations, whereas α is aimed at the first.

Thinking in terms of the first interpretation, suppose we visualize a triad of unit vectors attached to a rigid body and lined up with axes $Y_1 Y_2 Y_3$. If the body (and triad) is rotated about an axis A according to $[\alpha]$, the new components of the unit vectors on the axes $Y_1 Y_2 Y_3$ are

$$\begin{bmatrix} \alpha_{11} & \alpha_{12} & \alpha_{13} \\ \alpha_{21} & \alpha_{22} & \alpha_{23} \\ \alpha_{31} & \alpha_{32} & \alpha_{33} \end{bmatrix} \begin{bmatrix} 1 & 0 & 0 \\ 0 & 1 & 0 \\ 0 & 0 & 1 \end{bmatrix} = [\alpha].$$

Thus $[\alpha]$ is a measure of the new orientation of the rigid body. A subsequent rotation about a particular axis B defined by $[\beta]$ gives an orientation described by the product $[\beta][\alpha]$. Here A and B are axes fixed in $Y_1 Y_2 Y_3$.

Conversely, the product $[\alpha][\beta]$ corresponds, according to the second interpretation of a triad first rotated negatively about B and then negatively about A, all with respect to the axes in the rigid body. Thus A and B are axis directions fixed in the body, whereas for the product $[\beta][\alpha]$, they were fixed in the space $Y_1 Y_2 Y_3$. From the point of view of an observer in $(Y_1 Y_2 Y_3)$-space, $[\beta][\alpha]$ describes rotations about fixed directions A and then B, where the direction of B is not dependent on $[\alpha]$. Conversely, he says $[\alpha][\beta]$ can be interpreted as a rotation $[\alpha]$ of the rigid body about A and then a rotation $[\beta]$ about B, where B is figured with respect to the body triad not the fixed triad. Such relationships are examined in some detail in Sections 5–1 and 5–2 and in problems at the end of the chapters.

As described above, the components $\{y\}$ of a vector can be transformed to the components $\{x\}$ in a positively rotated coordinate system $X_1X_2X_3$ by

$$\{x\} = [\alpha]'\{y\} = [\gamma]\{y\}. \tag{A–17}$$

Thus two vectors A and B can each have the component transformations

$$\{A_x\} = [\gamma]\{A_y\},$$
$$\{B_x\} = [\gamma]\{B_y\}.$$

However, A and B may be related by the tensor T in the two forms

$$\{A_x\} = [T_x]\{B_x\},$$
$$\{A_y\} = [T_y]\{B_y\}, \tag{A–18}$$

where T can be represented in either case by the nine elements of a square matrix. To find the relation between $[T_x]$ and $[T_y]$, note that we can premultiply by $[\gamma]$ as

$$[\gamma]\{A_y\} = [\gamma][T_y]\{B_y\} = [\gamma][T_y]\,[[\gamma]^{-1}[\gamma]]\,\{B_y\}$$
$$= [\gamma][T_y][\gamma]^{-1}[\gamma]\{B_y\}$$
$$= [\gamma][T_y][\gamma]\{B_x\} = \{A_x\},$$

so that by comparison with Eq. (A–18) we find the *similarity transformation* for the tensor T,

$$[T_x] = [\gamma][T_y][\gamma]^{-1}. \tag{A–19a}$$

Since $[\gamma]$ is an orthogonal transformation, we can also write

$$[T_x] = [\gamma][T_y][\gamma]'. \tag{A–19b}$$

As demonstrated in Section 5–3 for the inertia tensor, it is always possible to find a transformation $[\gamma]$ which puts T into a diagonal form. In this *eigenvalue problem* for symmetric tensors, we always get three real eigenvalues or roots. In the eigenvalue problem of Section 5–1 for finding the single rotation equivalent to two successive ones, we found that the unsymmetrical orthogonal transformation matrix $[\alpha]$ has only one real root and that of unit magnitude. We found the direction cosines $\{R\}$ of this real root from the equation

$$[\alpha]\{R\} = \{R\}, \tag{A–20}$$

which is the specialization for a real root of unit magnitude of the more general case for a root of magnitude λ,

$$[\alpha]\{R\} = \{R\}\lambda. \tag{A-21}$$

When we have three real roots, such as for the inertia tensor, we can handle all three roots simultaneously and write

$$[I][\gamma] = [\gamma][\lambda] = [\gamma] \begin{bmatrix} I_A & 0 & 0 \\ 0 & I_B & 0 \\ 0 & 0 & I_C \end{bmatrix}, \tag{A-22}$$

or premultiplying by $[\gamma]'$,

$$[\gamma]'[I][\gamma] = [\lambda]. \tag{A-23}$$

These are both special cases of the even more general problem of finding the similarity transformation which diagonalizes the matrix $[a]$ and in which the roots may be real or complex, as

$$[\gamma][a][\gamma]' = [\lambda]. \tag{A-24}$$

We can show that the *trace* (sum of terms on the main diagonal) of the matrix $[a]$ is unchanged by such an orthogonal similarity transformation. If we write

$$[b] = [\gamma][a][\gamma]', \tag{A-25}$$

we can subtract $\lambda[1]$ from both sides (where here λ is any number) and get

$$
\begin{aligned}
[b] - \lambda[1] &= [\gamma][a][\gamma]' - \lambda[1] \\
&= [\gamma][a][\gamma]' - [\gamma][\gamma]'\lambda[1] \\
&= [\gamma][a][\gamma]' - [\gamma]\lambda[1][\gamma]' \\
&= [\gamma]\,[[a] - \lambda[1]]\,[\gamma]'.
\end{aligned}
$$

We can take determinants of both sides*, such as

$$
\begin{aligned}
|[b] - \lambda[1]| &= |\gamma|\,|[a] - \lambda[1]|\,|\gamma'| \\
&= |\gamma|\,|\gamma'|\,|[a] - \lambda[1]| \\
&= |[a] - \lambda[1]|,
\end{aligned}
$$

---

* See Hildebrand, Ref. 22, Sections 1.18 and 1.19.

since $|\gamma|\,|\gamma'| = 1$.　Thus

$$\begin{vmatrix} b_{11} - \lambda & b_{12} & b_{13} \\ b_{21} & b_{22} - \lambda & b_{23} \\ b_{31} & b_{32} & b_{33} - \lambda \end{vmatrix} = \begin{vmatrix} a_{11} - \lambda & a_{12} & a_{13} \\ a_{21} & a_{22} - \lambda & a_{23} \\ a_{31} & a_{32} & a_{33} - \lambda \end{vmatrix}.$$

Expanding both sides in λ, we get

$$-\lambda^3 + (b_{11} + b_{22} + b_{33})\lambda^2 + \cdots = -\lambda^3 + (a_{11} + a_{22} + a_{33})\lambda^2 + \cdots$$

so that by equating coefficients,

$$\text{Trace } [b] = \text{Trace } [a], \tag{A--26}$$

which is one of the more useful invariants of the transformation.

The eigenvalue problems discussed here are generalized in Chapter 9 to problems in which the transformations are no longer simply orthogonal in three-space. Instead, we look for simultaneous diagonalization of several symmetric matrices in n-space. Here the transformation matrices are orthogonal only in a general sense and may contain complex elements. In fundamentally unsymmetrical problems, it is helpful to introduce an adjoint set of relationships and define biorthogonality in order to diagonalize the matrices and define binormal coordinates.

INDEX

Acceleration, 10, 15
  absolute, 3
  of earth's surface, 58
  (*see also* Motion)
Accelerometer, 290, 318
Adjoint matrix, 364
Aircraft stability equations, 293
Albatross, 84
Andronow (Ref. 20), 337, 339
Angular acceleration
  in general motion, 193
  in planar motion, 38
Angular displacements, 181
  infinitesimal, 191
  not vectors, 185
  in planar motion, 37
  successive, 188
Angular momentum (*see* Momentum, moment of)
Angular velocity
  absolute, 3
  Euler's angles, 199
  in planar motion, 38
  rate of change, 193
Aristotle, 3

Beam, elastic
  dynamic deformation of, 137
Bernoulli's equation, 176
Bessel, 299
  functions, 321
Billiard ball, 249
Bisplinghoff (Ref. 9), 137, 138

Center, 332
  force (*see* Force)
  of gravity (*see* Gravity)
  of mass (*see* Mass)
Clock, 339
Coefficients, constant, 299
  functions of independent variable, 299

matrix of (*see* Matrix)
Coin, rolling, 252
Collisions
  elastic, 92
  plastic, 92
Complex plane, 305
Conic sections (*see* Orbits, gravitational)
Constants, of integration, 301, 308
Constraints, 249
Contact point
  motion of, 135, 251
Continuum, or continuous medium, 138
Control volume, 153
  (*see also* Free-body diagram)
Coordinate systems
  cartesian, 15
  cylindrical, 17, 18
  for rigid-body kinematics, 199
  for rotational motion, 196
  rotations of, 187
  spherical, 17, 24, 52
Coordinate transformations
  to cylindrical, 21
  in linear systems, 309
  matrices for, 185
  for rotation, 238
  to spherical, 24
Coordinates
  generalized, 327
  independent, 96, 249
  transformation of, 96
Coriolis acceleration, 48
Coriolis moment, 164
Coriolis, theorem of, 47
Coulomb friction, 332
  (*see also* Force)
Coulomb scattering, 105
  angle of, 127
Cramer's rule, 22, 189, 364
Curvature, radius of, 15
  of space-time, 5

373